DATE DUE			
Jul 4 '73			
Nov 26 '73			
May 11 '76			
GAYLORD M-2			PRINTED IN U.S.A.

PRINCIPLES OF INSECT
CHEMOSTERILIZATION

PRINCIPLES OF INSECT
CHEMOSTERILIZATION

edited by:

GERMAIN C. LABRECQUE

and

CARROLL N. SMITH

ENTOMOLOGY RESEARCH DIVISION
UNITED STATES DEPARTMENT OF AGRICULTURE
GAINESVILLE, FLORIDA

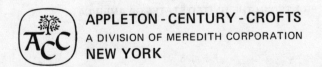

APPLETON - CENTURY - CROFTS
A DIVISION OF MEREDITH CORPORATION
NEW YORK

Copyright © 1968 by

MEREDITH CORPORATION

6117-1

Library of Congress Card Number: 67-28062

F-53096

CONTRIBUTORS

WAYLAND J. HAYES, Jr., Medical Director, Chief, Toxicology Section, United States Public Health Service, Communicable Disease Center, Atlanta, Georgia

WALDEMAR KLASSEN, Radiation Biology and Insect Genetics Section, Metabolism and Radiation Research Laboratory, Entomology Research Division, USDA, State University Station, Fargo, North Dakota

E. F. KNIPLING, Entomology Research Division, United States Department of Agriculture, Plant Industry Station, Beltsville, Maryland

GERMAIN C. LA BRECQUE, Entomology Research Division, United States Department of Agriculture, Gainesville, Florida

LEO E. LACHANCE, Radiation Biology and Insect Genetics Section, Metabolism and Radiation Research Laboratory, Entomology Research Division, USDA, State University Station, Fargo, North Dakota

A. W. LINDQUIST, Entomology Research Division, Agricultural Research Service, United States Department of Agriculture, Beltsville, Maryland

DAVID T. NORTH, Radiation Biology and Insect Genetics Section, Metabolism and Radiation Research Laboratory, Entomology Research Division, USDA, State University Station, Fargo, North Dakota

RALPH B. TURNER, Entomology Research Division, Pesticide Chemicals Research Branch, United States Department of Agriculture, Gainesville, Florida

D. E. WEIDHAAS, Entomology Research Division, United States Department of Agriculture, Plant Industry Station, Beltsville, Maryland

PREFACE

Interest in the possibility of using chemosterilants to control insect pests is widespread and research in the field continues to expand, as indicated by the increasing number of published papers. Much progress has been made in the chemical, biological, and toxicological evaluation of chemosterilants since the term was coined by the editors a brief six years ago. The wealth of new information has induced the authors to prepare this volume to serve as a basis for continued research and as a guide to new workers entering the field. It includes a comprehensive discussion of the potential uses of chemosterilants, the methods and results of their evaluation in the laboratory and the field, the chemistry of selected compounds representative of the important types of chemosterilants, the cytogenetic and cellular basis of their action and, most importantly, their toxicological aspects—most importantly because research with these compounds should not be undertaken without full awareness of their hazards and limitations.

The surge of interest in chemosterilants since 1960 is remarkable, the more so since only a single practical application can be cited at the time this is written, i.e., the release of tepa-sterilized Mexican fruit flies along the border between California and Mexico to prevent the northward movement of the species. This interest springs largely from the demonstrated effectiveness of released males of several species sterilized by gamma radiation, the indication that some species can be sterilized chemically for release with less deleterious effects than those induced by radiation, and the hope that research will develop selective methods of application and chemicals that will permit the sterilization of a large portion of the natural population without hazard to man or beneficial animals. This book is intended to delineate and evaluate what has been accomplished; it should suggest where future research should lead, and provide warning as to the limitations of the chemicals and methods, as well as the hazards associated with their use. It is not intended primarily as a review of literature; a complete list of the known chemosterilants is not presented and the bibliographical references, though extensive, are not exhaustive.

The editors wish to emphasize that much of the potential usefulness of chemosterilants would be in regulatory programs or programs conducted by governmental agencies, as opposed to individual usage, and that the safety of any method would depend on the particular compound and the way it would be used.

GERMAIN C. LA BRECQUE
CARROLL N. SMITH

CONTENTS

PRINCIPLES OF INSECT
CHEMOSTERILIZATION

1

Introduction

A. W. LINDQUIST

ENTOMOLOGY RESEARCH DIVISION
AGRICULTURAL RESEARCH SERVICE
U.S. DEPARTMENT OF AGRICULTURE
BELTSVILLE, MARYLAND (ret'd)*

In introducing the subject of chemosterilants as a potential means of controlling destructive insects, it is advisable to briefly evaluate the strength of the insect enemy, to review the reasons why present means of combating arthropods need strengthening, and to discuss the sterile-male concept.

First, we should consider that insects are one of man's most important enemies. They destroy a sizable part of his growing food crops, torment livestock, attack stored food and other products, and take an enormous toll of our forests. The total annual loss caused by insects over the world exceeds 25 billion dollars.

In addition, insects are transmitters of some of the most serious diseases of man and animals. Malaria, carried

---

*Present address: Rt. 1, Bridgeport, Kansas.

1

by *Anopheles* mosquitoes, has been a scourage of mankind for thousands of years. This disease has been estimated to have killed 2 million persons every year and sicken approximately two hundred million people so that they are unable to perform effective work. Other important insect-borne diseases of man are yellow fever, typhus, encephalitis, bubonic plague, and filariasis to mention a few. Livestock diseases, such as anaplasmosis, anthrax, trypanosomiasis, and cattle fever, are carried by insects and cause great economic loss.

The common methods employed to combat insects include the use of insecticides, biological control, cultural practices, mechanical devices, and draining and filling. The use of insecticides is the most widely applied single method of control. Their extensive use has led directly to three problems that have hindered control. The first of these is the insecticide residues, and although no known deaths or illnesses have resulted from the residues in food, it is considered a potential health hazard. An enormous amount of research has been done to determine the minute amounts of insecticides in numerous crops following the use of various formulations of different insecticides. Concurrent studies have been done on the effect of these materials on animals. The second problem concerns possible hazard of insecticides to fish and wildlife. The third great problem associated with insecticide usage is the development of insect resistance or tolerance to chemicals. Approximately 100 species of insects are resistant, to a greater or lesser degree, to several of our most effective insecticides. An immense amount of research has been directed toward development of alternate insecticides and physiological and biochemical work on the nature of resistance and ways to overcome it. It is little wonder, then, that entomologists have sought new ways to control noxious insects.

Knipling as early as 1937 considered that with insects having a low population, it would be possible to rear, sterilize, and release more males of the species than existed in nature. A preponderance of released sterile males of five or ten to one over native males should achieve control or eradication of the species. The sterile male would seek out the native females and render them reproductively ineffective. A continuous and systematic release would thus annihilate the species. The screwworm, a serious livestock pest, was the target of Knipling's early work.

Sterility in the screwworm was induced by exposure to gamma radiation. The sterile-male technique actually worked

in laboratory cages (Bushland and Hopkins, 1951 and 1953).
Proof of the soundness of the gamma-induced sterile male
method was provided by the eradication of the screwworm from
the 170-sq. mile Island of Curacao (Baumhover et al., 1955,
and Lindquist, 1955).

This destructive livestock insect was subsequently eradicated from Florida and the southeastern states by the release
of 3 1/4 billion sterile flies over 85,000 sq miles for a 17-
month period (Knipling, 1960, Lindquist, 1961). The highly successful eradication of this insect from a large area ranks as
one of the most outstanding entomological accomplishments of
all time.

Could certain chemicals be used instead of radiation
for sterilizing large numbers of insects? The chemicals might
cost less and be more practical than gamma radiation. Furthermore, insects in a natural population might somehow be
exposed to chemical sterilants without the necessity of rearing and releasing vast numbers of treated insects. Insects
might be lured to chemical attractants, lights, or mechanical
devices and thus be exposed to a chemosterilant. The sterile
insects would then be available to mate with the native population and nullify reproduction. Resting places might be treated
with a chemosterilant with good results. The possible use of
chemical sterilants presents an intriguing and exciting area
for research.

Prior to 1958 there was little reference indeed to chemosterilization of insects. There were, however, a few papers
on cytotoxic or mutational effects of chemicals on *Drosophila*.
Auerbach and Robson (1947) and Auerbach (1947) determined
that mustard gas and related compounds could induce germinal
mutations; Haddow et al. (1948) reported on the cytotoxic effect
of a long series of aryl-2-halogenoalkylamines; Bird (1950)
showed that alkylating chemicals produced sterilant effects; and
Goldsmith and Frank (1952) showed that folic acid antagonist
(aminopterin) would induce sterility in the female. Mitlin et al.
(1957) published on the effect of mitotic poisons on house fly
oviposition; and LaBrecque and his colleagues (1960, 1961) reported on the use of chemicals that either affect metabolism or
cause sexual sterility in the house fly. These highly important
studies stimulated a greatly expanded search and synthesis of
new chemicals for other, safer compounds that would sterilize
insects. An extensive screening program was initiated by the
U.S. Department of Agriculture to find chemicals that would
sterilize insects other than the house fly, i.e., the boll weevil,

the gypsy moth, the tropical fruit fly, the codling moth, the cabbage looper, and others.

Smith, LaBrecque, and Borkovec (1964) presented an excellent review of insect chemosterilant research, possible uses, and biochemical characteristics of the chemicals.

There are now over 400 papers reporting on results of research on chemosterilization of insects. These papers originate in numerous foreign countries, whereas studies of gamma-induced sterility come from comparatively few. This is understandable because of the high cost and limited availability of cobalt sources for entomological work and the ready availability of chemosterilants for research purposes.

Even though the research on chemosterilants has not led, as yet, to practical and exciting new ways to control insects, it should be mentioned that interest in chemosterilants has stimulated an immense amount of valuable research in the behavior, sexual habits, ecology, genetics, and cytogenetics of insects. This alone has advanced our knowledge of insects and possible ways to control destructive forms.

Several thousand chemicals have been evaluated on many species of insects. It is surprising that the search for new compounds has progressed so fast when it is considered that it takes approximately 30 days for the evaluation of one chemical on the house fly. Chemicals that kill an insect can be detected in a day or two, but testing of chemosterilants involves treating the insect, mating treated and untreated specimens, and determining hatchability of eggs.

Preliminary field tests (LaBrecque et al., 1962 and 1963) on the house fly, using a chemosterilant-treated sugar bait showed remarkably good overall reduction of the population. The limiting factor in these tests was the possible hazard of the chemosterilants to warm-blooded animals. Numerous other small-scale field tests are under way, using light traps or chemicals as lures, for the cabbage looper, codling moth, tobacco budworm, tropical fruit fly, and others. Although there has not been a smashing success in control or eradication of an insect species on a large-area basis such as with the screw-worm, there is every justification for continuing and extending the research.

REFERENCES

Auerbach, C., 1947. The induction by mustard gas of chromosomal in-
stabilities in *Drosophila*. Proc. Roy. Soc. Edinburgh, 62:307.
_____, and J. M. Robson. 1947. The production of mutations by chem-
ical substances. Proc. Roy. Soc. Edinburgh, 62:271.
Baumhover, A. H., A. J. Graham, B. A. Bitter, D. E. Hopkins, W. D.
New, F. H. Dudley, and R. C. Bushland. 1955. Screw-worm
through control release of sterilized flies. J. Econ. Entom.
48(4):462–466.
Bushland, R. C., and D. E. Hopkins. 1951. Experiments with screw-
worm flies sterilized by X-rays. J. Econ. Entom, 44(5):725–
731.
Bird, M. J. 1950. Production of mutations in *Drosophila* using four
aryl-2-halogenoalkylamines. Nature, 165 (4195):491–492.
_____, and D. E. Hopkins. 1953. Sterilization of screw-worm flies with
X-rays and gamma rays. J. Econ. Entom., 46(4):648–656.
Goldsmith, E. O., and I. Frank. 1952. Sterility in the female fruit fly,
Drosophila melanogaster, produced by the feeding of a folic
acid antagonist. Amer. J. Physiol. 171:726–727.
Haddow, A., G. A. R. Kon, and W. C. J. Toss. 1948. Effects upon tu-
mours of various haloalkylarylamines. Nature (London), 162:
824.
Knipling, E. F. 1955. Possibilities of insect control or eradication
through the use of sexually sterile males. J. Econ. Entom.,
48(4):459–462.
_____. 1960. Eradication of the screw-worm fly. Sci. Amer. 203(4):
54–61.
LaBrecque, G. C. 1961. Studies with three alkylating agents as house
fly sterilants. J. Econ. Entom., 54(4):684–689.
_____, P. H. Adock, and C. N. Smith. 1960. Tests with compounds
affecting house fly metabolism. J. Econ. Entom., 53(5):802–
805.
_____, C. N. Smith, and D. W. Meifert. 1962. A field experiment in the
control of house flies with chemosterilant baits. J. Econ. Entom., 55(4):449–451.
_____, D. W. Meifert, and R. L. Fye. 1963. A field study on the con-
trol of house flies with chemosterilant techniques. J. Econ.
Entom., 56(2):150–152.
Lindquist, A. W. 1955. The use of gamma radiation for control or
eradication of the screw-worm. J. Econ. Entom., 48(4):467–
469.
_____. 1961. New ways to control insects. Pest Control 29(6):9, 11–12,
14, 16, 18–19, 36, 38, 40.
Mitlin, N., B. A. Butt, and T. J. Shortino. 1957. Effect of mitotic poisons on house fly oviposition. Physiol. Zool. 30(2):133–136.
Smith, C. N., G. C. LaBrecque, and A. B. Borkovec. 1964. Insect chemosterilants. Ann. Rev. Entom, 9:269–284.

2

The Potential Role of Sterility for Pest Control

E. F. KNIPLING

ENTOMOLOGY RESEARCH DIVISION
AGRICULTURAL RESEARCH SERVICE
U.S. DEPARTMENT OF AGRICULTURE
BELTSVILLE, MARYLAND

INTRODUCTION

The sterility techniques for controlling insects and other pests are receiving the attention of an increasing number of research scientists. The techniques involved permit the application of certain principles of population suppression that could lead to more efficient or more desirable solutions to many important insect problems. Certain sterility procedures should prove equally useful for meeting many vertebrate pest problems.

The extent to which the sterility techniques will be employed for regulating pest populations will be contingent on the degree of progress that is made in several fields of research. It will be necessary to develop safe chemical sterilants or other ways of achieving the appropriate type of sterility. Application of the techniques will require a good understanding of the biology, behavior, ecology, and population dynamics of the pests involved. If sterility involves the natural population, practical ways of ·achieving the necessary level of sterility must be perfected. If the sterility technique involves the release of reared insects, such insects must be mass produced at a reasonable cost. Up to the present time, two methods of producing sterility have been investigated most extensively. One method involves the exposure of the organism to x-rays or gamma rays from Cobalt 60 isotopes (Bushland and Hopkins, 1951, 1953). The other involves the use of chemicals that produce sterility. These methods cause dominant lethal effects in the genetic material. Sterility can also be achieved by crossing species or races of insects. In this chapter we will not be concerned with the merits or limitations of various ways to induce sterility. We are concerned here with the fundamentals of population suppression by the use of the sterility techniques, irrespective of the methods used to produce sterility in the organism. A full understanding of the fundamental principles involved in the suppression of pest populations by various other systems of control is also necessary, since different methods of control affect population trends in different ways. Such understanding of the merits and limitations of different methods will suggest ways to integrate the sterility method with other systems of control.

Before proceeding with a discussion of the ways that sterility can be used to advantage in the control of insect populations, it is necessary to point out that two systems of employing sterility are involved in using sterility to suppress insect populations. One system involves the mass production, sterilization, and release of sterile organisms so that they will interfere with reproduction in the natural wild fertile population. The other system involves the sterilization of the required proportion of the natural population by appropriate means so the sterilized individuals cannot reproduce and at the same time, they further control reproduction by competing with the remaining fertile individuals in the natural population. Each system takes advantage of the effect that sterile insects can have on the reproductive capacity of the fertile individuals of the same species in the population. The two systems, however, have entirely different effects on population trends. The techniques for practical application of the methods are entirely different. The criteria that will determine the circumstances under which each system might be practical or impractical are also entirely different. Therefore, scientists interested in pursuing research on the sterility methods of pest control should fully understand the principles of population suppression involved in each method. They should also have an appreciation of the merits and limitations of each method. Under certain circumstances it may be advantageous to integrate the two methods of control.

APPLICATION OF THE STERILITY TECHNIQUE BY THE RELEASE OF STERILE INSECTS

BASIC PRINCIPLES INVOLVED

The basic principles involved in insect population control by the release of sterile insects have been discussed by the author in a number of publications (Knipling, 1955, 1959, 1964a). These principles can be explained by the use of a simple insect population model showing the trend of a stable hypothetical insect population subjected to the release of a constant number of sterile insects for several successive generations. This hypothetical model is shown in Table 1. The assumption is made that an untreated population consisting of 1,000,000 males and 1,000,000 females is stable and will neither increase nor decrease in number. Population density regulating factors are ignored. If 2,000,000 fully competitive sterile males (or 2,000,000 of each sex) are released, the ratio of sterile to fertile individuals in the population will be 2:1. Ac-

TABLE 1

THEORETICAL TREND OF A HYPOTHETICAL INSECT
POPULATION SUBJECTED TO CONTROL BY THE
RELEASE OF STERILE INSECTS

Assumed natural population of males and females each generation	No. of sterile males released each generation	Ratio of sterile to fertile males competing for each virgin female	Percentage of females mated to sterile males	Theoretical no. of male and female progeny produced
1,000,000	2,000,000	2:1	66.7	333,333
333,333	2,000,000	6:1	85.7	47,619
47,619	2,000,000	42:1	97.7	1,107
1,107	2,000,000	1,807:1	99.95	Less than 1

cordingly, one third of the natural wild females can be expected to mate with wild fertile males and two thirds with the released sterile males. Thus, theoretically, only 333,333 progeny of each sex will be produced, instead of 1,000,000 of each sex. In the next generation, the release of an additional 2,000,000 sterile males will result in a sterile to fertile ratio of 6:1. Only one seventh of the 333,333 wild fertile females will be expected to mate with fertile males and only 47,619 progeny of each sex will be produced. The greatly reduced numbers of progeny will then be subjected to an even higher ratio of sterile to fertile insects when 2,000,000 sterile males are again released. Theoretical elimination of the wild population will result in the fourth generation, where the number of sterile and fertile insects of each sex will be 2,000,000 to 1,107, respectively. This represents a sterile to fertile ratio of 1,807:1. Since the ratio exceeds the number of fertile insects in the population, no fertile matings could be expected.

The significant feature of insect population control by the sustained release of a constant number of sterile insects is that each release achieves a higher and higher ratio of sterile to fertile insects and, therefore, becomes progressively more efficient. This is true, however, only if the initial release rate is high enough to cause a decline in the natural population. If the initial release rate is not high enough to offset the net capacity for increase, and the natural population continues to increase in numbers, each subsequent release will result in a lower sterile to fertile ratio with a consequent progressive decrease in efficiency each generation.

The theoretical effect of sterile-insect releases, as shown in Table 1, cannot be expected to occur in actual insect control operations. Under favorable circumstances and in the absence of control efforts, an insect population will have the capacity to increase, especially when the starting population represents a low density for the environment. The ability of insect populations to increase from one generation to the next is a vitally important factor to overcome in the successful application of the sterile-insect release system. The potential rate of increase of most insect populations is very high indeed. A single female of many insect species may deposit 100 or more eggs, and thus is capable of producing 100 or more progeny. Due to parasitism, predation, and many other natural hazards, however, the actual rate of increase is much lower than the maximum potential. The net increase rate will vary with the species and the circumstances. For some insects like the tsetse flies (*Glossina* spp.), the net increase rate per generation probably seldom exceeds twofold. For others, like the house fly (*Musca domestica* L.), the codling moth (*Carpocapsa pomonella* L.) or the Mediterranean fruit fly (*Ceratitis capitata* (Wied.)), the net increase rate under favorable conditions may be as high as ten or even twentyfold per generation. Therefore, in order to achieve a downward trend in the natural population, it is obviously necessary to release enough sterile insects to more than offset the net increase capacity of the natural population.

If we assume a given insect has a net capacity to increase fivefold each generation, the ratio of fully competitive sterile to fertile insects will have to be 4:1 in order to keep the natural population stable. However, when the increase rate is fivefold, a sustained release rate sufficient to achieve an initial sterile to fertile ratio of 9:1 will have the effect shown in column 2 of Table 2. The first column of figures in Table 2 shows the relative trend of an uncontrolled population increasing at a fivefold rate. The treated population, as shown in Table 2, has essentially the same trend as that shown for the stable population depicted in Table 1. However, it shows the need for starting with a higher sterile to fertile ratio in order to offset the assumed fivefold net increase potential of the reproducing insects. Theoretically, an initial ratio as low as five sterile to one fertile will be adequate to start a downward trend in the natural population when the net increase rate is only

TABLE 2

TREND OF AN INSECT POPULATION SUBJECTED TO
STERILE-INSECT RELEASES WHEN THE NORMAL
INCREASE RATE IS FIVEFOLD

Generation	Uncontrolled natural population (5× increase rate)	Controlled population Natural population	Sterile population	Ratio sterile to fertile
1	1,000,000	1,000,000	9,000,000	9:1
2	5,000,000	500,000	9,000,000	18:1
3	25,000,000	131,625	9,000,000	68:1
4	125,000,000	9,535	9,000,000	942:1
5	625,000,000	50	9,000,000	180,000:1

fivefold. Actually, starting with this lower overflooding ratio, theoretical elimination of the population will be achieved with fewer insects than will be required starting with a 9:1 ratio. However, in these models we are concerned with the overall population. In actual practice the density of the insects will vary in different parts of the environment. Moreover, the distribution of sterile insects can never be uniform. Therefore, in control operations, the initial ratio should be sufficiently high to be certain that an overall reduction in the population will occur in all parts of the environment from the start. If the net increase potential for the insect to be controlled is likely to be as high as twentyfold, a sterile to fertile ratio in excess of 19:1 would, theoretically, be adequate to start a downward trend. Again, however, in actual practice, the sterile to fertile ratio probably should be at least 40:1. In some instances, the sterility procedures might reduce the vigor and competitiveness of the organism. Allowance must be made for this factor. If the sterile insects are only half competitive on the average, all release rates would have to be doubled to achieve the effects depicted in the models.

USE OF STERILE-INSECT RELEASES ALONE FOR INSECT POPULATION CONTROL

The discussion in the foregoing section emphasizes the necessity of having an adequate sterile to fertile ratio in order to achieve control of insect populations. Since the number of individual insects present in natural populations of most well-established insect species is very large, it naturally follows that the use of sterile insects alone will not be practical for the control or elimination of insects in many situations. However, certain species of insects are normally present in relatively low numbers, especially during the low period in the population cycle. Screw-worm flies (*Cochliomyia hominivorax* Coq.), are seldom numerous in the environment even during periods of abundance for this species. The density probably does not exceed 1,000 per square mile in most situations. During low periods in the population density cycle, the number of flies per square mile might be of the order of 10 to 20. Since relatively low-cost methods for mass rearing screwworm flies have been perfected, it is entirely feasible and practical to deal with this insect problem by the use of sterile-insect releases alone. This has been amply demonstrated in the Southeastern United States as well as in the southwestern United States and in northern Mexico.

It may be practical under certain circumstances to use sterile-insect releases alone to control or eliminate other important insects. However, at the present time, too little is known about the actual population density and the degree of fluctuations in the density of most economic insects to appraise the potential role of sterile-insect releases alone as a practical means of control. More basic information on the natural population density of economic insects in general might show that the method will have broader application than is generally realized. There is reason to believe that population of insects such as the *Heliothis* complex, the tobacco hornworm (*Protoparce sexta* [Johannson]), tropical fruit flies (*Trephrididae*), and the sugarcane borer (*Diatraca saccharalis* F.) vary widely from season to season and from year to year. With increasing progress in reducing the cost of mass rearing insects, it may be possible eventually to apply the sterile-release technique alone for a wide range of insect species. When it is practical to achieve the required dominance over the natural population with sterile insects, complete elimination of the natural population can be expected if it exists in an isolated area. If a population can be brought under control, but elimination is not feasible because of nonisolation, virtually complete control might be maintained by the continuous release of relatively few sterile insects throughout the area to be protected or in a barrier zone. The width of a barrier zone which would be necessary would depend on the flight range of the species.

Insects are also subject to natural catastrophes that may reduce the population to levels far below a normal low-density level. It may be possible to capitalize on such catastrophes and apply the sterile-insect release system alone when it would not otherwise be practical. Two good examples of such situations can be cited. The oriental fruit fly, *Dacus dorsalis*, was temporarily greatly reduced on Guam in 1962 and 1963 because of tropical typhoons that destroyed many of the insects and most of the host plants. The U.S. Department of Agriculture Fruit Fly Investigations Unit in Hawaii took advantage of the low population in applying the sterile-insect release method (unpublished manuscript). A high ratio of sterile to fertile flies was achieved by the release of a relatively few flies. Under normal circumstances, it might have required from 50 to 100 million sterile flies per week to accomplish elimination of the population. This probably would not have been practical. With a greatly reduced natural population, however, the release of several million sterile flies per week achieved eradication within a few generations and at a cost lower than would have been necessary by other means that require essentially the same cost regardless of the density of the insect population.

Another example of a natural catastrophe for an insect population which might have permitted the practical use of sterile insects alone as a means of control can be cited for the sugarcane borer in Louisiana. An extremely cold winter in 1961–62 reduced the natural population in the spring to a level that probably did not exceed 20 to 25 moths per acre (Charpentier and Mathes, 1962). The normal spring population is generally of the order of several hundred moths per acre. The use of sterile insects alone probably would not be practical as a means of population control under normal circumstances. If mass-rearing procedures and satisfactory methods of producing sterility, however, had been perfected, it might have been entirely practical in 1963 to overflood the natural population to further reduce the population and then continue a sterile-insect release program at a lower level to maintain control of this major sugarcane pest at a cost considerably lower than is required with insecticides. Moreover, an effective program of this nature should eliminate all losses and obviate the need for insecticides that may be potentially hazardous in the environment.

USE OF STERILE INSECTS TO PREVENT THE ESTABLISHMENT OF INCIPIENT INFESTATIONS

The release of sterile insects should play an important role in the future to prevent the spread of insects to new areas or to eliminate incipient infestations. In order to take full advantage of this method of control, it will be necessary to perfect rearing, sterilizing, and releasing procedures in advance of the anticipated need for the technique. The sterility method is now employed by the U.S. Department of Agriculture and the California Department of Agriculture to prevent the establishment and spread of the Mexican fruit fly, *Anastrepha ludens* (Loew), along the California-Mexico border area. The Mexican fruit fly is a major and continuing threat to the California fruit industry because of the presence of low-level populations of the insect in Tijuana, Mexico, that come from infested fruit shipped into the area from other parts of Mexico. The number of insects responsible for this threat each year does not exceed more than a few thousand. It is, therefore, possible to maintain a very high ratio of sterile to fertile flies by releasing only about one million flies each week during the warmer months of the year. Formerly, the threat to the establishment and spread of the insect was met by employing insecticide sprays. The use of sterile Mexican fruit fly releases in lieu of sprays is not only a more economical procedure, but avoids the objectionable feature of repeated spraying with insecticides.

There should be many circumstances where the continuous release of sterile insects could be employed to prevent the establishment of insects in critical areas. The Mediterranean fruit fly is a constant threat to the Florida citrus industry because of introductions of the insect in the Miami area. On several occasions during recent years, it has been necessary to institute an insecticide spray program to eliminate incipient infestations. The release of sterile flies before infestation gets out of hand should be a practical solution to such a problem in the future. It is possible also that the continuous release of a few million sterile flies per week in the Miami area would provide assurance that the few insects present in infested commodities that might escape detection by quarantine officials would not become established.

The above are examples of the value or potential value of sterile-insect releases to prevent establishment or to eliminate incipient insect populations before they can grow and spread. This procedure conceivably could have wide application throughout the world. However, it should again be emphasized that in order to be in a position to apply the method to the best advantage for specific insects, it will be necessary to develop all necessary procedures in advance. Early detection of introduced pests and quick action in instituting eradication efforts is important regardless of the control procedure employed, but it is particularly advantageous in applying the sterile-insect release method because, as previously noted, the cost and degree of effectiveness of the technique are governed by the ratio of sterile to fertile insects that must be achieved. If the natural population is at a very low level, an overwhelming ratio could be achieved by releasing relatively few sterile insects. If the detection of incipient infestations of certain insects is difficult and costly, and low-cost methods of rearing the insect are available, it may in some circumstances be more economical to continue the release of sterile insects than to establish and maintain intensive surveys.

THE INTEGRATION OF STERILE-INSECT RELEASES WITH OTHER SYSTEMS OF CONTROL

It was stated earlier that the natural population of most well-established insects is generally too high to make it economically feasible to rear and release the number of sterile insects required for population control.

This limitation to the practical use of sterile insects does not mean, however, that the sterility procedure involving the release of sterile insects cannot play an important role in meeting insect problems when used in conjunction with other methods of control. In fact, it is the writer's opinion that the greatest potential value of the sterile-insect release system will be to integrate sterile-insect releases with other systems of insect population control until natural population levels are reached where sterile-insect releases alone become the most economical procedure to follow. This possibility has been discussed in considerable depth (Knipling, 1964a).

The sterile-insect release method is inherently an inefficient system for controlling insects when natural populations are high, but potentially is a highly efficient system when the natural populations are low. Fortunately, certain other systems of insect population control, notably the use of insecticides, have contrasting merits in this regard. The use of insecticides is highly efficient in terms of the number of individual pests destroyed when natural populations are high and becomes progressively less efficient in terms of the number of individual pests destroyed when natural populations are low. Thus, the opportunity is presented to combine two contrasting systems to great advantage in dealing with the elimination or continuous control of insect populations.

The potential advantage of integrating the insecticide system and the sterile-insect release system over either system alone can be demonstrated by the use of hypothetical insect-control models.

TABLE 3

HYPOTHETICAL TRENDS IN AN INSECT POPULATION
TREATED WITH AN INSECTICIDE EACH GENERATION
UNTIL THEORETICAL ZERO IS ACHIEVED[a]

Generation	No. of insects treated	No. of survivors	No. of progeny
1 (Parent)	1,000,000	20,000	200,000
2	200,000	4,000	40,000
3	40,000	800	8,000
4	8,000	160	1,600
5	1,600	32	320
6	320	6	60
7	60	< 2	0

[a] The model assumes 98% control each generation and a tenfold increase for survivors.

Table 3 depicts the trend of a hypothetical insect population of 1,000,000 individuals when it is subjected each generation to insecticide treatments that destroy 98 percent of the
individuals. Each pair of the survivors is assumed to produce
20 progeny or a tenfold increase from one generation to the
next. The significant feature of insect population control by the
use of insecticides is that each treatment can be expected to
produce the same level of kill regardless of the population density. In this model the treatments directed against the initial
parent population will destroy 980,000 individuals if the level
of kill is 98 percent. Allowing for a tenfold increase of the
20,000 reproducing survivors, the second generation would then
consist of 200,000 insects. In the second generation, however,
the same dosage of insecticides and the same level of kill
could be expected to kill only 196,000. In each subsequent generation, the number of individuals killed becomes progressively
less. It would be just as costly to kill 98 percent of 320 insects
in the sixth generation as it was to kill 98 percent of 1,000,000
insects in the first generation. In the hypothetical model, it
would require more insecticide treatments to eliminate the
last one percent of the population than it did to eliminate the
first 99 percent. The model is hypothetical, but it is representative of practical experience in the use of insecticides for
the elimination of insect populations.

TABLE 4

HYPOTHETICAL TRENDS IN AN INSECT POPULATION
SUBJECTED TO RELEASE OF STERILE INSECTS[a]

Generation	No. of fertile insects	No. of sterile insects	Ratio sterile to fertile	No. of progeny
1 (Parent)	1,000,000	49,000,000	49:1	200,000
2	200,000	49,000,000	245:1	8,130
3	8,130	49,000,000	6,027:1	0

[a]All insects reproducing are assumed to increase tenfold.

Table 4 shows the requirements for the elimination of
a similar hypothetical insect population when subjected to
sterile-insect releases, if the initial release rate is designed
to reduce reproduction by 98 percent. This would require a
sterile to fertile ratio of 49:1 or the release of 49,000,000
sterile insects. The same rate of release during the second
generation would have a much greater effect because, theoretically, the ratio of sterile to fertile insects would increase
to 245:1. Theoretical elimination of the population would occur
in the third generation, when the ratio of sterile to fertile insects reaches 6,027 to 1. A total of 147 million insects, however, would be required to achieve elimination of the population. If the initial population of 1,000,000 insects represented
a high density for the area occupied by the population, the use
of sterile insects alone would in all probability be impractical.
    Table 5 shows the advantage of combining the use of
insecticides and sterile-insect releases. The model assumes
98 percent kill of the initial parent population with insecticides.
The reduced population (20,000) is then subjected to sterile-
insect releases. At this reduced level only 980,000 sterile
insects would be necessary to achieve a ratio of 49 sterile to 1
fertile. This ratio should reduce reproduction by 98 percent
or the same as the insecticide treatment at all population levels
and the same as the 49,000,000 sterile-insect release rate when
the natural population is at the original level of 1,000,000 insects. The continued release of 980,000 sterile insects would
then become progressively more effective until the natural
population reaches theoretical zero.

Thus, by taking advantage of the merits of each system of control, it is possible in this hypothetical situation to achieve complete control by employing insecticide treatments for one generation along with the release of 2,940,000 insects. Whereas insecticides alone, theoretically, would require treatments for seven generations, and sterile insects alone would require the release of 147,000,000 insects.

The fundamentals of insect population suppression depicted by Table 5 should be of great significance in exploiting the potential role that sterile-insect releases might play in meeting insect problems. The advantage of sterile-insect releases when integrated with other systems is not limited to integration with chemical insecticides. Cultural programs may be used to drastically reduce the natural population of certain insects. The use of insect pathogens, predator releases, or attractants, followed by the release of sterile insects, may be the most effective and desirable way to deal with other insect problems.

There are many important insect problems throughout the world that might be solved by developing and applying the integrated approach. The cotton boll weevil (*Anthonomous grandis*) in the United States might be cited as a promising candidate insect that eventually might be dealt with by an integrated approach. Knipling (1964a) has discussed details of the procedures that might be followed in eliminating boll weevil populations by integrating insecticide applications and sterile-insect releases. This integrated program might also provide the means for effective and practical elimination of tsetse fly populations

TABLE 5

HYPOTHETICAL TRENDS IN AN INSECT POPULATION
AGAINST WHICH INSECTICIDE TREATMENTS AND
STERILE-INSECT RELEASES ARE BOTH UTILIZED

Generation	Initial population	Natural population	Sterile population	Ratio sterile to fertile	Expected progeny
1 (Parent)	1,000,000[a]	20,000	980,000	49:1	4,000
2		4,000	980,000	245:1	163
3		163	980,000	6,027:1	0

[a]98% killed with insecticides.

in Africa (Knipling, 1964a, 1964b). The codling moth in various
parts of the world is another major insect problem that might
eventually be dealt with by the integration of insecticide application and sterile-insect releases. Proverbs and Newton
(1962) have shown that codling moths sterilized by gamma rays
can effectively suppress the reproductive potential of this
insect. B. A. Butt and his associates of the U.S. Department of
Agriculture laboratory, Yakima, Washington (personal com-
munications), have also obtained promising results in laboratory tests using moths sterilized with chemosterilants. Insecticides are now used intensively for controlling the codling moth.
Natural populations in commercial orchards are kept at a low
level in many areas because of the intensive use of insecticides.
By similarly limiting the development of codling moths in non-
commercial trees in the vicinity of commercial orchards, it
should be possible to reduce the total population in an area to
a level that would make it economically advantageous to sub-
stitute the use of sterile codling moth releases to either
achieve elimination in completely isolated areas or to maintain control on a continuing basis in a community or region
that may not be isolated.

BASIC REQUIREMENTS AND FACTORS THAT DETERMINE THE FEASIBILITY OF EMPLOYING THE STERILE-INSECT RELEASE TECHNIQUE

The foregoing discussion suggests that the sterile-insect
release system should play an important role in insect control
in the future. The method will not be feasible or practical for
controlling most of the destructive insects. Fortunately, however, the technique should play its most useful role in eliminating or controlling on a continuing basis many of the key insect
pests that are responsible for the most destructive losses. It is
more likely to be practical and economically advantageous to
rear and release the many sterile insects required than to use
chemicals if the intensive use of chemicals is necessary to
maintain control. Moreover, the control of insects by the sterile-
insect release system, when applied to total populations in
isolated or large areas, makes it feasible to achieve elimination
or maintain complete suppression of insect populations, thereby
eliminating all damage. Current procedures for the control of
most major insects are not only costly, but often the damage

caused by the insect, in spite of control efforts, amounts to millions of dollars annually.

The sterile-insect release system will not offer a simple and easy solution to any insect problem. Development of the technique will require difficult, costly, and complex research. Actual application of the technique, once it is developed, will require more complex operations and greater precision in applying the control method than are generally involved in current insect-control procedures. The feasibility of employing the sterile-insect release system to advantage for controlling a specific insect will be governed by a number of factors. The basic requirements and the type of information needed to appraise or establish the feasibility of employing the sterile-insect release technique are listed below:

1. Availability of a method of inducing sterility without serious adverse effects on the mating behavior and competitiveness of the male insects.

2. A practical method of rearing the insect in large numbers.

3. Quantitative information on the natural population density, especially at the lowest level in the population density cycle.

4. A practical way of further reducing natural populations to levels manageable with sterile insects if this is necessary or economically advantageous.

5. Information on rate of population increase as a guide for determining the necessary rate of overflooding with sterile insects.

6. The cost of reducing the natural population plus the cost for rearing and releasing the required number of sterile insects should be favorable in relation to costs of other methods of control plus the losses that occur in spite of control costs.

7. If complete elimination cannot be achieved because of reinfestations by migrating insects or because of new introductions, the cost of maintaining complete control by continuing sterile-insect releases must be favorable in relation to the costs for other available methods and the additional losses caused by the insect.

8. There could be justification for employing the sterile-insect release method, even if the method is more

costly than current ways to control or eradicate insect populations, if hazards to man and his environment are an important consideration when other
methods of control are employed.

9. Sterile insects to be released must not cause undue
damage to crops or livestock, or create hazards for
man and animals that outweigh the benefits of achieving or maintaining population control.

APPLICATION OF THE STERILITY TECHNIQUE
BY STERILIZING THE NATURAL POPULATION

It has already been noted that the technique of controlling insect and other pest populations by sterilizing the natural
population is basically different from the technique involving
the rearing and releasing of sterile organisms. Both methods
involve sterility, but any effort to categorize the two sterility
techniques as the same system of pest control can only lead to
confusion in efforts to appraise the merits and limitations of
sterility as a way to deal with pest problems. Different principles are involved in the manner in which population trends
are regulated by the two methods of control. The basic requirements for developing and putting each system into practice differ drastically. There may be circumstances in which
the two systems might be integrated to advantage, but they
should never be regarded as the same technique.

Pest populations subjected to treatment with chemosterilants, or any other feasible way of sterilizing individuals in
the natural population, follow the same trend as those subjected to treatment with conventional killing agents. The big
difference is that the sterility system is potentially more effective because two separate effects are produced by the sterilization procedure. The sterilized individuals cannot reproduce–an effect equivalent to killing in terms of reduced reproductive capacity of the population. But an extra effect is
achieved because the sterilized individuals can in turn reduce
the reproductive capacity of the remaining normal individuals
in the population. This writer has referred to this as the
''bonus effect.'' The advantage of the sterility procedure in
reducing the reproductive capacity in natural insect and other
pest populations over the killing system was first postulated
by Knipling (1959).

PRINCIPLES INVOLVED

In order to achieve the bonus effect, the sterility procedure must not destroy mating behavior and competitiveness of the sterilized organisms. Unless considerable mating competitiveness is retained, the method will have no theoretical advantage over killing, except to the extent that the sterile organisms might affect the reproductive potential by competing with the fertile organisms for food and living space. This factor alone could be highly significant in some situations, especially among vertebrate pests. However, if sexual competitiveness is maintained, the sterilized organisms will not only be incapable of reproducing, but they in turn will also have the ability to reduce the reproductive potential of the normal unsterilized population. Theoretically, if fully competitive, the sterilized organisms would be capable of adversely affecting the reproductive capacity of the remaining normal fertile organisms in a population to the same degree that the original population is affected by the sterilizing procedure. For example, if 50 percent of both sexes of a natural population were sterilized and the sterilized individuals were fully competitive, the sterile individuals would reduce the reproductive capacity of the remaining fertile population by 50 percent. If 90 percent were sterilized, the sterile individuals would reduce the reproductive capacity of the remaining individuals by 90 percent. The system might be regarded as a combined chemical-biological control method. The effects of the chemosterilant on the treated organism would be chemical; the effects of the sterilized organism would be biological.

Table 6 shows the maximum theoretical effect on the reproductive potential of a pest population when different levels of sterility are achieved in the natural population.

If a method of inducing sterility and a method of killing are equally efficient, the potential advantage of the sterility system over the conventional killing system is clearly indicated by Table 6. It was noted earlier that sterility has the same effect as killing insofar as the initial impact on reproduction is concerned. The extra immediate effect due to the sterility procedure is achieved only if the sterilized organisms retain normal sexual behavior. In such an event, the relative advantage over killing increases progressively as the level of sterility becomes higher. The figures in Table 6 show that in terms of the number of reproducing organisms, a sterility

TABLE 6

THE MAXIMUM EFFECT ON REPRODUCTION RESULTING
FROM DIFFERENT STERILITY LEVELS IN NATURAL
PEST POPULATIONS

Sterility level, %	Maximum reduction in reproductive potential, %
25	43.75
50	75
75	93.75
80	96
90	99
99	99.99

level of 50 percent would be two times as effective as 50 percent kill. At the 90 percent sterility level, the sterility system
is nine times as effective as the killing system in terms of the
number of individuals that would reproduce. At the 99 percent
sterility level, the advantage is 100 fold. A translation of the
percentage figures into actual numbers might be more enlight-
ening: If there were 20,000 individuals in the pest population
and 99 percent were killed, 200 individuals would remain to
reproduce. If 99 percent were sterilized, 200 would be capable
of reproducing, but since the ratio of sterile to fertile individuals in the population would be 99:1, only two individuals would
be expected to reproduce.

Information in Table 6 is presented to show the expected effects on one generation. The difference in trends of
insect populations subjected to treatment in successive generations with a sterility agent versus a conventional killing agent
may be noted in Table 7. In this model, it is assumed that both
sexes of the insects are sterilized and that there are no adverse effects on mating behavior or length of life. The rate
of increase of all fertile mated pairs is assumed to be fivefold. The insects are assumed to survive and reproduce for
one generation only.

The sterility system in this hypothetical model would
achieve theoretical elimination of the population by the sixth
generation, whereas the killing method would achieve theoretical elimination in 21 generations. The sterility method, although much more effective, has the same limitations as the

TABLE 7

RELATIVE TREND (THEORETICAL) OF INSECT POPU-
LATIONS SUBJECT TO: (1) NO CONTROL, (2) 90% KILL
WITH INSECTICIDES EACH GENERATION, (3) TREATMENT
THAT PRODUCES 90% STERILITY EACH GENERATION

	Number of insects resulting from		
Generation	No control (at assumed 5× increase rate)	Insecticide giving 90% kill applied each generation	Treatment producing 90% sterility applied each generation
1 (Parent)	1,000,000	1,000,000	1,000,000
2	5,000,000	500,000	50,000
3	25,000,000	250,000	2,500
4	125,000,000[a]	125,000	125
5	125,000,000	62,500	6
6	125,000,000	31,250	0
11	125,000,000	976	
16	125,000,000	31	
21	125,000,000	1	

[a]Assumed maximum population for the environment.

killing system in terms of the effect in relation to the population density. It can be assumed that it would require just as
much chemosterilant and the same treatment procedure to
achieve 90 percent sterility in 100 individuals as in 1,000,000.
Thus, like insecticides, it can be concluded that chemosterilants will be highly efficient in terms of the number of individuals in a population that are sterilized when the pest population
is high and highly inefficient in terms of the number of individuals sterilized when the population is low. In contrast, reference
is made to the earlier discussion of the principles involved in
the control of insect populations by rearing and releasing
sterile insects. The rearing and releasing procedure becomes
increasingly effective as the natural population density declines.

Since the two sterility systems differ in their potential
efficiency, depending on the natural population density, it is apparent that the integration of the two systems could be advantageous in some cases in the same way that the integration of
conventional chemical control procedure and sterile-insect

releases might prove advantageous. For example, if an insect population were under control by the use of a chemosterilant as depicted in the last column of Table 7, it might be more practical to rear and release sterile insects after the natural population is reduced to 50,000 than to apply another chemosterilant treatment. It should be pointed out, however, that it would be necessary to employ insecticides for four generations to reduce the natural population to a level comparable to the 50,000 level achieved by the use of a chemosterilant for one generation.

OTHER POTENTIAL ADVANTAGES OF THE STERILITY SYSTEM IN NATURAL PEST POPULATION CONTROL

The foregoing discussion has emphasized the importance of the bonus effect in reducing the reproductive potential of pest populations. It is the writer's opinion that this is the chief advantage of the sterility technique over the killing technique. However, there are other potential advantages in the sterility procedure that could be of great significance in pest population control. The killing procedure can reduce reproduction in a pest population only to the degree that individuals in a population are killed.

The sterility procedure, on the other hand, could have the following separate effects on the reproductive potential of a pest population.

1. The reproductive potential of the population is reduced to the extent that sterility is achieved in the natural population. This reduction is the same as that achieved by killing at the same level.
2. The reproductive potential of the pest population is further reduced to the extent that sterilized individuals will compete for mates with unsterilized individuals. This bonus effect could be equal to the initial sterilizing or the initial killing effect.
3. The sterilized individuals, through movement, can affect the reproductive potential of individuals outside the area treated (space effect).
4. Among long-lived organisms, the sterilized individuals can affect the reproductive potential of the popu-

lation in subsequent generations (time effect).

5. The sterilized individuals will compete with unsterilized individuals for food and shelter in the environment during their normal survival period.

The relative importance of the five different factors in reducing the reproductive capacity of a pest population will vary with the individual species and the circumstances.

The importance of the second factor, which has been referred to as the "bonus effect," has already been discussed in some detail. However, it might be well to repeat that this effect, when sterile organisms are fully competitive, is equal to the direct effect of sterilization.

The third factor, involving movement in and out of the environment occupied by the treated population, may be significant among highly mobile animals. Sterilized individuals from the treated environment can move into untreated areas and affect the reproductive potential of unexposed fertile individuals. Likewise, unsterilized individuals from the surrounding unexposed environment can move into the treated area and be affected by the sterilized individuals.

The fourth factor, the time factor, will be of no significance among short-lived animals that do not live long enough to mate with individuals in the generation that follows. Many insects are short lived and would not survive to overlap the next generation. Insects that have only one generation a year and do not overwinter as adults could have no impact on reproduction during the next generation. But among long-lived animals, including certain insects that survive long enough to overlap a subsequent generation, the time factor is one of the most important advantages of the sterility system over the killing system. In view of the potential significance of this factor, it will be discussed in more detail in the following section of this report.

The fifth factor could be of considerable importance for a short period of time in limiting the available food supply for all animals in the population or in occupying favorable areas where the animals are less subject to predation or other hazards. In contrast; a high kill of an animal population could be expected to give an immediate advantage to the surviving population because of less competition for available food per individual and because the survivors could select the most favorable sites for protection from predation or adverse weather.

INFLUENCE OF THE SURVIVAL-TIME FACTOR
ON THE REPRODUCTIVE POTENTIAL
OF INSECT POPULATIONS

As previously stated, the length of survival can be a significant factor in determining the advantage of the sterility over the killing system of insect population control. In projecting the effects of sterilization as shown in Tables 6 and 7, it was assumed that the insects survived for only one generation. On the other hand, if some of the insects, either fertile or sterile, live long enough to overlap reproduction during the next generation, this would be an *advantage* to the pest that has been subjected to control by killing, but a *disadvantage* to the pest that has been subjected to control by the sterility procedure. Many insects, including such important pests as the boll weevil and tsetse fly are relatively long lived, and a substantial portion of the individuals of one generation could be expected to live long enough to overlap reproduction in at least one subsequent generation.

To evaluate the theoretical effects of the survival-time factor on the reproductive potential of insect populations, a hypothetical population model will again be employed. This is shown in Table 8.

It is assumed that one half the insects emerging in one generation will survive and be capable of reproducing during the next generation. All successful reproducing pairs of insects, regardless of age, are assumed to produce 10 progeny. This would represent a fivefold increase. On the basis of these assumptions, the population subjected to 90 percent kill in the parent generation would consist of 3,025,000 individuals by the third generation. If none of the insects survived to reproduce during the second generation, the total insects in the third generation would number only 2,500,000. If neither sterile nor fertile insects from the first generation overlapped the second generation, the number of insects in the third generation would theoretically be 250,000. Thus, the survival-time factor would cause a reduction in population buildup by more than 50 percent when the sterility system is used, but cause an increase in population by about 20 percent when the killing system is used. Actually, the estimated effect on reproduction in the population subjected to the sterility treatment is probably conservative. If the female insects are completely monogamous, none of the surviving females from the parent generation that

TABLE 8

THEORETICAL TRENDS OF INSECT POPULATION SUB-
JECTED TO: (1) NO CONTROL, (2) 90% KILLED IN THE
FIRST GENERATION, (3) 90% STERILIZED IN THE FIRST
GENERATION. IT IS ASSUMED THAT ONE HALF THE IN-
SECTS SURVIVE TO OVERLAP THE NEXT GENERATION[a]

Generation	(1) Uncontrolled population 5× increase rate	(2) 90% killed (fertile survivors)	(3) 90% sterilized (fertile survivors)	Sterile survivors
1 (Parent)	1,000,000	100,000	100,000	900,000
2	5,500,000	550,000	100,000[b]	450,000
3	30,250,000	3,025,000	115,905	0

[a]All reproducing insects are assumed to produce five progeny.
One half of the insects produced in one generation survive to reproduce in the next generation.

[b]Half of these would represent survivors of the first or parent
generation and the other half represent progeny of insects that reproduced successfully during the first or parent generation.

mated originally with sterile males would produce progeny during the second generation. In the model as constructed, the assumption is made that all surviving unsterilized females from
the first generation would produce progeny if mated to fertile
males during the reproductive period of the second generation.
For a species in which the females are monogamous for life,
the population level in the third generation would be about
90,000 instead of 115,000.

HOW THE STERILITY TECHNIQUE MIGHT BE
EMPLOYED AGAINST SPECIFIC INSECTS

There is reason to believe that sterility-producing
agents comparable in effectiveness and safety to insecticides
will eventually be developed. In such an event, we might consider how such material could be employed to advantage in
controlling a specific insect. Knipling (1962b) calculated the
relative theoretical effect on comparable boll weevil populations if an insecticide and a chemosterilant, each effective

at a 95 percent level, were employed against representative overwintered boll weevil populations. The relative effects of such treatments are shown in Table 9.

Theoretically, complete elimination of reproduction in a population of 200 boll weevils on one acre of cotton would result if 95 percent of the parent population were sterilized, whereas, a substantially large population could be expected by the end of the season (F_3 generation) if 95 percent kill were achieved in the parent population. Insecticide treatments that kill 95 percent of the insects would have to be applied each generation for three successive generations in order to achieve

TABLE 9

THEORETICAL TRENDS IN POPULATIONS OF BOLL
WEEVILS SUBJECTED TO: (1) NO CONTROL, (2) 95% KILL
OF PARENT GENERATION WITH INSECTICIDES, (3) 95%
STERILITY OF PARENT GENERATION WITH CHEMO-
STERILANTS[a]

		Number of weevils resulting from	
Generation	No treatment	Treatment of parent generation with insecticide giving 95% kill	Treatment of parent generation with chemosterilant giving 95% sterility
Parent[b]	200	200 reduced to 10 fertile	200 (converted to 190 sterile and 10 fertile)[e]
F_1	1,100	55	100 (95 sterile and 5 fertile)[e]
F_2	6,000	300	0
F_3[c]	6,000+ [d]	1,637	0

[a]The model assumes a spring population of 200 boll weevils per acre and a fivefold increase of reproducing boll weevils each generation, plus 50% survival of boll weevils that emerged in previous generations.

[b]Represents hibernating survivors.

[c]It is assumed that weevils emerging as the F_3 generation will constitute the hibernating population.

[d]The maximum population level would depend on number of fruiting forms present for growth and development during the F_2 generation.

[e]Odds would favor absence of fertile matings.

theoretical elimination of a population on one acre.

If chemosterilants are not sufficiently selective to permit safe use when applied to the insect in its natural habitat in the same way insecticides are now employed, selectivity in use might be achieved by incorporating the chemosterilants in specific attractants.

Baits that will attract both sexes of an insect are one of the promising ways of control. The use of a chemosterilant instead of a toxicant in such baits would have the advantage discussed earlier: a greater effect on reproduction would be achieved if the insects coming to the baited traps were allowed to return to the environment after sterilization instead of being destroyed. In some instances attractants might not be sufficiently effective to achieve the required level of control when the insects are destroyed. However, with the increased effect on the reproduction potential of the population when a substantial portion of the population is sterilized, the sterility procedure could represent the difference between success and failure in insect control. For example, the use of an attractant that would lead to a kill of 75 percent of an insect population each generation might not provide adequate control to prevent the buildup of a damaging population. However, the sterilization of 75 percent would theoretically reduce reproduction by 93.75 percent each generation, which in all probability would be adequate to control the insect population buildup.

One of the most challenging areas of research in entomology is in the field of insect sex attractants. Chemists and entomologists are exploring the potential usefulness of these sex pheromones for insect control. Accordingly, it should be pointed out that the full impact of the sterility procedure cannot be realized by destroying only one sex of an animal population. If 90 percent of the males of an insect population are sterilized when the insects are drawn to a sex attractant, the maximum decline in reproduction that could result would be 90 percent. But if 90 percent of both sexes are attracted to a bait and sterilized, the maximum decline in reproduction would be 99 percent. If females are the aggressor and are drawn to a sex attractant produced by the males, the effects of killing and sterilization should be the same. Even when males are the aggressor and are attracted to a sex attractant produced by the female, there is relatively little advantage to sterilizing the males instead of killing them, if the attractant is in continuous competition with the virgin females (based on estimates made by Knipling and McGuire, 1966). However, sterilization of males coming to attractants that do not necessarily compete with sex pheromones produced by the females with respect to time and place; or the sterilization of males if they are selectively attracted to physical attractants, such as light, could have a substantial advantage over the killing of males. For example, the sterilization rather than the destruction of males of the oriental fruit fly *(Dacus dorsalis)* coming to methyl eugenol, could provide a much more efficient means of achieving population control of this important fruit pest. Methyl eugenol is a powerful male lure for this insect (Steiner, et al., 1965). The possible advantage of using a chemosterilant instead of a toxicant in combination with methyl eugenol has not been investigated as a means of control of the oriental fruit fly. Powerful male lures are also known for other important species of the tropical fruit fly group.

STERILITY FOR REGULATING VERTEBRATE PEST POPULATIONS

The sterility principle should prove useful for regulating vertebrate pest populations. Not only is the method potentially more efficient than the present system of destruction or removal, but the method should be more acceptable to the public. In most circumstances, the objective in vertebrate pest control will be to regulate the number of animals in an area rather than to eliminate the populations.

The same basic principles that affect population trends in insects are applicable to vertebrate pests if sexual behavior and aggressiveness of the sterilized animals are not impaired. Wildlife biologists or rodent specialists must develop necessary information on the behavior and population dynamics of each species and take into account many factors in appraising the feasibility of applying the technique in practical control operations. However, regardless of the species, if it is practical to regulate an animal population effectively by destruction or removal of a substantial part of the population, it should be even more practical to regulate the population by applying the sterility method. Irreversible sterility would naturally have the greatest impact, especially among long-lived species.

Sterility lasting even for one breeding season, however, could have a greater impact on the reproductive capacity of the population than would result from the destruction or removal of the same number of animals in a given area. Temporary sterility would obviously require repeated application over a period of several generations in order to substantially lower the population.

The theoretical effect of the sterility technique on population trends of any organism can be calculated by establishing hypothetical models that reflect representative density levels and trends of untreated populations in comparison to populations subjected to different levels of sterility. Knipling (1959, 1962a) has previously calculated the theoretical effects of the sterility procedure versus the killing procedure when applied to hypothetical vertebrate animal populations.

It should be emphasized that the full effect of the sterility procedure will be realized only if mating competitiveness, mating behavior, and length of life of the sterilized individuals are not adversely affected. Sterility that destroys mating behavior, such as castration, could have no advantage over killing or removal of the same portion of the population insofar as the reproductive capacity of the population is concerned. The presence of sterile individuals in an environment would have some temporary adverse effects on the reproductive capacity of the remaining fertile population because of competition for food, favorable habitats, and so forth. However, if the sterility does not adversely affect mating behavior, all of the advantages over killing as a means of pest control cited for insects should apply in the case of vertebrate pests. The "time" factor would appear to be of particular importance among long-lived vertebrate pests.

Table 10 (Knipling 1962a) shows the calculated trends of a vertebrate pest population subjected to 95 percent kill of an original parent population as compared with the trend of a similar population subjected to a treatment that causes irreversible sterility in 95 percent of the parent population. It is assumed that the sterility treatment does not adversely affect the length of life or sexual behavior of the animal. It is also assumed that the species is monogamous. This hypothetical model clearly shows the great potential advantage of the sterility technique among pests that would be expected to survive for a number of generations. The population dynamics of different species of animals vary. Allowances must be made for factors such as survival rate, length of life, reproductive

TABLE 10

THEORETICAL TREND OF A VERTEBRATE ANIMAL
POPULATION SUBJECTED TO: (1) 95% KILL OR (2) 95%
STERILIZATION

Generation	Population trend after 95% kill of initial population		Population trend after 95% sterility of initial population	
Parent	1,000	50	1,000	(50 fertile, 950 sterile)
F_1		75	505	(30 fertile, 475 sterile)
F_2		112	253	(18 fertile, 235 sterile)
F_3		168	126	(9 fertile, 117 sterile)
F_4		252	64	(5 fertile, 59 sterile)
F_5		378	32	(3 fertile, 29 sterile)
F_6		587	16	(2 fertile, 14 sterile)
F_7		880	8	(1 fertile, 7 sterile)
F_8		1320	4	(0 fertile, 4 sterile)
F_9		1980	2	(0 fertile, 2 sterile)
F_{10}		2970	1	(sterile)

behavior, and reproductive capacity in appraising the relative
effectiveness of the two systems of control. However, regardless of difference in species, the proper type of sterility will
have the basic advantages depicted. Polygamous mating habits
in a species could reduce the relative difference in effect of
the two systems of control. However, sterility might be
achieved in various ways. Polygamous mating habits may not
be a serious disadvantage if ova are fertilized by sperms from
sterilized males and the embryos fail to develop. This would
be highly significant, especially for animals that have restricted breeding periods. Only the biologist familiar with the
particular animal to be controlled can determine the potential
merits of the sterility procedure, because it is vitally important to understand the life history and habits of the animal.
Also, many factors must be considered in applying the control
techniques. Nevertheless, if an appropriate material or method
for producing sterility can be developed that is comparable in
efficiency to that of a lethal material when used in essentially
the same way, the sterility technique should be more efficient
than the lethal agent for regulating populations of any species,
whether it be a carnivorous animal, bird, rodent, fish, game
animal, or any other vertebrate.

The pigeon problem in urban areas might serve as an

example of the possible advantage of the sterility principle for regulating an animal population. Pigeons are regarded by many as a desirable species. They furnish esthetic value for many in city parks and elsewhere. On the other hand, an over-abundance of the birds can create problems of sanitation around food or feed-handling areas, roosting and nesting sites, or in other places where the birds congregate. An overpopulation might also result in starvation and diseases among the birds and thus affect the well-being of the entire pigeon population.

To test the potential advantage over killing of regulating a pigeon population and by the use of an effective and safe sterility agent (if such an agent were developed), three initially similar and ecologically isolated hypothetical populations will be established. One will remain untreated, and two will be subjected to control for one generation. Of the two populations subjected to control, one will be treated with a hypothetical lethal agent that destroys 80 percent of the birds and the other will be treated with a hypothetical irreversible sexual sterilant that sterilizes 80 percent of both sexes without otherwise adversely affecting their mating behavior or length of life. For the normal uncontrolled population, the parent population declines by one half each generation, because of normal environmental hazards, but each pair produces two juveniles that reach maturity and become potential parents for the next generation. Thus the increase rate of the population is 1.5-fold per generation. Each of the three populations is assumed to start with 100,000 reproducing parents. The maximum density that the environment will maintain is assumed to be 500,000. For the two populations subjected to control, the rate of decrease and increase for all reproducing pairs are the same as for the uncontrolled population. The mortality rate of sterile and fertile birds is assumed to be the same. All population density dependent factors below the 500,000 population level are ignored in establishing the increase or decrease rates for the three populations.

The number of individual birds that would be present in the three populations each generation is shown in Table 11. The population trends are also shown graphically (Fig. 1).

The uncontrolled population would reach the maximum population density by the fifth generation. The population subjected to 80 percent kill in the parent generation would regain the original population level by the fifth generation and reach the maximum density level by the ninth. The population sub-

TABLE 11

THEORETICAL TRENDS OF THREE HYPOTHETICAL
PIGEON POPULATIONS, EACH IN DIFFERENT URBAN
AREAS, WHEN SUBJECTED TO: (1) NO TREATMENT,
(2) A TREATMENT THAT KILLS 80% OF THE BIRDS IN THE
THE FIRST GENERATION, (3) A TREATMENT THAT PRO-
DUCES IRREVERSIBLE STERILITY IN 80% OF BOTH SEXES
IN THE FIRST GENERATION[a]

Genera-tions	No treatment	80% kill of 1st generation	80% sterility of 1st generation		
				Sterile	Fertile
1	100,000	20,000	100,000	80,000	20,000
2	150,000	30,000	54,000	40,000	14,000
3	225,000	45,000	30,627	20,000	10,627
4	337,500	67,500	19,000	10,000	9,000
5	500,000	101,250	13,765	5,000	8,765
6	500,000	151,875	12,529	2,500	10,029
7	500,000	227,813	14,288	1,250	13,038
8	500,000	341,719	19,669	625	19,044
9	500,000	500,000	27,305	312	26,993

Number of pigeons

[a]All fertile mated pairs are assumed to produce two adult
progeny each year, but one half of the parents disappear because of
normal environmental hazards each year.

jected to the sterility treatment would reach a low level of
about 12,000 birds by the sixth generation and then gradually
increase. The level would be only about 27,000 by the ninth
generation, however, when the population treated with a lethal
agent reached the assumed maximum density level of 500,000.
The population subjected to the sterility treatment would begin
to increase at a normal rate during about the tenth generation.
    As previously pointed out in the discussion on insects,
the degree of advantage of the sterility technique over the killing technique depends on the percentage of the population
sterilized or killed. The same principle should apply in the
case of vertebrate pest control. If the theoretical effects of
a 90 percent sterility level were compared with a 90 percent
kill level, the effect would be even greater in favor of the
sterility procedure than is shown in Table 11 and in Figure 1.
The sterilization of 90 percent of the pigeons would result in
almost complete elimination of the population. A 95 percent
sterility level in the initial parent population would, accord-

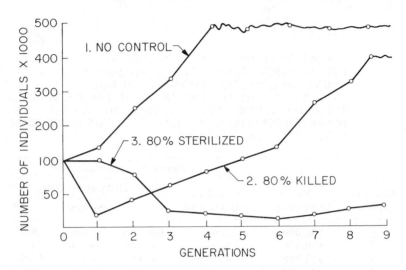

FIG. 1. The theoretical trends of hypothetical pigeon populations subjected to (1) no control, (2) control by destroying 80 percent of
the initial population, (3) control by sterilizing 80 percent of the initial
population. (Basic assumptions are discussed in the text.)

ing to the basic assumptions, result in complete elimination
of the isolated pigeon population. The population decline would
follow the same general trend indicated for the hypothetical
animal population in Table 10, except that it would take longer
for a starting animal population of 100,000 to reach theoretical zero.

Wildlife biologists are exploring the sterility method of
vertebrate pest population control (Wetherbee, 1964). The use
of chemicals that produce sterility in animals, whether for controlling invertebrate or vertebrate pests, will no doubt create
potential problems of safety to other organisms in the environment just as does the use of any toxicant. The degree of safety
that can be achieved in the use of a sterility agent will depend
on the progress that can be made in developing materials that
are highly selective in action against the target species or in
developing selective ways to use the materials.

Suitable ways to administer the sterility agents to animals in the natural population would obviously be the most
practical procedures to consider in most circumstances. If
trapping procedures offer the only practical way to regulate
an animal population, however, the sterility principle should

still prove useful. If animals are trapped, the removal of the females and sterilization of males for return into the environment would theoretically have a much greater adverse impact on the reproductive potential of a population than the destruction or removal of both sexes. If destruction or removal of any of the trapped animals is impractical or undesirable, the sterilization of both sexes and their return into the environment should have the same effect as the destruction or removal of the females and the return of sterile males into the environment.

In order to apply the sterility principle to advantage over the killing method, it will no doubt be essential that the control program be directed as uniformly as possible to the total pest population. Because of considerable movement of most animals from place to place, an individual owner of a small tract could not expect much advantage in pest population control by employing a sterility agent. The advantage of the sterility procedure over the killing procedure will not be immediately realized even if applied to the total population in a large area because of the survival of the sterilized animals. However, it is the sterile survivors that produce the final advantage of the sterility system of animal population control.

REFERENCES

Bushland, R. C., and D. E. Hopkins. 1951. Experiments with screw-worm flies sterilized by x-rays. J. Econ. Entom., 44(5): 725–731.

_____, and D. E. Hopkins. 1953. Sterilization of screw-worm flies with x-rays and gamma rays. J. Econ. Entom., 46(4):648–656.

Charpentier, L. J., and Ralph Mathes. 1962. Sugarcane borer over-wintering population and outlook. The Sugar Bulletin, April, 40[14]:158.

Knipling, E. F. 1955. Possibilities of insect control or eradication through the use of sexually sterile males. J. Econ. Entom., 48(4):459–462.

_____. 1959. Sterile male method of population control. Science, 139(3380):902–904.

_____. 1962a. The sterility principle of population control. Proc. First Intl. Conf. on Wildlife Disease Assn. High View, N.Y. June 24–27.

_____. 1962b. Potentialities and progress in the development of chemo-sterilants for insect control. J. Econ. Entom., 55(5):782–786.

_____. 1964a. The potential role of the sterility method for insect population control with special reference to combining this method with conventional methods. U.S. Dept. Agr. Research Service. ARS 33–98, Nov.

_____. 1964b. The sterility principle of insect population control. Pesticides Abstracts and News Summary, Section A, 10,587–10,603.

_____. and J. W. McGuire, 1966. Population models to test theoretical effects of sex attractants used for insect control. Agric. Information Bulletin 308:20. Agri. Res. Serv. U.S. Dept. Agric.

Proverbs, M. D., and J. R. Newton. 1962. Suppression of the reproductive potential of the codling moth by gamma irradiated males in caged orchard trees. J. Econ. Entom., 55(6):934–936.

Steiner, L. F., W. C. Mitchell, E. J. Harris, T. T. Kozuma, and M. S. Fujimoto. 1965a. Oriental fruit fly eradication by male an-nihilation. J. Econ. Entom., 58(5):961–964.

Wetherbee, D. K. 1964. Vertebrate pest control by biological means. Presented as part of a Symposium held by Section O (Agriculture) at 1964 Annual Meeting of Amer. Ass. for Advancement of Science, Montreal, Canada. Unpublished.

3

Laboratory Procedures

GERMAIN C. LA BRECQUE

ENTOMOLOGY RESEARCH DIVISION
INSECTS AFFECTING MAN AND ANIMALS BRANCH
GAINESVILLE, FLORIDA

INTRODUCTION

The elimination of the screwworm *Cochliomyia homini-vorax* (Coquerel) from the United States indicates the practicality of the sterile-male approach for the control of insect pests. Since that time, interest in this approach has increased steadily, especially with regard to chemosterilants. Chemosterilants are chemicals that (1) cause sexual sterility by preventing the development of sperm or ovum, (2) cause the death of the sperm or ovum after it has been produced, or (3) so severely injure the genetic make-up of the sperm and ovum that fertilization, if accomplished, will not result in viable progeny. Other desirable properties are species specificity, and low chronic toxicity to warm-blooded animals.

To find chemicals possessing such properties, numerous laboratories have initiated screening programs along the following lines. Entomologists and chemists have selected chemicals suspected of possessing antimitotic, antimetabolic, or anticarcinogenic properties. These chemicals have been included in programs similar to those now in use in screening insecticides to obtain a rapid qualitative index of biological activity. The promising sterilant is then used as a basis for the further selective evaluation of related structures. Approximately 400 chemicals have been found that indicated biological activity, and these have been used to determine the effect of chemosterilants on insect metabolism, population dynamics, behavior, and many other factors.

SCREENING

A convenient technique used in a formal screening program was developed in 1958 and is still in use at the U.S. Department of Agriculture laboratory of Insects Affecting Man and Animals in Gainesville, Florida. In their tests with house flies [*Musca domestica* (L.)], a specific amount of the candidate sterilant is incorporated in an essential portion of the adult diet consisting of either sugar or a standard-adult nutriment.[1] The standard-adult nutriment was chosen because it had been used for over 15 years in maintaining the house fly colonies and because the flies prefer this diet to any other. Concurrent studies

---

[1]Six parts granulated sugar, six parts powdered nonfat dry milk, and one powdered egg yolk.

with treated sugar have been included, however, because the proteinaceous base of the standard-adult nutriment may have some deleterious effect on some of the candidate chemoster- ilants. In these screening tests, the treated diet, including 1.0 percent of the candidate sterilant and an adequate water supply, is introduced into a cage containing 100 newly eclosed adults of mixed sexes. Cages containing 100 flies with untreated sugar or adult nutriment are used as controls. After 3 days, the flies in the cages are examined to note if any mortality has been caused by the chemical, and untreated adult nutriment is added to those cages containing only treated sugar to provide protein for ovum development. When the flies are 6 to 7 days old, aged, moist larval medium is placed in the cage for oviposition. Four to six hours later, the oviposition medium is withdrawn, submerged in water, and stirred to disassemble the egg masses. A random sample of 100 eggs is collected and placed on a small piece of moistened black cloth, which in turn is laid on moist larval medium in a small rearing container. If no eggs are laid, oviposition medium is offered again at 1- and 2-day inter- vals until it has been offered five times, or until the flies have oviposited. After the eggs have been exposed to the larvel me- dium for 24 hrs, they are examined for hatch. The larvae are then allowed to crawl through or from the cloth into the rearing medium and, about a week after oviposition, the pupae are counted to determine the number of larvae that have reached the pupal stage of development. Sterility is based on the number of pupae derived from 100 eggs. With house flies, egg hatch is not considered a good criterion of sterilant effect; hatch may be delayed on account of dryness; excess moisture in the cloth may rupture the eggs giving appearances of hatching, or more con- ceivably, low concentrations of aziridines, s-triazines, and di- methyl amine compounds would allow the lethality induced to be expressed in the newly hatched larvae rather than in the em- bryos (Morgan and LaBrecque, 1964). Reduction in pupal count could be derived from larval mortality in dried or contaminated larval medium but concurrent untreated checks in like medium would normally uncover this fact. Failure of a female to oviposit is also considered a criterion in the evaluation of a compound as a chemosterilant.

Since the treated diet is offered to mixed sexes, the tech- nique does not demonstrate whether sterility has been induced in the male, the female, or both sexes. Further studies with the males, however, will show whether they have been sterilized.

As soon as it becomes apparent that the chemical produces sterility, 10 males are removed from the cage and introduced into a cage containing 10 sexually mature virgin females reared on an untreated diet. Three days later, oviposition medium is made available and sterility assessed following the procedure described previously. If the results of the second mating show sterility, the compound obviously sterilized the males. If the second mating indicates fertility, it may mean that the sterilant effect in the male is transitory. If seems more plausible, however, to assume that the chemical was a chemosterilant of females only. To determine whether the lack of progeny was not caused by noninseminated eggs deposited by virgin females, or to ascertain whether sperm motility was not affected by the chemosterilant, females from the test cages are also removed, the spermathecae are excised in insect's ringer solution (0.1 g potassium chloride, 0.0135 g calcium chloride, 0.012 g sodium bicarbonate, and 0.75 g of sodium chloride in 100 ml of distilled water), crushed on a slide and examined under magnification for the presence of motile sperm.

Chemicals are first tested at a concentration of 1.0 percent. Those that cause sterility or mortality are tested at lower concentrations to find the minimum effective concentration. Compounds that induce sterility are also tested at 2.5 and 5.0 percent to determine the maximum range that will produce sterility without too much mortality. This screening procedure appears to be more extensive than necessary for a preliminary evaluation. It can be justified, however, since a comprehensive determination of the sterilant properties of the compound can be derived with a relatively small amount of chemical, which is often all that is available. To date, the Gainesville organization has screened over 4,000 chemicals and uncovered over 360 compounds possessing insect-chemosterilant activity.

Other investigators also use the house fly as a test organism in chemosterilant-screening programs. Kenaga (1965) initiates his tests by selecting 100 pupae. These are placed in a paper dish on the floor of a 1-ft^3 screened cage. The procedure follows that previously described for the adult nourishment. He uses 1.0 percent of the candidate chemosterilant in the food as the initial concentration, and the oviposition medium is offered to the adults 3 to 4 days after eclosion and remains in the cage for 3 days. Kenaga's assessment of sterility also differs in that it is based on larval count. When the cup of larval medium is removed from the cage, it is filled with tepid water to the point where the medium is immersed. The water forces the larvae to the surface in their attempt to escape drowning. In cups containing larvae from eggs laid by an equal number of control females, the number of larvae usually found amounts to several thousand, which makes the effect of the chemical on egg viability rather easy to determine visually. In the test larval containers, larval counts are estimated except when less than 50 larvae are found. If no larvae are found, the medium is examined for unhatched eggs. The percent sterility produced by the candidate chemical is derived by deducting the number of larvae in the treatment from the number obtained in the control group (arbitrarily set at 2,000). This number is then divided by the number of larvae in the control group and multiplied by 100.

J. T. Chang et al. (1963) use the house fly *Musca domestica vicina* Macq. as their screening insect. The freshly eclosed adults are exposed for 24 and 48 hrs to a milk powder containing 1.0 and 0.5 percent of the candidate chemosterilant. Sterility is based on the number of eggs laid and the percentage hatch over a period of 14 days.

McFadden and Rubio (1965) also utilize the feeding approach to determine the sterilant effect of candidate chemosterilants on the reproductive capacity of the Mexican fruit fly *Anastrepha ludens* (Loew). They present the chemical in a mixture of orange juice and sugar. The orange juice crystals are diluted in water in a ratio of 1:3 and neutralized with NaOH. The pH of the solution is set at 7.0 because many chemicals, particularly the aziridines, break down rapidly in acidic solutions. Three milliliters of the diluted juice are mixed with 4 g of sugar and poured on the bottom of a petri dish. Enough chemical is added to the solution to form a 1.0 or a 0.1 percent concentration. After the mixture has dried for 1 day, it is placed in a cage containing 50 male and 50 female fruit flies, 1 day old. The flies are allowed to feed at will on a treated diet and a dietary supplement of protein hydrolysate for 21 days. Cages containing untreated food are used as controls. At weekly intervals from the start of the test, the caged populations are checked for mortality. On the 12th and 19th days, oviposition medium is placed in the cages, the eggs are collected and approximately 200 are placed on blotting paper moistened with 0.07 percent of sodium benzoate in water to prevent fungal contamination. The blotting papers are then placed in petri dishes and incubated for 7 days, after which the hatch is determined. Compounds that cause sterility or death in the adults are then retested to deter-

mine the effective range of concentration that induces sterility
without excessive mortality.

Mosquitoes at the Gainesville, Florida laboratory are
also used as a test organism for potential sterilants. In this
screening program, 50 to 100 adult *Aedes aegypti* L. mosquitoes are allowed to emerge in a cage 20 by 20 by 25 cm in di-
mension. The mosquitoes are fed continuously on a sugar solution containing 1 percent of the candidate sterilant. No other
food is available. Four days after peak emergence, the mosquitoes are given a blood meal, and eggs are collected on wet filter
paper provided in small beakers. The mosquitoes are then given
a second blood meal, and a second collection of eggs is made.
The eggs are allowed to stand on wet filter paper for 4 days,
after which they are counted. The eggs are then flooded and the
percentage hatch is determined. The compounds are evaluated
by determining adult survival, number of eggs deposited; and
percent hatch. Compounds showing promise are tested at other
concentrations.

Crystal (1963) in his screening program with the screw-
worm *Cochliomyia hominivorax* (Coquerel) selects 100 flies of
mixed sexes less than 24 hr old and exposes them daily to
freshly prepared quantities of honey containing 1.0 percent of
the candidate chemical for 1 week. The food is made available to
the flies by spreading it on gauze and applying it to the screen
forming the roof of the cage. The pH of the formulation is adjusted to avoid use of an acid medium. Whenever mortality is
induced at the initial test concentration, the test is rerun at
lower concentrations until enough insects survive to derive reliable data as to the sterilant effectiveness of the compound.
In each series of tests, control experiments are run for baseline data. On the eighth day after emergence, 20 females, when
available, are withdrawn from the cage, and placed in individual
vials containing ground lean beef for evaluation of fecundity
(average number and hatchability of eggs laid per female).

Ascher (1957), Mitlin et al. (1957), and Ristich et al.
(1965) with house flies, and Hays and Cochran (1964) with *Conotrachelus nenuphar* (Herbst.) and Keiser et al. (1965) with teph-
ritids also use the feeding approach with appropriate variations
in the diet and in the methods of fecundity evaluation.

Other methods are also used in the screwworm screening programs. Crystal (1963) conducts a companion screening
program using topical applications as a confirmation of results
obtained by feeding. Young adults less than 24 hr old are anes-

thetized with CO_2, after which 2.0 to 2.5 μl of a 10 percent acetone solution of the sterilant is applied to the body of each fly.
In each test, 20 flies of each sex are treated with 200 to 250 μg
of the test chemical. Fertility is evaluated in the same manner
as that described in his oral feeding evaluations.

Often it is more practicable to screen against stages
other than the adult stage, or it is advantageous to determine
whether the sterilant is effective against other stadia. At
Gainesville, Florida, sterilants are also screened against immature house flies In this program, 25 g of dry larval medium
is moistened with 25 ml of water. Fifty eggs are then placed
on moistened patches of black cloth, and washed off the cloth
into the dampened medium with 15 ml of water; 72 hr later, 25
ml of water containing 0.25 g of the chemical in suspension or
solution is then poured in the medium. Twenty-four hours later,
the medium is examined to determine the condition of the larvae.
Two days later, the pupae are examined for abnormalities. At
this time the pupae in the medium are placed in a cage with nutriment and water added. Five days after eclosion, oviposition
medium is made available in each cage of adult flies. When
possible, a sample of 100 eggs is collected, and the number that
hatch as well as the number of pupae derived from the larvae of
the hatched eggs are recorded. If oviposition failed to occur
after initial exposure to the ovipositional medium, it is made
available at least two more times.

SECONDARY TESTS

FEEDING

House flies. For determination of sterilant and related
activity, LaBrecque (1961) and Painter and Kilgore (1965) studied the effect of various groups of chemosterilants on house fly
growth, behavior, and metabolism by following the technique in
the screening procedure. Kenaga (1965) also using the modified
screening technique, investigated in detail the effects of organotin compounds on house flies. Mitlin et al. (1957) in their investigations incorporated such substances as metabolic antagonists, alkaloids, and other compounds in skimmed milk. If the
sterilant was insoluble in water, however, it was first dissolved
in an appropriate solvent prior to inclusion into the milk diet.
Ascher (1965), in his studies with oviposition inhibitors, pre-

conditioned his flies to a sugar and water diet for 3 days prior to introducing the flies to a reconstituted milk diet treated with the sterilant and sugar on cotton pads.

Chang and Chiang (1964) admixed the chemicals in sugar and exposed the flies to the mixture for 3 days. Ristich et al. (1965) in their studies on the chemosterilant properties of apholate dissolved the sterilant in a volatile solvent; the solution was later slurried in granular sugar and the solvent evaporated. Twenty grams of bait were introduced into the cage containing the flies. The sterilant was then kept in the cages until three sets of eggs were collected. Tahori et al. (1965), in their evaluation of phosphon (2, 4-dichlorobenzyltributyl phosphonium chloride), fed 3-day-old flies with milk and water treated with the chemical.

Screwworms. Chamberlain (1962) fed confined *Cochliomyia hominivorax* (Coquerel) adult flies a mixture containing a concentration of the chemosterilant. The mixture consisted of the chemical mixed in water and diluted with honey and blood at various concentrations, whereas Crystal (1963) evaluated sterility in screwworms by using the techniques described in the screening program section.

Mosquitoes. Weidhaas et al. (1961) used the procedure described in the screening section to study the effects of chemosterilants against the yellow-fever and malaria mosquitoes. Glancey (1965) followed the procedure closely in his evaluation of hempa. Mulla (1964), in his studies with southern house mosquitoes, *Culex p. quinquefasciatus,* provided the adults with cotton pads soaked in a 5 percent solution of sugar containing the desired concentration of the sterilant for a period of 24 hr, after which the treatment was removed and the normal diet introduced.

Fruit flies. Against *Drosophila melanogaster* (Meigen), Goldsmith Goldsmith and Frank (1952) placed newly emerged females or males in Pearls synthetic medium supplemented with the sterilant. Following 7 days of exposure, the flies were transferred to stock yeasted banana rations and mated. With the same species, Cantwell and Henneberry (1963) simply exposed 3- to 4-day-old males and females to the chemosterilant admixed in a sugar yeast bait for 24 hr. Orphanidis (1963) held newly eclosed adults of the Mediterranean fruit fly for 4 days on drinking water and a diet consisting of 22 percent yeast and 78 percent honey. On the fifth day the diet was withdrawn and replaced for 24 and 48 hr with one containing 20.4 percent yeast,

77.6 percent honey, 1 percent chemosterilant, and 0.5 percent aqueous solution of NaOH. The same procedure was used earlier against the olive fly (*Dacus oleae Gmel*) except that in this instance the untreated diet was withdrawn on the third day and was replaced with one containing 1 percent sterilant, 32 percent yeast, 16 percent sugar, 16 percent banana broth, 34 percent water, and 0.5 percent NaOH solution (Orphanidis 1963). McFadden and Rubio (1965) followed the procedure described in their screening technique against Mexican fruit flies, however, Keiser et al. (1965) sterilized the Mediterranean fruit fly [*Ceratitis capitata* (Wiedemann)], the Oriental fruit fly [Dacus dorsalis (Hendel)], and the melon fly [*Dacus curcurbitae* (Coquillet)], by incorporating the dissolved chemosterilant with hydrolyzed protein fruit and exposing this diet to the adults for the duration of the test. On the other hand, Keiser et al. often simply dissolved the sterilant in water, and offered this solution to the flies for 3 days following eclosion.

Eye gnats. Schwartz (1965) sterilized *Hippelates pusio* Loew by allowing them to feed *ad libitum* for 3 days on dental rolls saturated with 7.0 percent aqueous sugar solution containing the sterilant. The treated rolls were then replaced with rolls containing honey for the duration of the test.

Face flies. Hair and Adkins (1964) followed the same procedure for inducing sterility in *Musca autumnalis* DeGeer as that utilized by LaBrecque for house flies except that the chemosterilant diet was slurried with water and made available to the adult fruit flies for only 24, 48, or 72 hr after which periods an untreated diet was placed in its stead through the fifth day.

Blow flies. Morgan and LaBrecque (1964) thoroughly mixed solutions or suspensions of the chemosterilant with ground meat which was given to adults of *Phaenicia cuprina* (Wiedemann). Fresh portions were supplied daily for five days, after which untreated meat was introduced; whereas to sterilize the sheep blow fly *Lucilia sericata* (Meigen), Yeoman and Warren (1965) mixed the sterilant in a liquid paste consisting of one part water to six parts icing sugar containing 1.5 percent of calcium phosphate. This diet was offered to the flies for varying periods of time following eclosion, after which it was replaced by the untreated diet.

Boll weevils. Oviposition and hatch were studied in tests with *Anthonomus grandis* Boheman when the germinated cottonseed diet of Vanderzant et al. (1959) with the agar omitted was used to feed chemosterilants to the adults. This diet was placed on pads of cotton and fed to weevils for 5 days (Lindquist et al., 1964). Hedin et al. (1964) incorporated the sterilant in the diet, however the diet was prepared from a reconstituted, freeze hydrated cotton square powder to which agar had been added. The diet was then adjusted to pH 7 prior to addition of the chemosterilant. The weevils were then allowed to feed for 5 days.

Curculios. Plum curculio adults were sterilized when fed a chemosterilant-treated diet consisting of 20 g of applesauce, 2 g of sucrose, 0.05 g of cholesterol, 0.3 g Wesson salts, 0.1 g choline chloride, 3.0 g of agar, 0.1 g of sorbic acid, and a trace of B vitamins in 100 ml of water for 14 days following adult emergence to the preoviposition period (Hays and Cochran, 1964).

Bees. Johanssen and Redmond (1965) were able to sterilize the queen of a colony of *Apis mellifera* by offering 0.05 percent apholate in a 1:1 sugar water sirup when 2 liters were used per colony in the standard feed frames.

Wasps. Grosch (1959) starved habrobracon wasps (*Microbracon hebetor* Say) until the abdomen was flattened, after which the wasp was allowed to feed on one drop of sugar solution containing the chemosterilant.

Moths. Young and Cox (1965) used essentially the same method as Grosch to induce sterility in the fall armyworm *Spodoptera frugiperda* J. E. Smith. To obtain a more quantitative determination of the amount of chemosterilant concerned, individual armyworms were exposed to a determined amount of sterilant in the following manner. Two loops, one inside of another at $90°$ were twisted together. The loops were then immersed in a 10 percent sucrose water solution containing the sterilant. By weighing the loop complex before and after the insect had consumed all of the solution it was possible to determine the amount of sterilant ingested (see Fig. 1).

In the majority of the representative feeding techniques cited, especially against Diptera, sugar or sugar water has been the main constituent of the chemosterilant carrier. Its acceptability by most insects, its solubility in water, its nutritional value, and its general availability make it an exceptional standard nutrient.

Another approach utilizing the feeding technique is to combine the sterilant with the natural diet or environment of the insect. Henneberry et al. (1964) and Creighton et al. (1966) exposed adult cucumber beetles *Diabrotica balteata* LeConte

FIG. 1. Loop feeder used to treat fall armyworm moths individually. (From Young and Cox, J. Econ. Entom., 58(5):883–888. Reprinted courtesy of The Entomological Society of America.)

for 48 hr to collard leaves dipped in a solution of the sterilant.
Chamberlain (1962) has been successful in reducing fertility in
adult screwworms by subjecting first and second instar larvae
to a chemosterilant-treated medium.

Perhaps the greatest success in inducing sterility in
adults by subjecting the immature stage to the sterilant has
been derived in mosquitoes. Dame and Ford (1964), and Glancey
(1965) with *Aedes aegypti* larvae, and Murray and Bickley (1964),
and Mulla (1964) with *Culex pipiens quinquefasciatus*, have successfully induced sterility in adults by subjecting some or all
of the immature stadia to various concentrations of the sterilant. Burden and Smittle (1963) sterilized adult German cockroaches [*Blattella germanica* (L.)] by treating the food (pulver-
ized compressed dog food) and exposing the food to second instar nymphs and successive stages, but Kenaga (1965) was but

partially successful evaluating a different group of chemicals against the same species by exposing the fourth nymphal instar.

The most interesting approaches in utilizing the natural diet have been those used by Eddy et al. (1965). In these experiments, mice were injected with chemosterilant solutions after which yellow-fever mosquitoes were allowed to feed on the treated mice for selected intervals following the i.p. injections. This same technique was followed by Vinson and Land (1965) with the house spider [*Theridon tepidariorium* (Koch)]. In this instance adult male roaches were injected with the chemosterilant then placed on the web and the spider allowed to feed.

RESIDUES

Insects differ in structure, behavior, and feeding mechanism. Often, intake of a chemosterilant by ingestion may not be the most practicable method of sterility induction. Weidhaas (1962) induced sterility in the common malaria mosquito by treating the inner surface of petri dishes with various quantities of the sterilant dissolved in acetone in sufficient volume to obtain calculated residues. The insects were then exposed to the residue for a definite period of time. The same technique was also followed by Mustafa and Naidu (1964) to induce sterility in the red cotton bug (*Dysdercus cingulatus* F.). Meifert et al. (1963) and LaBrecque (1966) with the house fly used 5 ml of a chemosterilant, methyl alcohol or acetone solution, and applied the residue by rotating the solution in the jar until dry. To insure constant exposure of the insects to the residue, they covered the mouth of the jars with an organdy cloth treated with a repellent to prevent the insects from resting on a surface not treated with the chemosterilant. Also, after definite exposure periods to the treated surface, the insects were allowed to escape into cages, for if the insects were anesthetized for transfer, they would have picked up additional amounts of the residue when they fell on the treated surface. Against the pink bollworm, *Pectinophora gossypiella* (Saunders), Ouye et al. (1965) also treated inner surfaces of half-pint jars with 2 ml of a solution containing the chemosterilant by rapidly rotating the jars until the solvent had completely evaporated. Harris (1962) with the stable fly *Stomoxys calcitrans* (L.) and Collier and Downey (1965) with the gypsy moth *Porthetria dispar* (L.) also used the same type container but they used 5 and 1 ml of carbon

tetrachloride respectively as a carrier to disperse the chemosterilant evenly on the glass surface. Howland et al. (1966) with
the cabbage looper, Trichoplusia ni (Hubner), applied their
residues by rotating the chemosterilant solution in a 500 ml
erlenmeyer flask. The chemosterilant solution also contained
1 percent each of an adjuvant X-77 (alkyloxylpolyoxyethylene
glycols, free fatty acids, isopropanol) and a food coloring.
The solution was poured in excess in the flask, rotated until the
surface appeared evenly coated, and then the excess poured out.
It was found that a flask treated with 2, 4, 8, or 16 percent of
the chemosterilant resulted in 30, 60, 120, and 240 mg of the
sterilant per flask. In experiments requiring a large number of
cabbage loopers, Howland followed the same procedure as that
described above, but in this instance he used 1-gallon open
mouth jars. Keiser et al. (1965) forced teneral fruit flies to
walk through 1-in. glass tubes, 7 in. long, to which a 5 percent
solution of the chemosterilant was applied. Forcing newly
emerged fruit flies to walk on moist cellulose sponges saturated with a chemosterilant solution also caused sterility in
both sexes of insects. Bertram (1963) and Bertram et al. (1964)
in their studies with anophelines, applied an aqueous solution
of the sterilant by pipette to white paper, which when dry was
inserted as internal lining to a plastic cylinder (4 by 13 cm).
The mosquitoes were held for various periods in the holder
tubes then transferred to an attached tube lined with clean paper.
Hays and Cochran (1964) in their studies with the plum curculio
placed prepupae in petri dishes treated with the sterilant. The
larvae were allowed to remain on the moistened surface for
15 min and then were transferred to pupation chambers.

Ever since organized research has been directed in the
field of chemosterilants, numerous compounds have been uncovered that have had effects on various species. A review of
some of the species sterilized by some of the previously described methods and some of the chemicals that have produced
this desired effect are listed in Table 1. If a complete list of
all chemosterilants is desired, however, Borkovec (1967) has
catalogued all compounds found as of April, 1966.

DIPPING

Another form of application consists of placing the sterilant on the cuticle itself by dipping various stages of insects

TABLE 1

SOME CHEMICALS AFFECTING THE REPRODUCTIVE
CAPACITY OF INSECTS AND RELATED SPECIES

Chemosterilant	Species	Reference
Aldrin	*Musca domestica* (L.)	LaBrecque et al., 1960
Allyltriphenyltin	*Musca domestica* (L.)	Fye et al., 1966
		Kenaga, 1965
	Tribolium confusum Jaquelin du Val	Kenaga, 1965
Amethopterin	*Aedes aegypti* (L.)	Weidhaas et al., 1961
	Anopheles quadri- maculatus Say	Weidhaas et al., 1961
	Ceratitis capitata (Wiedemann)	Keiser et al., 1965
	Cochliomyia hominivorax (Coquerel)	Crystal, 1963 Crystal, 1964a
	Dacus cucurbitae Coquillet	Keiser et al., 1965
	Dacus dorsalis Hendel	Keiser et al., 1965
	Drosophila melanogaster (Meigen)	Goldsmith and Frank, 1952
	Musca domestica (L.)	LaBrecque et al., 1960 Painter and Kilgore, 1964
Aminopterin	*Cochliomyia hominivorax* (Coquerel)	Crystal, 1963 Crystal, 1964a
	Drosophila melanogaster (Meigen)	Goldsmith and Frank, 1952
	Musca domestica (L.)	Mitlin et al., 1957
	Theridon tepidariorum Koch.	Vinson and Land, 1965
4-Amino-1H-pyrazolo[3, 4-d]=pyrimidine sulfate	*Anastrepha ludens* (Loew)	Shaw and Rivi- ello, 1962
	Cochliomyia hominivorax (Coquerel)	Crystal, 1963
3-Amino-1,2,4-triazole	*Musca domestica* (L.)	Fye et al., 1966
5-Amino-*v*-triazolo[4, 5-d]=pyrimidin-7(6H) one	*Cochliomyia hominivorax* (Coquerel)	Gouck et al., 1963

TABLE 1 (CONTINUED)

Chemosterilant	Species	Reference
Amphotericin B	*Tetranychus telarius* (L.)	Harries, 1963
Anisol	*Musca domestica* (L.)	Ascher, 1964
Antimony dimercapto-succinate	*Cochliomyia hominivorax* (Coquerel)	Crystal, 1964
Antimycin A	*Tetranychus telarius* (L.)	Harries, 1963
Aphamide	*Aedes aegypti* (L.)	Weidhaas et al., 1961
	Anopheles quadri-maculatus Say	Weidhaas et al., 1961
	Blattella germanica (L.)	Burden and Smittle, 1963
	Cochliomyia hominivorax (Coquerel)	Crystal, 1963
	Conotrachelus nenuphar (Herbst.)	Hays and Cochran, 1964
	Musca domestica (L.)	LaBrecque, 1961
	Panonychus citri (McGregor)	Cressman, 1963
Apholate	*Acyrthosiphon pisum* (Harris)	Balla and Robinson, 1966
	Aedes aegypti (L.)	Dame et al., 1964
		Weidhaas et al., 1961
	Anopheles quadrimacu-latus Say	Weidhaas et al., 1961
		Weidhaas, 1962
	Anthonomus grandis Boheman	Hedin et al., 1964
		Lindquist et al., 1964
	Apis mellifera	Johansen and Redmond, 1965
	Blattella germanica (L.)	Burden and Smittle, 1963
	Bombyx mori (L.)	Sugai and Hirano, 1965

TABLE 1 (CONTINUED)

Chemosterilant	Species	Reference
Apholate	*Ceratitis capitata* (Wiedemann)	Keiser et al., 1965 Orphanidis, 1963a
	Callosobruchus chinensis (L.)	Shinohura and Nagasawa, 1963 Nagasawa and Shinohura, 1964a
	Cochliomyia hominivorax (Coquerel)	Chamberlain, 1962 Crystal and LaChance, 1963 Crystal, 1963
	Conotrachelus nenuphar (Herbst.)	Roach and Buxton, 1965
	Culex pipiens quinque-fasciatus Say	Mulla, 1964 Murray and Bickley, 1964
	Dacus cucurbitae Coquillet	Keiser et al., 1965
	Dacus dorsalis Hendel	Keiser et al., 1965
	Diabrotica balteata LeConte	Creighton et al., 1966
	Drosophila melanogaster (Meigen)	Cantwell and Henneberry, 1963
	Dysdercus cingulatus (F.)	Mustafa and Naidu, 1964
	Epilachna varivestis Mulsant	Henneberry et al., 1964 Carillo et al., 1963
	Fannia canicularis (L.)	Davis and Eddy, 1966
	Glossina morsitans (Westw.)	Chadwick, 1964
	Hippelates pusio Loew	Schwartz, 1965
	Hylemya brassicae (Bouché)	Swailes, 1966

TABLE 1 (CONTINUED)

Chemosterilant	Species	Reference
Apholate	*Lucilia sericata* (Meig.)	Millar, 1965
		Yeoman and Warren, 1965
	Musca autumnalis DeGeer	Adkins, Jr., 1965
		Hair and Adkins, 1964
	Musca domestica (L.)	Gouck et al., 1963
		Gouck, 1964
		Kenaga, 1965
		LaBrecque, 1961
		Loaeza and Corona, 1965
		Painter and Kilgore, 1964
		Ratcliffe and Ristich, 1965
	Panonychus citri (McGregor)	Cressman, 1963
	Phaenicia cuprina (Wiedemann)	Morgan and LaBrecque, 1964
	Popillia japonica (Newman)	Ladd, 1966
	Portheria dispar (L.)	Collier and Downey, 1965
	Spodoptera frugiperda (S. E. Smith)	Young and Cox, 1965
	Stomoxys calcitrans (L.)	Harris, 1962
	Tetranychus cinnabarinus (Baisduval)	Smith et al., 1965
	Tetranychus telarius (L.)	Smith et al., 1965
	Trichoplusia ni (Hübner)	Henneberry and Kishaba, 1966
		Howland et al., 1965
Azaserine	*Cochliomyia hominivorax* (Coquerel)	Crystal, 1963

TABLE 1 (CONTINUED)

Chemosterilant	Species	Reference
1-Aziridine= carboxanilide	*Musca domestica* (L.)	Gouck et al., 1963 Gouck and LaBrecque, 1964
Benzene	*Musca domestica* (L.)	Ascher, 1964
Benzeneboronic Acid	*Musca domestica* (L.)	LaBrecque et al., 1960
Benzyl[bis(1-aziri= dinyl)phosphinyl]= carbamate	*Anastrepha ludens* (Loew) *Cochliomyia hominivorax* (Coquerel) *Musca domestica* (L.)	McFadden and Rubio, 1965 Crystal, 1964a Gouck and LaBrecque, 1964
Benzyltriphenyltin	*Musca domestica* (L.)	Kenaga, 1965
2,5-Bis(1-aziridinyl)- *p*-benzoquinone	*Musca domestica* (L.)	Fye et al., 1965
2,5-Bis(1-aziridinyl)- 3,6-bis(2-methoxy= ethoxy)-*p*-benzo- quinone	*Cochliomyia hominivorax* (Coquerel)	Crystal, 1963 Crystal and LaChance, 1963 LaChance and Crystal, 1963
2,5-Bis(1-aziridinyl)- 3,6-bis(2-methoxy= ethoxy)benzoquinone	*Musca domestica* (L.)	LaBrecque and Gouck, 1963
P,*P*-bis(1-aziridinyl)- *N*-butylphosphinic amide	*Musca domestica* (L.)	Fye et al., 1966
1,4-Bis(1-aziridinyl= carbonyl)piperazine	*Musca domestica* (L.)	Fye et al., 1965
2,4-Bis(1-aziridinyl)- 6-chloropyrimidine	*Musca domestica* (L.)	Fye et al., 1966
2,4-Bis(1-aziridinyl)- 6-diazomethyl-S- triazine	*Cochliomyia hominivorax* (Coquerel)	Gouck et al., 1963
Bis(1-aziridinyl) 3,4- dichlorophenylureido phosphine oxide	*Musca domestica* (L.)	Ratcliffe and Ristich, 1965
2,5-Bis(1-aziridinyl)- 3,6-dipropoxy-*p*- benzoquinone	*Musca domestica* (L.)	LaBrecque and Gouck, 1963

TABLE 1 (CONTINUED)

Chemosterilant	Species	Reference
P,P-bis(1-aziridinyl)- *N*-ethylphosphinic amide	*Anastrepha ludens* (Loew) *Musca domestica* (L.)	McFadden and Rubio, 1965 Fye et al., 1965
Bis(1-aziridinyl)(hexa- hydro-1H-azepin-1-yl) phosphine oxide	*Cochliomyia hominivorax* (Coquerel)	Crystal, 1965a
Bis(1-aziridinyl)hexahy- dro-1H-azepin-1-yl) phosphine sulfide	*Musca domestica* (L.)	Fye, 1967
2,5-Bis(1-aziridinyl)= hydroquinone	*Musca domestica* (L.)	Fye et al., 1965
P,P-Bis(1-aziridinyl)- *N*-(*p*-methoxyphenyl)= phosphinic amide	*Musca domestica* (L.)	LaBrecque and Gouck, 1963
2,4-Bis(1-aziridinyl)- 6-methylamino-*s*- triazine	*Anastrepha ludens* (Loew) *Musca domestica* (L.)	McFadden and Rubio, 1965 Fye et al., 1966
2,4-Bis(1-aziridinyl)- 6-methyl-5-nitro= pyrimidine	*Anastrepha ludens* (Loew) *Musca domestica* (L.)	McFadden and Rubio, 1965 Gouck and LaBrecque, 1964
Bis(1-aziridinyl)= morpholino-phosphine oxide	*Musca domestica* (L.)	LaBrecque and Gouck, 1963
P, P-Bis(1-aziridinyl)- *N*-octylphosphinic amide	*Musca domestica* (L.)	Fye et al., 1965
Bis(1-aziridinyl)= phenylphosphine sulfide	*Musca domestica* (L.)	Fye et al., 1965
1-[Bis(1-aziridinyl)= phosphinyl]-3-(3,4- dichlorophenyl)-urea	*Cochliomyia hominivorax* (Coquerel) *Musca domestica* (L.)	Crystal, 1965a Fye et al., 1966
1-[Bis(1-aziridinyl)= phosphinyl]-3-(*o*- nitrophenyl)urea	*Musca domestica* (L.)	Fye et al., 1966
4,8-Bis(1-aziridinyl)= pyrimido[5,4-*d*]= pyrimidine	*Musca domestica* (L.)	Fye et al., 1965
3,9-Bis(1-aziridinyl)- 2,4,8,10-tetraoxa- 3,9-diphosphaspiro= [5,5]undecane-3,9- dioxide	*Musca domestica* (L.)	Ratcliffe and Ristich, 1965

TABLE 1 (CONTINUED)

Chemosterilant	Species	Reference
P,P-Bis(1-aziridinyl)- *N*-1,3,4-thiadiazol-2- yl phosphinic amide	*Anastrepha ludens* (Loew)	McFadden and Rubio, 1965
2,4-Bis(1-aziridinyl)- *s*-triazine	*Musca domestica* (L.)	Fye et al., 1965
5-[Bis(2-chloroethyl)= amino]-6-methyluracil	*Musca domestica* (L.)	Fye. et al., 1965
5-[Bis(2-chloroethyl) amino] uracil	*Anastrepha ludens* (Loew) *Musca domestica* (L.)	McFadden and Rubio, 1965 Fye et al., 1965
N,N'-Bis(2-chloroethyl)- 2,4-dimethylbenzyl= amine hydrochloride	*Musca domestica* (L.)	Gouck and LaBrecque, 1964
1,1-Bis(2-chloroethyl)- 3-ethyl-2-thiourea	*Cochliomyia hominivorax* (Coquerel)	Crystal, 1963
1,1-Bis(2-chloroethyl)- 3-(p-methoxyphenyl) urea	*Cochliomyia hominivorax* (Coquerel)	Crystal, 1963 Gouck et al., 1963
Bis-(p-chlorophenyl)- pentafluoroethyl= carbinol	*Musca domestica* (L.)	Ascher, 1962
Bis-(p-chlorophenyl)- trifluoromethyl= carbinol	*Musca domestica* (L.)	Ascher, 1962
Bis(dimethylglyoximato)- bis(ethylenimine)= cobalt chloride	*Anastrepha ludens* (Loew)	McFadden and Rubio, 1965
Bis(ethylenediamine)= bis-(ethylenimine)= cobalt tribromide	*Anastrepha ludens* (Loew)	McFadden and Rubio, 1965
1,4-Bis(3-hydroxy= propionyl)piperazine dimethanesulfonate	*Musca domestica* (L.)	Gouck and LaBrecque, 1963
Bis(2-methyl-1-aziri= dinyl)phenylphosphine	*Cochliomyia hominivorax* (Coquerel)	Crystal, 1963
Bis(triphenyltin)= dodecylsuccinate	*Musca domestica* (L.)	Kenaga, 1965
Bis(triphenyltin)= ethylenebis-(dithio= carbamate)	*Musca domestica* (L.)	Kenaga, 1965
Bis(triphenyltin)sulfide	*Musca domestica* (L.)	Kenaga, 1965
Bithionol	*Cochliomyia hominivorax* (Coquerel)	Crystal, 1964b
Bromobenzene	*Musca domestica* (L.)	Ascher, 1964
P-Bromo-*N,N*-dimethyl= benzenesulfonamide	*Cochliomyia hominivorax* (Coquerel)	Gouck et al., 1963

TABLE 1 (CONTINUED)

Chemosterilant	Species	Reference
1,3-Butadienylenebis (triphenyltin)	*Musca domestica* (L.)	Kenaga, 1965
1,3-Butadienyltri= phenyltin	*Musca domestica* (L.)	Kenaga, 1965
2-Butenyltriphenyltin	*Musca domestica* (L.)	Kenaga, 1965
0-Butyl bis(1-aziri= dinyl)phosphino= thioate	*Musca domestica* (L.)	Fye et al., 1965
Butyltriphenyltin	*Musca domestica* (L.)	Kenaga, 1965
Butyric acid, 2-phenylhydrazide	*Musca domestica* (L.)	Gouck and LaBrecque, 1964
Calcium arsenate	*Rhagoletis pomonella* (Walsh)	Pickett and Patterson, 1963
Captan	*Tetranychus telarius* (L.)	Hunter, 1961
Chlorambucil	*Anastrepha ludens* (Loew)	Shaw and Riviello, 1962
	Cochliomyia hominivorax (Coquerel)	Crystal, 1963
Chlorobenside	*Musca domestica* (L.)	Ascher and Hirsch, 1961
	Tetranychus urticae (Koch)	Meltzer, 1956
1-(p-Chlorobenzoyl)= aziridine	*Anastrepha ludens* (Loew)	McFadden and Rubio, 1965
p-Chloro-N,N-bis(2-chloroethyl)benzyla-mine hydrochloride	*Musca domestica* (L.)	Gouck and LaBrecque, 1964
0-2-Chloroethyl bis(1-aziridinyl)phosphino-thioate	*Musca domestica* (L.)	Fye et al., 1965
2-Chloroethyl 6-chloro-piperonyl sulfide	*Musca domestica* (L.)	Gouck and LaBrecque, 1964
2-Chloroethyl ethane= sulfonate	*Musca domestica* (L.)	LaBrecque and Gouck, 1963
2-Chloroethyl methane= sulfonate	*Musca domestica* (L.)	LaBrecque and Gouck, 1963
Chloromethotrexate	*Cochliomyia hominivorax* (Coquerel)	Crystal, 1964a
2-Chloro-N-(3-methoxy= propyl)acetamide	*Cochliomyia hominivorax* (Coquerel)	Gouck et al., 1963
4-Chlorophenyl-benzene sulfonate	*Tetranychus urticae* Koch	Meltzer, 1956

TABLE 1 (CONTINUED)

Chemosterilant	Species	Reference
6-Chloropiperonyl methyl sulfide	*Musca domestica* (L.)	Gouck and LaBrecque, 1964
Chloroquine	*Cochliomyia hominivorax* (Coquerel)	Crystal, 1964c
Colchicine	*Ceratitis capitata* (Wiedemann)	Keiser et al., 1965
	Cochliomyia hominivorax (Coquerel)	Chamberlain and Hopkins, 1960
	Conotrachelus nenuphar (Herbst.)	Hays and Cochran, 1964
	Dacus cucurbitae (Coquillet)	Keiser et al., 1965
	Dacus dorsalis Hendel	Keiser et al., 1965
	Musca domestica (L.)	Gouck and LaBrecque, 1964
		Mitlin et al., 1957
Coumarin	*Musca domestica* (L.)	Mitlin and Baroody, 1958b
Cumene	*Musca domestica* (L.)	Ascher, 1964
Cycloheximide (3-[2-(3,5-dimethyl-2-oxocyclohexyl)-2-hydroxyethyl]= glutarimide)	*Musca domestica* (L.)	LaBrecque and Gouck, 1963
	Panonychus citri (McGregor)	Jeppson et al., 1966
	Panonychus ulmi (Koch)	Harries, 1963
	Tetranychus pacificus (McGregor)	Jeppson et al., 1966
	Tetranychus telarius (L.)	Harries, 1961
Cycloheximide; acetate derivative	*Panonychus citri* (McGregor)	Jeppson et al., 1966
	Tetranychus pacificus (McGregor)	Jeppson et al., 1966
Cycloheximide; aceto= acetate derivative	*Panonychus citri* (McGregor)	Jeppson et al., 1966
	Tetranychus pacificus (McGregor)	Jeppson et al., 1966
Cycloheximide; oxime derivative	*Panonychus citri* (McGregor)	Jeppson et al., 1966

TABLE 1 (CONTINUED)

Chemosterilant	Species	Reference
Cycloheximide; oxime derivative	*Tetranychus pacificus* (McGregor)	Jeppson et al., 1966
Cycloheximide; semi= carbazone derivative	*Panonychus citri* (McGregor)	Jeppson et al., 1966
	Tetranychus pacificus (McGregor)	Jeppson et al., 1966
Cyclopentadienyl= triphenyltin	*Musca domestica* (L.)	Kenaga, 1965
Cyclopropyltriphenyltin	*Musca domestica* (L.)	Kenaga, 1965
Cytovirin	*Panonychus ulmi* (Koch)	Harries, 1963
	Tetranychus telarius (L.)	Harries, 1961
0-Decyl bis(1-aziri= dinyl)phosphinothioate	*Musca domestica* (L.)	Fye et al., 1965
2,4-Diamino-6-(2-furyl)- s-triazine	*Musca domestica* (L.)	Fye et al., 1966
2,4-Diamino-6-iso= propyl-s-triazine	*Musca domestica* (L.)	Fye et al., 1966
2,4-Diamino-6-(1- piperidyl)-s-triazine	*Musca domestica* (L.)	Fye et al., 1966
N,N-Di-n-butyl furo- amide	*Musca domestica* (L.)	LaBrecque and Gouck, 1963
Dichloromethotrexate	*Cochliomyia hominivorax* (Coquerel)	Crystal, 1964
N,N-Di-(2-chloroethyl)- p-toluidine	*Drosophila melanogaster* (Meigen)	Bird, 1950
N,N-Di-(2-chloroethyl)- p-anisidine	*Drosophila melanogaster* (Meigen)	Bird, 1950
2,2'-Dichloro-N-methyl= diethylamine	*Musca domestica* (L.)	Piquett and Keller, 1962
2,2'-Dichloro-N-methyl= diethylamine hydro= chloride	*Musca domestica* (L.)	Gouck and LaBrecque, 1964
0-2,4-Dichlorophenyl 0-methyl isopropyl= phosphoramidothioate	*Musca domestica* (L.)	Fye et al., 1966
Di-(p-chlorophenyl)= pentafluoroethyl= carbinol	*Musca domestica* (L.)	Ascher, 1957
Di-(p-chlorophenyl)- trifluoromethyl= carbinol	*Musca domestica* (L.)	Ascher, 1957
trans-Dichlorotetrakis- (ethylenimine)chro- mium chloride	*Anastrepha ludens* (Loew)	McFadden and Rubio, 1965
Diethylene glycol di-2- methyl-1-aziri= dinecarboxylate	*Musca domestica* (L.)	LaBrecque and Gouck, 1963

TABLE 1 (CONTINUED)

Chemosterilant	Species	Reference
Diethylstilbesterol	*Conotrachelus nenuphar* (Herbst.)	Hays and Cochran, 1964
N^2,N^2-Dimethylmelamine	*Musca domestica* (L.)	Fye et al., 1966
1,4-Dimethyltetra= methylene methane= sulfonate	*Musca domestica* (L.)	Fye et al., 1965
1,3-Dimethyl-2-thiourea	*Musca domestica* (L.)	LaBrecque and Gouck, 1963
Disodium methyl arsonate	*Musca domestica* (L.)	Fye et al., 1966
Dithiazanine	*Cochliomyia hominivorax* (Coquerel)	Crystal, 1964b
1,1'-Dithiobisaziridine	*Cochliomyia hominivorax* (Coquerel)	Crystal, 1963
	Musca domestica (L.)	Fye et al., 1965
6,8-Dimethylpyrimido[5, 4-e]-as-triazine- 5,7{6H,8H}-dione	*Musca domestica* (L.)	Fye, 1967
1,1'-Dithiobis[2-methyl= aziridine]	*Musca domestica* (L.)	Fye et al., 1965
Dopan	*Musca domestica vicina*	Chang et al., 1963
Emetine	*Cochliomyia hominivorax* (Coquerel)	Crystal, 1964
Endoxan	*Musca domestica vicina*	Chang et al., 1963
	Musca domestica (L.)	LaBrecque and Gouck, 1963
Enovid	*Conotrachelus nenuphar* (Herbst.)	Hays and Cochran, 1964
Ethyl [bis(1-aziri= dinyl) phosphinyl]= carbamate	*Anastrepha ludens* (Loew)	McFadden and Rubio, 1965
	Cochliomyia hominivorax (Coquerel)	Crystal, 1964b
	Musca domestica (L.)	Gouck and LaBrecque, 1964
0-Ethyl bis(1-aziri= dinyl)phosphinothioate	*Musca domestica* (L.)	Gouck and LaBrecque, 1964
0-Ethyl bis(2-methyl-1- aziridinyl)phosphino= thioate	*Musca domestica* (L.)	Fye et al., 1965

TABLE 1 (CONTINUED)

Chemosterilant	Species	Reference
Ethylenebis (triphenyl=tin)	*Musca domestica* (L.)	Kenaga, 1965
Ethylenimine	*Cochliomyia hominivorax* (Coquerel)	Crystal, 1963
Ethyl methanesulfonate	*Bracon hebetor* Say	Lobbecke and Von Borstel, 1962
4-Fluorobutyl methane=sulfonate	*Musca domestica* (L.)	Fye et al., 1965
5-Fluorodeoxyuridine	*Musca domestica* (L.)	Painter and Kilgore, 1964
2-Fluoroethyl methane=sulfonate	*Cochliomyia hominivorax* (Coquerel)	Gouck et al., 1963
	Musca domestica (L.)	Gouck and LaBrecque, 1964
5-Fluoroörotic acid	*Anthonomus grandis* Boheman	Ridgway et al., 1966
	Cochliomyia hominivorax (Coquerel)	Crystal, 1963
3-Ethoxy-2-oxobutyral-dehyde bis-thiosemi-carbazone	*Musca domestica* (L.)	Kohls et al., 1966
Ethyl bis(1-aziridinyl) phosphinate	*Musca domestica* (L.)	Fye, 1967
	Musca domestica (L.)	LaBrecque and Gouck, 1963
5-Fluorouracil	*Anastrepha ludens* (Loew)	McFadden and Rubio, 1965
	Anthonomus grandis Boheman	Ridgway et al., 1966
	Ceratitis capitata (Wiedemann)	Keiser et al., 1965
	Cochliomyia hominivorax (Coquerel)	Crystal, 1963
	Dacus cucurbitae (Coquillet)	Keiser et al., 1965
	Dacus dorsalis Hendel	Keiser et al., 1965
	Musca domestica (L.)	Kilgore and Painter, 1962
		LaBrecque et al., 1960
		Painter and Kilgore, 1964

TABLE 1 (CONTINUED)

Chemosterilant	Species	Reference
Folic acid	*Conotrachelus nenuphar* (Herbst.)	Hays and Cochran, 1964
Formyl-sarcolysin	*Musca domestica vicina*	Chang et al., 1963
1,1'-Fumaroylbis= aziridine	*Musca domestica* (L.)	Fye et al., 1966
Furfural	*Musca domestica* (L.)	Ascher, 1964
Hemel	*Fannia canicularis* (L.)	Davis and Eddy, 1966
	Musca domestica (L.)	Chang et al., 1964
		Fye et al., 1965
Hempa	*Aedes aegypti* (L.)	Glancey, 1965
	Fannia canicularis (L.)	Davis and Eddy, 1966
	Musca domestica (L.)	Chang et al., 1964
		Fye et al., 1965
		LaBrecque et al., 1966
N,N'-Heptamethylene bis (1-aziridine= carboxamide)	*Anastrepha ludens* (Loew)	McFadden and Rubio, 1965
	Musca domestica (L.)	Fye et al., 1966
N,N'-Hexamethylenebis[1-aziridinecarboxamide]	*Musca domestica* (L.)	Gouck and LaBrecque, 1964
		Ratcliffe and Ristich, 1965
Hexaphenylditin	*Musca domestica* (L.)	Kenaga, 1965
5-Hydroxy-4-6-dimethyl-3-pyridinemethanol hydrochloride	*Musca domestica* (L.)	LaBrecque and Gouck, 1963
Hydroxytriphenyltin	*Blattella germanica* (L.)	Kenaga, 1965
	Musca domestica (L.)	Fye et al., 1966
		Kenaga, 1965
	Tribolium confusum Jaquelin du Val	Kenaga, 1965
Hydroxyurea	*Musca domestica* (L.)	Kissam and Hays, 1966
Hygromycin B	*Tetranychus telarius* (L.)	Harries, 1963

TABLE 1 (CONTINUED)

Chemosterilant	Species	Reference
2-Imidazolidinethione	*Musca domestica* (L.)	Gouck and LaBrecque, 1964 LaBrecque and Gouck, 1963
2-Imidazolidinone	*Musca domestica* (L.)	Simkover, 1964
	Oncopeltus fasciatus (Dallas)	Simkover, 1964
Imidodicarboxylic acid dihidroxide	*Anastrepha ludens* (Loew)	McFadden and Rubio, 1965
Isobutyric acid, 2-phenylhydrazide	*Musca domestica* (L.)	Gouck and LaBrecque, 1964
Lead arsenate	*Rhagoletis pomonella* (Walsh)	Pickett and Patterson, 1963
Mechlorethamine	*Cochliomyia hominivorax* (Coquerel)	Crystal, 1963
6-Mercapto purine	*Musca domestica vicina*	Chang et al., 1963
Metepa	*Aedes aegypti* (L.)	Dame and Schmidt, 1964
	Anopheles quadrimaculatus Say	Dame and Schmidt, 1964
	Callosobruchus chinensis (L.)	Nagasawa and Shinohara, 1964b Shinohara and Nagasawa, 1963
	Ceratitis capitata (Wiedemann)	Keiser et al., 1965 Orphanidis, 1963b
	Cochliomyia hominivorax (Coquerel)	Chamberlain and Barrett, 1964 Crystal, 1963
	Culex p. quinquefasciatus Say	Mulla, 1964
	Dacus cucurbitae (Coquillet)	Keiser et al., 1965
	Dacus dorsalis Hendel	Keiser et al., 1965

TABLE 1 (CONTINUED)

Chemosterilant	Species	Reference
Metepa	*Dacus oleae* Gmel	Orphanidis and Patsacos, 1963
	Diabrotica balteata LeConte	Creighton et al., 1966
	Fannia canicularis (L.)	Davis and Eddy, 1966
	Glossina morsitans (Westw.)	Chadwick, 1964
	Hippelates pusio Loew	Schwartz, 1965
	Musca domestica (L.)	Dame and Schmidt, 1964
		Gouck, 1964
		Kenaga, 1965
		LaBrecque et al., 1963
		Ratcliffe and Ristich, 1965
	Pectinophora gossypiella (Saunders)	Ouye et al., 1965
	Phaenicia cuprina (Wiedemann)	Morgan and LaBrecque, 1964
	Popillia japonica Newman	Ladd, 1966
	Porthetria disper (*L.*)	Collier and Downey, 1965
	Stomoxys calcitrans (*L.*)	Chamberlain and Barrett, 1964
		Harris, 1962
	Trichoplusia ni (Hübner)	Henneberry and Kishaba, 1966
		Howland et al., 1965
1-Methanesulfonyl= aziridine	*Musca domestica* (L.)	Parish and Arthur, 1965
Methionine	*Musca domestica* (L.)	LaBrecque et al., 1960
Methiotepa	*Cochliomyia hominivorax* (Coquerel)	Crystal, 1963

TABLE 1 (CONTINUED)

Chemosterilant	Species	Reference
Methiotepa	*Blattella germanica* (L.)	Burden and Smittle, 1963
	Musca domestica (L.)	Gouck and LaBrecque, 1964 Kenaga, 1965 LaBrecque et al., 1963
(1-Methylallyl)tri= phenyltin	*Musca domestica* (L.)	Kenaga, 1965
(2-Methylallyl)tri= phenyltin	*Musca domestica* (L.)	Kenaga, 1965
Methyl apholate	*Blattella germanica* (L.)	Burden and Smittle, 1963
	Musca domestica (L.)	LaBrecque and Gouck, 1963
(*a*-Methylbenzyl)tri= phenyltin	*Musca domestica* (L.)	Kenaga, 1965
o-Methyl bis(1=aziri- dinyl)phosphinothioate	*Musca domestica* (L.)	Fye, 1967
Methyl[bis(1-aziridinyl)= phosphinyl)carbamate	*Cochliomyia hominivorax* (Coquerel)	Crystal, 1964a
Methyl bis(*beta* chloro= ethyl)amine hydro= chloride	*Musca domestica* (L.)	Mitlin et al., 1957
Methyl-2,3-dichloro= propionate	*Musca domestica* (L.)	Gouck and LaBrecque, 1964
N,N'-Methylenebis= [acrylamide]	*Musca domestica* (L.)	Gouck and LaBrecque, 1964
p,p'-Methylenebis[1- aziridinecarboxan= ilide]	*Musca domestica* (L.)	Gouck and LaBrecque, 1964
1,1'-[4,4'-methylene= bis(benzoylaziridine)]	*Cochliomyia hominivorax*	Crystal, 1963 Gouck et al., 1963
	Musca domestica (L.)	Gouck et al., 1963
N-(4,5-Methylenedioxy- 2-propylphenyl)= chrysanthemumamide	*Cochliomyia hominivorax* (Coquerel)	Gouck et al., 1963
1-Methyl-4-methylamino- 1*H*-pyrazolo[3,4-*d*]= pyrimidine	*Cochliomyia hominivorax* (Coquerel)	Crystal, 1963

TABLE 1 (CONTINUED)

Chemosterilant	Species	Reference
N,N'-(2-methyl-m-pheny=lene)bis-1-aziridine=carboxamide	*Anastrepha ludens* (Loew)	McFadden and Rubio, 1965
	Musca domestica (L.)	Fye et al., 1966
N,N'-(4-Methyl-m-pheny=lene)bis-1-aziridine=carboxamide	*Musca domestica* (L.)	Gouck and LaBrecque, 1964
		Ratcliffe and Ristich, 1965
Methyl tretamine	*Cochliomyia hominivorax* (Coquerel)	Crystal, 1963
		Crystal and LaChance, 1963
6-Methyluracil	*Musca domestica* (L.)	Painter and Kilgore, 1964
Monocrotaline	*Musca domestica* (L.)	Gouck and LaBrecque, 1964
Morzid	*Cochliomyia hominivorax* (Coquerel)	Crystal, 1963
	Musca domestica (L.)	LaBrecque et al., 1960
beta Naphthoxyacetamide	*Musca domestica* (L.)	LaBrecque et al., 1960
β-Naphthyldi-(2-chloro-ethyl)-amine	*Drosophila melanogaster* (Meigen)	Bird, 1950
β-Naphthyldi-(2-chloro-propyl)-amine (Mixture of isomers)	*Drosophila melanogaster* (Meigen)	Bird, 1950
Nitrogen mustard	*Bracon hebetor* Say	Lobbecke and Von Borstel, 1962
	Musca domestica vicina	Chang et al., 1963
Nitromin	*Musca domestica vicina*	Chang et al., 1963
N,N'-Octamethylene=bis (1-aziridine=carboxamide)	*Anastrepha ludens* (Loew)	McFadden and Rubio, 1965
	Musca domestica (L.)	Fye et al., 1966
Pactamycin	*Musca domestica* (L.)	Kohls et al., 1966
N,N'-Pentamethylene=bis-1-aziridine=carboxamide	*Anastrepha ludens* (Loew)	McFadden and Rubio, 1965
	Musca domestica (L.)	Fye et al., 1966
Phenothiazine	*Cochliomyia hominivorax* (Coquerel)	Crystal, 1964b

TABLE 1 (CONTINUED)

Chemosterilant	Species	Reference
N,N'-p-Phenylenebis-1-aziridinecarboxamide	*Musca domestica* (L.)	Fye et al., 1966
N,N'-(o-phenylenedi=methylene)bis(1-aziri=dine carboxamide)	*Anastrepha ludens* (Loew)	McFadden and Rubio, 1965
2-Phenylhydrazide of 3-ethoxypropionic acid	*Musca domestica* (L.)	LaBrecque and Gouck, 1963
Phenyl metepa	*Musca domestica* (L.)	LaBrecque et al., 1963
1-Phenyl-2-thiourea	*Musca domestica* (L.)	Mitlin and Baroody, 1958a
Phosphon(2,4-dichloro=benzyltributyl phos-phonium chloride)	*Musca domestica* (L.)	Tahori et al., 1965
	Prodenia litura Fabricius	Tahori et al., 1965a
1,4-Piperazinediylbis=[bis(1-aziridinyl)=phosphine oxide]	*Musca domestica* (L.)	Gouck and LaBrecque, 1964 LaBrecque and Gouck, 1963
Piperonyl butoxide	*Musca domestica* (L.)	Mitlin and Baroody, 1958b
Porfiromycin	*Musca domestica* (L.)	Kohls et al., 1966 Fye, 1967
Potassium arsenite	*Musca domestica* (L.)	Gouck and LaBrecque, 1964
Progesterone-diethyl=stilbesterol	*Conotrachelus nenuphar* (Herbst.)	Hays and Cochran, 1964
N-Propyl-1-aziridine=carboxamide	*Musca domestica* (L.)	Gouck and LaBrecque, 1964 Gouck et al., 1963
O-Propyl bis(2,2-dimethyl-1-aziri=dinyl)phosphino=thioate	*Musca domestica* (L.)	Fye et al., 1965
Purine	*Cochliomyia hominivorax* (Coquerel)	Gouck et al., 1963
p-Quinone	*Musca domestica* (L.)	Mitlin and Baroody, 1958b

TABLE 1 (CONTINUED)

Chemosterilant	Species	Reference
Reserpine	*Musca domestica* (L.)	Hays, 1965
	Anastrepha ludens (Loew)	Benschoter, 1966
2-Ribofuranosyl-*as*-triazine-3-5(2*H*,4*H*)= dione	*Cochliomyia hominivorax*	Crystal, 1963
Sarcolysin	*Musca domestica vicina*	Chang et al., 1963
Sterculia foetida	*Musca domestica* (L.)	Beroza and LaBrecque, 1967
Stilbazium iodide	*Cochliomyia hominivorax* (Coquerel)	Crystal, 1964c
Streptovitacin A	*Panonychus ulmi* (Koch)	Harries, 1963
1,1'-Sulfinylbis= aziridine	*Cochliomyia hominivorax* (Coquerel)	Crystal, 1963
1,1'-Sulfinylbis(2-methylaziridine)	*Cochliomyia hominivorax* (Coquerel)	Crystal, 1963
1,1'-Sulfonylbis= aziridine	*Musca domestica* (L.)	Parish and Arthur, 1965
1,1'-Sulfonylbis[2-methylaziridine	*Musca domestica* (L.)	Fye et al., 1965
Tartar emetic	*Cochliomyia hominivorax* (Coquerel)	Crystal, 1964b
Tedion	*Musca domestica* (L.)	Ascher and Hirsch, 1961
	Tetranychus urticae Koch	Meltzer, 1956
Tepa	*Acyrthosiphon disum* (Harris)	Bhalla and Robinson, 1966
	Aedes aegypti (L.)	Weidhaas et al., 1961
	Anastrepha ludens (Loew)	McFadden and Rubio, 1965 Shaw and Riviello, 1965
	Anopheles labranchiae	D'Alessandro et al., 1966
	Anopheles quadri-maculatus Say	Weidhaas et al., 1961
	Blattella germanica (L.)	Burden and Smittle, 1963

TABLE 1 (CONTINUED)

Chemosterilant	Species	Reference
Tepa	*Ceratitis capitata* (Wiedemann)	Keiser et al., 1965
		Orphanidis et al., 1963a
	Cochliomyia hominivorax (Coquerel)	Crystal, 1963
		Gouck et al., 1963
	Conotrachelus nenuphar (Herbst.)	Roach and Buxton, 1965
	Culex pipiens quinque-fasciatus Say	Mulla, 1964
	Dacus cucurbitae (Coquillet)	Keiser et al., 1965
	Dacus dorsalis Hendel	Keiser et al., 1965
	Dacus oleae Gmel	Orphanidis and Patsacos, 1963
	Diabrotica balteata LeConte	Creighton et al., 1966
	Fannia canicularis (L.)	Davis and Eddy, 1966
	Glossina morsitans (Westw.)	Dame, 1965
	Hippelates pusio Loew	Schwartz, 1965
	Musca autumnalis DeGeer	Hair and Adkins, 1964
	Musca domestica (L.)	Gouck, 1964
		Kenaga, 1965
		LaBrecque, 1961
	Panonychus citri (McGregor)	Cressman, 1963
	Popillia japonica Newman	Ladd, 1966
	Porthetria dispar (L.)	Collier and Downey, 1965
	Spodoptera frugiperda (J. E. Smith)	Young and Cox, 1964
	Stomoxys calcitrans (L.)	Harris, 1962
	Trichoplusia ni (Hübner)	Henneberry and Kishaba, 1966
		Howland et al., 1965

TABLE 1 (CONTINUED)

Chemosterilant	Species	Reference
Tetrahydrofuran	*Musca domestica* (L.)	LaBrecque and Gouck, 1963 Ascher, 1964
N,N'-Tetramethylene= bis (1-aziridine= carboxamide)	*Anastrepha ludens* (Loew)	McFadden and Rubio, 1965
	Cochliomyia hominivorax (Coquerel)	Crystal, 1965a
	Musca domestica (L.)	Fye et al., 1966
Tetraphenyltin	*Musca domestica* (L.)	Kenaga, 1965
Thiabendazole	*Cochliomyia hominivorax* (Coquerel)	Crystal, 1964b
Thiobis[triphenyltin]	*Musca domestica* (L.)	Fye et al., 1966
Thiotepa	*Aedes aegypti* (L.)	Bertram, 1963 Bertram et al., 1964 White, 1966
	Anopheles gambiae var. *gambiae* Giles	Bertram, 1963
	Anopheles gambiae var. *melas* (Theo)	Bertram, 1963
	Cochliomyia hominivorax (Coquerel)	Crystal, 1963 Crystal and LaChance, 1963
	Musca domestica (L.)	Kenaga, 1965 LaBrecque et al., 1960 Painter and Kilgore, 1964
	Musca domestica vicina	Chang, J.T. et. al., 1963
	Pseudaletia separata Walker	Chang, J.T. and Chiang, 1963
Thiourea	*Musca domestica* (L.)	LaBrecque et al., 1960 Mitlin and Baroody, 1958a
1-*p*-Toluoylaziridine	*Musca domestica* (L.)	Fye et al., 1965
1-*m*-Toluoylaziridine	*Musca domestica* (L.)	Fye et al., 1965

TABLE 1 (CONTINUED)

Chemosterilant	Species	Reference
1-*o*-Toluoylaziridine	*Musca domestica* (L.)	Fye et al., 1965
Tretamine	*Ceratitis capitata* (Wiedemann)	Keiser et al., 1965
	Cochliomyia hominivorax (Coquerel)	Crystal, 1963
	Cochliomyia hominivorax (Coquerel)	Crystal and LaChance, 1963
	Dacus cucurbitae (Coquillet)	Keiser et al., 1965
	Dacus dorsalis Hendel	Keiser et al., 1965
	Musca domestica (L.)	LaBrecque et al., 1960
as-Triazine-3,5(2H,= 4H)-dione	*Musca domestica* (L.)	LaBrecque and Gouck, 1963
3,4,4'-Trichloro= carbanilide	*Musca domestica* (L.)	Fye et al., 1966
Triphenyltin acetate	*Musca domestica* (L.)	Fye et al., 1966 Kenaga, 1965
Triphenyltin, *p*-aceta= midobenzoate	*Musca domestica* (L.)	Kenaga, 1965
Triphenyltin borate	*Musca domestica* (L.)	Kenaga, 1965
Triphenyltin chloride	*Musca domestica* (L.)	Fye et al., 1966 Kenaga, 1965
Triphenyltin dimethyl= thiocarbamate	*Musca domestica* (L.)	Kenaga, 1965
Triphenyltin fluoride	*Musca domestica* (L.)	Kenaga, 1965
Triphenyltin iodide	*Musca domestica* (L.)	Kenaga, 1965
Triphenyltin methacry= late	*Musca domestica* (L.)	Kenaga, 1965
Triphenyltin stearate	*Musca domestica* (L.)	Kenaga, 1965
Triphenyltin, 10-unde- cenoate	*Musca domestica* (L.)	Kenaga, 1965
Triphenyl vinyl tin	*Musca domestica* (L.)	Kenaga, 1965
Triphenyl (*p*-vinyl= benzyltin, polymers	*Musca domestica* (L.)	Kenaga, 1965
Tris(*p*-aminophenyl)= carbonium chloride	*Cochliomyia hominivorax* (Coquerel)	Crystal, 1964b
Tris(*p*-aminophenyl)= carbonium pamoate	*Cochliomyia hominivorax* (Coquerel)	Crystal, 1964b
N[Tris(1-aziridinyl)= phosphoranylidene] benzenesulfonamide	*Anastrepha ludens* (Loew) *Musca domestica* (L.)	McFadden and Rubio, 1965 Fye et al., 1966

TABLE 1 (CONTINUED)

Chemosterilant	Species	Reference
2,4,6-Tris(1-aziridinyl)-2,4,6-tris(dimethyl= amino)-2,2,4,6,6-hexahydro-1,3,5,2,4,6-triazatriphosphorine	*Cochliomyia hominivorax* (Coquerel) *Musca domestica* (L.)	Gouck et al., 1963 Gouck et al., 1963 Gouck and LaBrecque, 1964
Tris(*d*-2-methyl-1-aziridinyl)phosphine	*Musca domestica* (L.)	Fye et al., 1965
Tris(*l*-2-methyl-1-aziridinyl)phosphine	*Musca domestica* (L.)	Fye et al., 1965
2,4,6-Tris[1-(2-methyl) aziridinyl]-*s*-triazine	*Musca domestica* (L.)	LaBrecque and Gouck, 1963
Tubercidin	*Musca domestica* (L.)	Kohls et al., 1966
Tyrosine	*Musca domestica* (L.)	LaBrecque et al., 1960
Uracil	*Musca domestica* (L.)	LaBrecque et al., 1960
Uracil-*y*-acetic acid	*Musca domestica* (L.)	LaBrecque et al., 1960
m-Xylohydroquinone	*Drosophila melanogaster* (Meigen) *Musca domestica* (L.)	Mukherjee, 1961 Ascher and Hirsch, 1963
N,N'-(alpha,alpha'-*m*-xylylene)bis[1-aziridinecarboxamide	*Musca domestica* (L.)	Gouck and LaBrecque, 1964

in a chemosterilant solution. This method is particularly suited to irradiation for inducing sterility in large numbers for in many insects, particularly in diptera, it can be used when the insect is in an immobile state. Unfortunately, in the case of house flies, the author has found that the sterilant does not penetrate the cuticle, although a trace is found in the tracheal tubes. The sterility is induced when the fly collects a sterilizing dose on its labellum and tarsi from the residue on the exterior of the pupal case in its effort to leave the puparium. Some of the insect species sterilized as prepupae, pupae or adults in this method are given in Table 2 and can serve as a guide if this method is chosen to induce sterility. The solvent and carrier

TABLE 2

STAGES AND SPECIES OF INSECTS THAT HAVE BEEN STERILIZED BY IMMERSION

Stadium	Insect	Chemosterilant and Concentration, %		Immersion time, min.	Reference
Prepupa	House fly	Apholate	0.5– 5.0	0.5–10.0	Gouck, 1964
		Metepa	0.5– 5.0	0.5–10.0	Gouck, 1964
		Tepa	0.5– 5.0	0.5–10.0	Gouck, 1964
	Screwworm	Apholate	1.0– 5.0	1.0–30.0	Chamberlain, 1962
Pupa	Face fly	Apholate	4.0	25.0	Hair and Adkins, 1964
	House fly	2,2'-Dichloro-n-methyl= diethylamine	5.0–20.0	30.0	Piquett and Keller, 1962
		Apholate	0.5– 5.0	0.5–10.0	Gouck, 1964
		Metepa	0.5– 5.0	0.5–10.0	Gouck, 1964
		Tepa	0.5– 5.0	0.5–10.0	Gouck, 1964
		Hempa	2.5–75.0	5.0–60.0	LaBrecque et al., 1966
	Mediterranean fruit fly	Apholate	40.0	0.5	Keiser et al., 1965
		Metepa	5.0	0.5	Keiser et al., 1965
		Tepa	5.0–40.0	0.5	Keiser et al., 1965
		Tretamine	40.0	0.5	Keiser et al., 1965
	Melon fly	Apholate	5.0–40.0	0.5	Keiser et al., 1965
		Metepa	5.0–40.0	0.5	Keiser et al., 1965
		Tepa	.63– 5.0	0.5	Keiser et al., 1965
		Tretamine	10.0	0.5	Keiser et al., 1965
	Mexican fruit fly	Tepa	5.0	1.0	Shaw and Riviello, 1964

TABLE 2 (CONTINUED)

Stadium	Insect	Chemosterilant and Concentration, %		Immersion time, min.	Reference
	Oriental fruit fly	Apholate	40.0	0.5	Keiser et al., 1965
		Metepa	10.0–40.0	0.5	Keiser et al., 1965
		Tepa	2.5–20.0	0.5	Keiser et al., 1965
		Tretamine	1.25–20.0	0.5	Keiser et al., 1965
	Tsetse fly	Tepa	5.0	1.0	Dame, 1965
Adult	Azuki bean weevil	Apholate	.03– 1.0	1.0	Shinohara and Nagasawa, 1963
		Metepa	.03– 1.0	1.0	Shinohara and Nagasawa, 1963
	Banded cucumber beetle	Metepa	.12– 1.0	(3 sec.)	Creighton et al., 1966
	Boll weevil	Apholate	.25– 2.0	0.33[a]	Lindquist et al., 1964
	Mexican bean beetle	Apholate	.5	5.0	Henneberry et al., 1964
	Plum curculio	Apholate	0.1–10.0	0.5	Roach and Buxton, 1965
	Two spotted spider mite	Apholate	.25– 2.0	---	Smith, F. F., et al., 1965
	I. cinnabarinus	Apholate	.25– 2.0	---	Smith, F.F., et al., 1965

[a]Dipped 1 to 3 times at various intervals.

for the sterilant varied in most tests but ethyl alcohol, methanol, acetone, acetonitrile in water, or water alone were the materials of choice.

TOPICAL APPLICATION

Possibly the most accurate method in the quantitative determination of sterilant necessary to induce sterility is by topical application. Although it is not practicable in inducing sterility in large numbers, it can be highly instrumental in determining the sterilant's mode of action, breakdown, and rapidity of transfer. The technique used has been described in the section on screening, however it consists generally of applying a definite concentration of the sterilant on the thorax or abdomen of the insect by means of a microapplicator. The volume usually ranges from 0.5 to 1.0 μl. Some of the species upon which this technique has been used are given below.

Azuki bean weevil	Nagasawa and Shinohara, 1965
Boll weevil	Lindquist et al., 1964
House flies	Ascher, 1964
	Chang, S. C. et al., 1964
	Chang and Chiang, 1964
	Gouck et al., 1963
Pink bollworm	Ouye et al., 1965
Screwworm	Chamberlain, 1962
	Crystal, 1964b
Tsetse fly	Chadwick, 1964

Chang and Borkovec (1964) and S. C. Chang et al. (1964) have carried the accuracy of the approach even further in house flies when they injected the sterilant solution directly into the tissue of the house fly.

The techniques of sterility induction covered thus far represent the majority of the approaches used by researchers in evaluating chemosterilants. Other methods can be found in the literature, but many are still in the developmental stage or utilized only in isolated instances. One method indicating great promise is that utilized by F. F. Smith et al. (1965) in which a coarse spray is applied on adult spider mites. Another is a technique utilized by Crystal (1965a), aerosol droplets containing the chemosterilant were sprayed on confined adult screwworms. These droplets are so fine that they penetrate into the insect's respiratory system without the change of breakdown by enzymes or digestion as would be encountered by the feeding technique.

SPECIAL TESTS

Once a chemosterilant has been uncovered, the critical phase of its laboratory evaluation begins. It is from a detailed study of the sterilant's effects in or on the insect that determination of field practicality is obtained.

RANGE OF CONCENTRATION

It is rather obvious that when a sterilant has been isolated in a screening program, regardless of the method by which sterility has been induced, the range of concentrations that produce sterility should be determined. A sterilant that produces sterility at one level, yet is lethal at a slightly higher concentration, but has no effect at a lower dosage, is rather limited in potential. Under field conditions, the insect would by necessity have to consume or absorb relatively the same limited dosage within the prescribed time as in the screening tests. However, should the range of sterility inducing concentrations be more extensive, in the vicinity of tenfold, the insect by chance contact, a single meal, or intermittent short exposures would have a greater opportunity of becoming sterilized.

SEX STERILIZED

The knowledge of whether both sexes are sterilized is mandatory. If only the female were sterile, the benefits derived would be of no greater significance than with the use of an insecticide, as the reproductive potential of the particular female alone would be eliminated. Some reports have indicated that sterile females have reduced populations to a degree greater than that expected at the same selective pressure and this bonus effect has been attributed to sperm depletion in the males. These instances are rare as most males are unfortunately equipped with either vast stores of sperm or mechanism for the rapid

replacement of expended sperm. The principle of sperm depletion should not be overlooked and is worthy of investigation, although a chemical that sterilizes both sexes is preferable.

A chemosterilant that produces only male sterility also
leaves something to be desired. Agreed that a marked population
reduction would be evident at the 90 percent level of selection,
once again a definite bonus would be lost as the remaining 10
percent fertile males: assuming an equal number of both sexes,
would be able to inseminate their equal number of females.
However, if 90 percent of the females were sterile, the chances
of a fertile cross are reduced by 90 percent giving a final 99
percent selection rate to the population. This advantage might
be slightly reduced if the female was of the multiple mating
type, but not necessarily so if the sperm of the initial mating
alone is utilized by the female for egg fertilization, or the sterilant in the sperm have the capabilities of translocating in
quantities to affect the sperm of subsequent fertile matings upon
admixture in the spermatheca.

Perhaps at this time we should discuss some of the techniques used in obtaining virgin insects. To insure virgins for
crosses, cockroaches are sexed at the last nymphal instar,
whereas the fall armyworm, *Tribolium*, and the banded cucumber beetle are separated during the pupal stage (Burden and
Smittle, 1963, Young and Cox, 1964, Kenaga, 1965, and Creighton et al., 1966). The screwworm, the boll weevil, the large
milkweed bug, and the face fly are sexed upon eclosion. (Chamberlain, 1962, Hedin et al., 1965, Simkover, 1964, and Hair and
Adkins, 1964.) Although house flies are normally sexed within
four hr following eclosion, Murvosh et al. (1964) indicated that
males and females will not mate for at least 16 and 24 hr, respectively. Because newly eclosed house flies have poorly differentiated external reproductive organs, aging is preferable to
insure positive sexual differentiation. Ascher (1965) places
hundreds of pupae individually in small test tubes; later, the
adults are segregated by sexes in separate cages. Another
method for obtaining virgin house flies is by the use of a physical deterrent to mating. In this method, the apparatus consists
basically of a boxed plexiglass plate. The plate is covered with
pupae, after which another plexiglass plate of identical measurements is fitted over the pupae, allowing for a space between
the plates of only 1 mm above the height of the pupae. Upon
eclosion, the adults are free to migrate laterally but cannot assume any copulating attitude because of lack of space. A virgin

state of all confined adults is assured over an extended period of time.

Fortunately, among some insects, mating is not a phenomenon exhibited too rapidly upon reaching the adult stage. Drosophila, the Azuki bean weevil, and the Mexican bean beetle can be sexed within 6 to 8 hr following adult emergence (Cantwell and Henneberry, 1963, Shinohara and Nagasawa, 1963, and Henneberry et al., 1964); the olive fruit fly, the southern house mosquito, and the eye gnat can be sexed within 24 hr (Orphanidis and Patsacos, 1963, Mulla, 1964, and Schwartz, 1965) with relative assurance of virginity. In some instances, with insects such as the Mediterranean fruit fly, the virginity period is extended to several days.

The majority of antimetabolites, except for examples like 5-fluoroorotic acid in house flies, will sterilize only adult females when presented in the diet. Ovaries in young adults are in a state of rapid proliferation, and the germ cells are in a state of high metabolic activity, apparently sensitive to outside factors, and are ideal sites for the antimetabolite's intervention. Ovaries attacked at this time show immediate cessation of development, followed by rapid degeneration and resorption. Although the effects of the metabolic antagonist are more readily evident at this stage of the insect, the same effects can be induced, but to a lesser degree, throughout the female's adult life, as long as gonotropic cycles are present. This degenerative phenomenon seldom occurs in the males, and the lack of it is attributed to the fact that (1) in the majority of males, gametic development in numbers adequate to satisfy numerous inseminations is nearly complete prior to ecdysis to the adult, and (2) the antagonistic effect of the chemical is lacking. It has been observed that if the chemical is injected into the insect at a preceeding stadium, where spermatogenesis is prevalent, sterility can be induced. This selective sterility has severely hampered the use and development of antimetabolites, but because (1) in most instances only minute quantities are necessary to produce sterility in females, (2) their effects can be reversed, and (3) they appear to possess less mutagenic activity than the nitrogen mustard derivatives, they should be included in screening programs. They definitely have a niche in sterilant studies particularly when used in combinations with compounds of other types, a recent development towards lowering some of the hazards involved in field dispersal of baits.

As previously stated, antimetabolites have high selectivity for inducing sterility in females, but the opposite is often true with other groups of chemicals. Dimethylamines such as hempa and hemel (S. C. Chang et al., 1964a) and some chemicals having s-triazine structures are more specific to males and produce sterility in this sex at concentrations often ten times lower than in females. Such sterilants at the lowest concentrations calculated to sterilize the male, could be admixed with an antimetabolite counterpart at low concentrations to sterilize females and thus significantly lower the toxicity hazards. Especially with alkylating agents and some antibiotics, combinations of these sterilants with antimetabolites should be investigated to determine whether sterilant activity could be obtained at lower dosages by simultaneous attack at two or more sites within the insect or by one chemical having a potentiation effect upon the other. Combinations should not be overlooked in secondary evaluations.

Experiments with sterilants should be designed to serve some applied goal as well as to contribute to the basic knowledge. Insects in the field seldom encounter more than a few sites where a chemosterilant would be available. Moreover, adults will vary in age and physical condition. Following the determination of sex sterilized as well as range of concentrations that produce sterility, the effect of the sterilant should be studied against both sexes, virgin or mated of various ages ranging from freshly eclosed to mature, to determine whether a single exposure derived by feeding, contact, or other methods will produce sterility.

Chemosterilants applied as baits in the field are normally applied to breeding and feeding sites as well as in areas of population congregation: these baits are in constant competition with many natural nutrients found in the environment. If an attractant could be included with the bait, areas to be treated could be selected, but unfortunately except for some species few attractants are available to date. It has also been reported by Sacca et al. (1965) that house flies were repelled from sugar baits containing metepa and hempa. These factors, i.e., competition with a natural attractant or repellence of the chemosterilant could severely hamper the results of a field trial. To overcome this, as screening programs are evolved, one test procedure should include the addition of normal food along with the treated food to give the insect a choice. If the candidate sterilant is too repellent it will be evidenced by lack of sterility. Fye and LaBrecque (unpublished data) have screened 23 promising sterilants, including metepa and hempa, to determine whether a repellency, if present, was sufficiently pronounced to influence the induction of sterility in house flies. At concentrations known to produce sterility, only *Sterculia foetida* (a low-order female sterilant) was ineffective when a choice of diets was made available.

PERMANENCE

　　Often a dosage will produce sterility but the effect will be transitory and the insect will regain fertility. Simple laboratory studies can be readily conducted to determine the duration of sterilant effectiveness. This can be accomplished by sterilizing groups of virgin males and females segregated by sex, and performing crosses with untreated virgin individuals of the opposite sex at various periods throughout the adult life span. It must be kept in mind that the higher the concentration of chemosterilant, the greater the chance of deleterious effect on the insect. Longevity has been markedly shortened by some sterilants, e.g., apholate, tepa, and metepa in house flies, (Murvosh et al, 1964a), the Mexican bean beetle (Henneberry et al., 1964), and the boll weevil, (Hedin et al., 1964). But it must also be kept in mind that permanence of sterility at the cost of marked reduction in longevity may be unnecessary. It has been reported that some house flies undergo over 20 gonotropic cycles in the laboratory as well as having a survival time of over six weeks, but these conditions are seldom encountered in the field. Normally, the period of greatest sexual activity is in the earlier part of adult life. It is at this time that the females are first ready to accept mates, the mating competitiveness of the male is at its height, the most rapid gonadial development occurs, and the largest number of eggs are laid. These activities decrease rapidly as the insect ages; especially the number of eggs laid. In nature, for example, many females of *Anopheles quadrimaculatus* die after laying a single clutch of eggs, far less than their potential capacity. Therefore, a sterilant concentration that produces sterility for only 50 percent of the adult life could, with some species, be as effective in the field as one that produces permanent sterility at the cost of reduced sexual aggressiveness and a shortened life span. It should also

be noted that the inherent hazards of the chemical would also
be reduced at lower concentrations.

SEXUAL COMPETITIVENESS

Another aspect to be considered is the effect of the sterilant on the sexual aggressiveness of the male. A. N. Davis
et al. (1959) found that radiosterilized male mosquitoes were
not as competitive as normal males. No reduction in sexual
competitiveness, however, was noted in chemosterilized mosquitoes by Weidhaas and Schmidt (1963), nor in house flies by
LaBrecque et al. (1962). Should a male be so incapacitated by
the sterilant that the sexual drive is reduced or eliminated, the
theoretical advantage of control by the sterile-male concept
could not be realized. Sexual competitiveness can be determined
by confining a definite number of normal males and chemosterilized males at various ratios with sexually mature virgin
females, and evaluating competitiveness by comparing egg sterility obtained to the theoretical values for each ratio of sterile
to fertile males. With some species it may be necessary to insure that the number of females is less than the total number
of males in order to obtain competition for the females. As in
many insects, coitus involves an extended period, during which,
if the number of males equals the number of females, even
males with reduced sex drives could possibly find a female
within the mating period of the aggressive male. Some suggested ratios of chemosterilized males, normal males, and
normal females range from 1:1:1 to 10:1:1.

The above technique is principally instrumental in the
determination of whether the sterilized males retain their
sexual aggressiveness. However, should field releases be con-
templated where sterile insects of both sexes would be released
into the environment, the effect of the released sterile females
should also be determined. Supposing a release is conducted
with a sterile-fertile ratio of 10:1. A prior competitiveness test
involving a ratio of 10 sterile males, 10 sterile females, 1 fertile male and 1 fertile female would shed some light on whether
the sterile female exerts some influence on the mating potential
of both released and wild males.

Since these procedures are somewhat laborious, a simple way of measuring sexual vigor was devised for the screw-
worm (Baumhover, 1965). Normally the male screwworm at-

tempts to mate repeatedly, while the female (after a single mating) rejects the male's overtures. The persistent harassment by the untreated males when they outnumber the females in a 3:1 ratio shortens the lifespan of the females. The extent to which the lifespan is shortened is a measure of the sexual vigor of the treated males; this test is known as the SAG test (sexual aggressiveness test).

RESISTANCE

When chlorinated hydrocarbon insecticides were discovered more than two decades ago, many researchers believed that the extinction of noxious insect pests was at hand. Some species of insects, however, have overcome not only chlorinated hydrocarbons but also some organophosphorous compounds by utilizing or developing mechanisms which could block or detoxify the lethal properties of the insecticides. To assume that insects could do the same with chemosterilants was not beyond reason. Sacca et al. (1966) obtained increased resistance in a colony of house flies treated with metepa, but not in a colony treated with hempa. Morgan et al. (1966) failed to develop any resistance to apholate in house flies when they subjected adults continuously to concentrations of apholate in the diet that produce less than 100 percent sterility for 80 generations. Their results indicated that in the earlier generations, there appeared to be a cumulative deleterious effect in the genetic material with fertility gradually reducing for about 30 generations. By the 80th generation, fertility approaching the level obtained at the start of the study was observed. These laboratory results support those obtained by Meifert et al. (1967) in field studies. In this test, semiweekly applications of metepa baits for two years failed to produce any marked resistance to the sterilant. Unfortunately, this situation has not been encountered when mosquitoes were subjected in the larval stage to sterilants. Hazard et al. (1964) found that the yellow-fever mosquito does develop resistance to apholate to a significant degree within a short period of time. Morever, these results have been substantiated by Klassen and Matsumura (1966), who found that larvae of the same species respond to metepa and develop resistance within a few generations.

HAZARDS

The nature of the aziridine sterilants demands that close surveillance be exercised not only at the site of distribution, but also in determining the amount that the insects carry, especially if they frequent human habitations. Dame and Schmidt (1964) found the total amount of radioactivity in and on house flies after three days of maintenance on dry food containing 0.4 percent of P^{32}-labelled metepa equalled the amount in 3.68 μg of metepa in male flies and 8.42 μg of metepa in female flies. Probably only a portion of the radioactivity represented unmetabolized metepe inasmuch as Plapp et al. (1962) demonstrated that house flies injected with metepa degraded 50 percent of the chemical in approximately one hr.

    Both studies, however, involved the use of radioactively tagged chemosterilants, and so limited studies to laboratory situations so that, except under controlled field conditions, this technique could not be used in the field to determine the uptake of a chemosterilant by the insects. This is especially true in the case of insects that share the same habitat as man and contaminate his food. Moreover the distribution of tagged bait severely limits its dispersal. Bowman and Beroza (1966) have recently developed an assay for chemosterilants in which the uptake of the chemical by the insect or the amount of contamination by regurgitation or by walking can be measured to an astounding degree. By a gas chromatograph method sensitive to 0.1 nanogram, they devised an analysis for nonmetabolized chemosterilant residues of tepa, apholate, metepa, methiotepa, and hempa, enabling a researcher to monitor minute amounts of chemosterilants. For the first time actual definitive analysis can be conducted during field studies to determine whether a sterilant does produce a hazard to the environment. This enables one to regulate the concentration of the sterilant to tolerable levels.

OTHER STUDIES

    If field releases are considered for overflooding a fertile population, to supplement a field bait or residue program, or if a chemosterilant is used to replace gamma irradiation as a less expensive and more mobile source of sterility induction, then pupal and adult dipping in chemosterilant solutions merits serious consideration. As will be discussed in a subsequent chapter, pupal dipping has been used successfully with Mexican fruit flies in field releases. To date there has been no report of sterility induction in insects within the pupal case, but rather, as previously cited, the insect contacts a sterilizing dose in the process of escaping the confines of the pupal case upon eclosion. Unfortunately, in house flies, the author has observed that although complete sterility is often obtained, less than 100 percent sterility is encountered on enough occasions to render this method of treatment unreliable. Failure to produce a consistent 100 percent sterility has been attributed to the degradation of the chemosterilant or the fact that when dipped house fly pupae are placed in large numbers in release containers, those on the uppermost layer do not contact enough sterilant to insure complete sterility. If a chemosterilant barrier were placed over the pupae, however, the freshly eclosed adults would have to migrate through an additional residual treatment and chances of the insect escaping the residual would be drastically lowered. It is mandatory that a high sterility be obtained when releases are contemplated. Should a field population be reduced to 10,000 insects and a release of 100,000 sterile insects be considered to overflood the existing population at a 10:1 ratio, its effect would be reduced to 4.5:1 if only 90 percent of the released insects are sterile.

Release programs usually involve the mass rearing of insects in which the sex ratio is approximately equal. Segregation of the insects by sex is costly and time consuming, and sterile females as well as males are usually released into the environment. The sterile females probably do not reduce the effectiveness of the control operation, and may actually contribute to its success. With some species, however, particularly those that are impossible or too difficult to rear economically in large numbers, it would be highly advantageous to exploit the potential of the females more fully. P. B. Morgan (1967). successfully sterilized male house flies by exposing them to booby-trapped females. Booby-trapping consisted of attaching small chamois pads treated with a chemosterilant on the dorsum of the abdomen. Preliminary results were encouraging. Following Crystal's (personal communication) report that fertility in male screwworms was greatly reduced by copulation with females topically treated with N, N'-tetramethylenebis (1-aziridinecarboxamide), further studies by Meifert et al. (in press) with this chemical on house flies revealed that topical applications on the padded females or applications directly on the dorsum of virgin females not only sterilized the males exposed to the females within a 15-day period, but the females were sterile also. It was also noted that when male house flies were treated topically with the sterilant and exposed to other males, these untreated males became sterile in attempts to copulate with the treated males. These highly promising results indicate that females can definitely contribute to population reduction in a release program. This method need not be limited to insects where difficulty in rearing is encountered, but could be applied where mass rearing techniques are available. Insects could be reared and then sprayed with a chemosterilant prior to release.

Another fascinating facet involving chemosterilants was investigated by Altman (1963). Upon learning that mosquitoes could be sterilized by exposure to tepa residues, he surmised that a sufficient amount should also be absorbed by the insect to possibly prevent the development of parasites within it. Using chicks infected with *Plasmodium gallinaceum*, he found that *Aedes aegypti* mosquitoes exposed to a 10 mg residue of tepa immediately before or after feeding had a marked reduction of infective rate as well as reduced oocyst counts. Similar exposures also caused a reduction in malaria transmission rates. Bertram et al. (1964) in similar tests with thiotepa obtained similar effects, but to a lesser extent.

The alkylating agents have stimulated much research on the fundamental problems encountered with chemosterilants. However, their mutagenicity and carcinogenicity preclude their indiscriminate use in all but severely controlled laboratory and field studies. Without these tools, however, many of the stumbling blocks inherent in the study of the chemical sterilant approach would not have been resolved. They have opened the way to research in other groups of chemicals principally in the area of dimethylamines, triazines, antimetabolites, organometallic compounds, and numerous other chemical structures where great promise is indicated.

REFERENCES

Adkins, T. R. Jr., 1965. Face fly control with a chemosterilant. Agric. Res. So. Car. Agric. Exper. Sta. II(2):5, 17–18.

Altman, R. M. 1963. The effects of tepa on *Plasmodium gallinaceum* in *Aedes aegypti*. The Amer. J. Hyg., 77(3):221–227.

Arkin, A. 1962. Recent developments in the etiology and chemotherapy of cancer. Bull. L. A. Weiss Mem. Hosp IV(1):9–15.

Ascher, K. R. S. 1957. Prevention of oviposition in the house fly through tarsal contact agents. Science, 125:938.

_____, 1962. Two new research approaches to the resistance problem using the house fly as experimental animal. J. Hyg. Epidem. (Praha) VI:256–264.

_____, 1964. Oviposition-inhibiting agents: a screening for simple model substances. Proc. XII Int. Cong. Entom. (London), July 8–16. p. 514.

_____, 1965. Oviposition inhibiting agents: a screening for simple model substances. Int. Pest Control, pp. 1–4.

_____, and Hirsch. 1961. Inhibition of oviposition in the house fly by inhibition of acaricides. (ovicides.). Estratto dalla Revista di Malariol., XL (nn4–6):1–7.

_____, and Hirsch. 1963. The effect of m-xylohydroquinone on oviposition in the house fly. Ent. Exp. et Applicata, 6(4):337–338.

Baumhover, A. H. 1965. Sexual aggressiveness of male screw-worm flies measured by effect on female mortality. J. Econ. Entom., 58(3):544–548.

Benschoter, C. A. 1966. Reserpine as a sterilant for the Mexican fruit fly. J. Econ. Entom., 59(2):333–334.

Beroza, M., and G. C. LaBrecque. 1966. Chemosterilant activity of oils, especially oil of *Sterculia foetida*, in the housefly. J. Econ. Entom. 60(1):196–199.

Bertram, D. S. 1963. Observations on the chemosterilant effect of an alkylating agent, thio-tepa, on wild caught *Anopheles gambiae* var, *melas* (Theo.) in Gambia, West Africa, and on laboratory bred *A.g. gambiae* Giles, and *Aedes aegypti* L. Trans. Roy. Soc. Trop. Med. Hyg., 57(5):322–335.

_____, S. C. Srivastava, and A. S. Msangi. 1964. Transmission of *Plasmodium gallinaceum* Brumpt to chicks by *Aedes aegypti* (L.) sterilized by an alkylating agent thiotepa. J. Trop. Med. Hyg., 67:51–57.

Bhalla, O. P., and A. G. Robinson. 1966. Effect of three chemosterilants on the pea aphid fed on an artificial diet. J. Econ. Entom., 59(2):378–379.

Bird, M. J. 1950. Production of mutations in *Drosophila* using four aryl-2-halogenalkylamines. Nature, 165 (London) (4195):491–492.

Borkovec, A. B. 1966. Insect chemosterilants. In   , Advances in Pest Control, vol. 7,   , New York, John Wiley & Sons.

Bowman, M. C., and M. Beroza. 1966. Gas chromatographic determination of trace amounts of insect chemosterilants, tepa, metepa, methiotepa, hempa, and apholate, and the analysis of tepa in insect tissue. J. Ass. Official Anal. Chem., 49(5):1046–1052.

Burden, G. S., and B. J. Smittle. 1963. Chemosterilant studies with the German cockroach. Fla. Entom., 46(3):229–234.

Cantwell, G. E., and T. J. Henneberry. 1963. The effects of gamma
    radiation and apholate on the reproductive tissues of *Droso-
    phila melanogaster* Meigen. J. Insect Path., 5(2):251–264.
Carillo, J. L., A. Ortega, and J. Rodriguez. 1963. Effecto esteril-
    izante de las radiociones gamma y del compuesto "apholate"
    sobre la conchuela del frijol. Agr. Tecn. en Mexico. 11(4):1–8.
Chadwick, P. R. 1964. Effect of two chemosterilants on *Glossina mor-
    sitans*. Nature (London), 204 (4955):299–300.
Chamberlain, W. F. 1962. Chemical sterilization of the screw-worm.
    J. Econ. Entom. 55(2):240–248.
_____ , and D. E. Hopkins. 1960. Effect of colchicine on screw-worms.
    J. Econ. Entom., 53(6):1133–1134.
_____ , and C. C. Barrett. 1964. A comparison of the amounts of metepa
    required to sterilize the screwworm fly and the stable fly. J.
    Econ. Entom., 57(2):267–269.
Chang, J. T., T. P. Tsao, and Y. C. Chiang. 1963. Studies on insect
    chemosterilants. I. Screen tests of 35 chemicals as insect
    chemosterilants. Acta Entom. Sinica., 12(4):394–401.
_____ , and Y. C. Chiang. 1963. Studies on insect chemosterilants. II.
    Thiotepa as a chemosterilant for armyworn moth (*Pseudaletia
    separata* Walker, Noctuidae.) Acta Entom. Sinica., 12(5–6):
    538–542.
_____ , and Y. C. Chiang. 1964. Studies on insect chemosterilants.
    III. The sterilizing effect of thiotepa on the common house fly
    Musca domestica vicina Macq. Acta Entom. Sinica., 13(5):679–
    688.
Chang, S. C., and A. B. Borkovec. 1964. Quantitative effects of tepa,
    metepa, and apholate on sterilization of male house flies. J.
    Econ. Entom., 57(4):488–490.
_____ , P. H. Terry, and A. B. Borkovec. 1964. Insect chemosterilants
    with low toxicity for mammals. Science, 144:57–58.
Collier, C. W., and J. E. Downey. 1965. Laboratory evaluation of cer-
    tain chemosterilants against the gypsy moth. J. Econ. Entom.,
    58(4):649–651.
Creighton, C. S., E. R. Cuthbert, Jr., and W. J. Reid, Jr. 1966. Fe-
    cundity and hatch of eggs from banded cucumber beetles treated
    with three aziridines: Preliminary tests. J. Econ. Entom.,
    59(1):163–165.
Cressman, A. W. 1963. Response of citrus red mite to chemical ster-
    ilants. J. Econ. Entom., 56(1):111–112.
Crystal, M. M. 1963. The induction of sexual sterility in the screw-
    worm fly by antimetabolites and alkylating agents. J. Econ.
    Entom., 56(4):468–473.
_____ , 1964a. Insect fertility: inhibition by folic acid derivatives.
    Science, 144(3616):308–309.
_____ , 1964b. Chemosterilant efficiency of bis(1-aziridinyl)phosphinyl
    carbamates in screw-worm flies. J. Econ. Entom., 57(5):726–
    731.

_____ , 1964. Antifertility effects of antihelminthics in insects. J. Econ. Entom., 57(4):606–607.

_____ , 1965a. Sexual sterilization of insects by aerosol administration of alkylating agents. J. Econ. Entom., 58(4):678–680.

_____ , 1965. First efficient chemosterilants against screwworm flies (Diptera:Calliphoridae). J. Med. Entom., 2(3):317–319.

_____ , and L. E. LaChance. 1963. The modification of reproduction in insects treated with alkylating agents. I. Inhibition of ovarian growth and egg production. J. Cell Comp. Physiol. 125(2):270–279.

D'Alessandro, G., C. Bruno-Smiraglia, and A. Lavagnino. 1966. Saggi di chemosterilizazione con tepa su *Anopheles labranchiae.* Estratto dalla Revista di Malariol. XLV:1–3.

Dame, D. A. 1965. Mass rearing and chemosterilization of *Glossina morsitans* (Westw.) Advances in Insect Population Control by the Sterile Male Technique. A Report of the Panel, Vienna, Austria. 20–24 July. Technical Report Series #44. pp 1–79.

_____ , and C. H. Schmidt. 1964. Uptake of metepa and its effect on two species of mosquitoes (*Anopheles quadrimaculatus* and *Aedes aegypti*) and house flies (*Musca domestica*) J. Econ. Entom., 57(1):77–81.

_____ , D. B. Woodward, and H. R. Ford. 1964. Chemosterilization of *Aedes aegypti* (L.) by larval treatments. Mosq. News, 24(1):1–6.

_____ , and H. R. Ford. 1964. Chemosterilization and its permanency in mosquitoes. Nature (London), 201(4920):733–734.

Davis, A. N., J. B. Gahan, D. E. Weidhaas, and C. N. Smith. 1959. Exploratory studies on gamma irradiation for the sterilization and control of *Anopheles quadrimaculatus.* J. Econ. Entom., 52(5):868–870.

Davis, H. G., and G. W. Eddy. 1966. Some effects of chemosterilants on the little house fly. J. Econ. Entom., 59(4):993–996.

Eddy, G. W., A. R. Roth, and L. R. Abrahamsen. 1965. Sterilant effect of some materials on *Aedes aegypti* (L.) feeding on treated mice. Mosq. News, 25(2):169–171.

Fye, R. L. 1967. Screening of chemosterilants against house flies. J. Econ. Entom., 60(2):605–607.

_____ , H. K. Gouck, and G. C. LaBrecque. 1965. Compounds causing sterility in adult house flies. J. Econ. Entom., 58(3):446–448.

_____ , G. C. LaBrecque, and H. K. Gouck. 1966. Screening tests for sterilization of adult house flies. J. Econ. Entom., 59(2):485–487.

Glancey, B. M. 1965. Hempa as a chemosterilant for the yellow-fever mosquito *Aedes aegypti* (L.) (Diptera Culicidae) Mosq. News, 25(4):392–396.

Goldsmith, E. D., and I. Frank. 1952. Sterility in the female fruit fly *Drosophila melanogaster* produced by the feeding of a folic acid antagonist. Amer. J. Physiol., 171(3):726–727.

Gouck, H. K. 1964. Chemosterilization of house flies by treatment in the pupal stage. J. Econ. Entom., 57(2):239–241.

_____, and G. C. LaBrecque. 1963. Studies with compounds affecting the development of house fly larvae. U.S. Dept. Agr., ARS, 33–87:1–7.

_____, M. M. Crystal, A. B. Borkovec, and D. W. Meifert. 1963. A comparison of techniques for screening chemosterilants of house flies and screwworm flies. J. Econ. Entom., 56(4): 506–509.

_____, and G. C. LaBrecque. 1964. Chemicals affecting fertility in adult house flies. J. Econ. Entom., 57(5):663–664.

Grosch, D. S. 1959. The effects of feeding antimitotic substances to adult female Habrobracon (Microbracon hebetor (Say)); Hymenoptera, Braconidae.) Ann. Entom. Soc. Amer., 52(3):294–298.

Hair, J. A., and T. R. Adkins, Jr. 1964. Sterilization of the face fly, Musca autumnalis, with apholate and tepa. J. Econ. Entom., 57(4):586–589.

Harries, F. H. 1961. Effect of certain antibiotics and other compounds on the two-spotted mite. J. Econ. Entom., 54(1):122–124.

_____, 1963. Effects of some antibiotics and other compounds on fertility and mortality of orchard mites. J. Econ. Entom., 56(4): 438–441.

Harris, R. L. 1962. Chemical induction of sterility in the stable fly. J. Econ. Entom., 55(6):882–885.

Hays, S. B. 1965. Some effects of reserpine, a tranquilizer on the house fly. J. Econ. Entom., 58(4):782.

_____, and J. H. Cochran. 1964. Evaluation of compounds affecting the reproductive potential of the plum curculio. J. Econ. Entom., 57(2):217–219.

Hazard, E. I., C. S. Lofgren, D. B. Woodard, H. R. Ford, and B. M. Glancey. 1964. Resistance to the chemical sterilant apholate in Aedes aegypti. Science, 145(3631):500–501.

Hedin, P. A., C. P. Cody, and A. C. Thompson Jr. 1964. Antifertility effect of the chemosterilant apholate on the male boll weevil. J. Econ. Entom., 57(2):270–272.

Henneberry, T. J., F. F. Smith, and W. L. McGovern. 1964. Some effects of gamma radiation and a chemosterilant on the Mexican bean beetle. J. Econ. Entom., 57(6):813–815.

_____, and A. N. Kishaba. 1966. Effects of some chemosterilants on the viability of eggs, fecundity, mortality, and mating of the cabbage looper. J. Econ. Entom., 59(1):156–159.

Howland, A. F., P. Vail, and T. J. Henneberry. 1965. Effect of chemosterilants on fertility of cabbage loopers. J. Econ. Entom., 58(4):635–637.

_____, P. Vailan, and T. J. Henneberry. 1966. Results of cage experiments with sterile-male releases and a chemosterilant technique for control of cabbage looper populations. J. Econ. Entom., 59(1):194–196.

Hunter, P. E. 1961. Effect of captan upon reproduction in the two-spotted spider mite, *Tetranychus telarius*. J. Econ. Entom. 54(1);204–206.

Jeppson, L. R., M. J. Jesser, and J. O. Complin. 1966. Cyclohexamide derivatives and mite control, with special reference to mites of citrus. J. Econ. Entom., 59(1):15–19.

Johansen, C. A., and R. D. Redmond. 1965. Toxicity of apholate to the honeybee. J. Apicultural Res., 4(1):55–59.

Keiser, I., L. F. Steiner, and H. Kamasaki. 1965. Effect of chemosterilants against the oriental fruit fly, melon fly, and Mediterranean fruit fly. J. Econ. Entom., 58(4):682–685.

Kenaga, E. E. 1965. Triphenyl tin compounds as insect reproduction inhibitors. J. Econ. Entom. 58(1):4–8.

Kilgore, W. W., and R. R. Painter. 1962. The effect of 5-fluorouracil on the viability of house fly eggs. J. Econ. Entom., 55(5):710–712.

Kissam, J. B., and S. B. Hays. 1966. Mortality and fertility response of *Musca domestica* adults to certain known mutagenic or antitumor agents. J. Econ. Entom. 59(3):748–749.

Klassen, W., and F. Matsumara. 1966. Resistance to a chemosterilant metepa in *Aedes aegypti* mosquitoes. Nature (London) 209(5028):1155–1156.

Knipling, E. F. 1964. The potential role of the sterility method for insect population control with special reference to combining this method with conventional methods. U.S. Dept. Agr., ARS, 33–98, pp. 1–54.

Kohls, R. E., A. J. Lemin, and P. W. O'Connel. 1966. New chemosterilants against the house fly. J. Econ. Entom., 59(3):745–746.

LaBrecque, G. C. 1961. Studies with three alkylating agents as house fly sterilants. J. Econ. Entom., 54(4):684–689.

_____, P. H. Adcock, and C. N. Smith. 1960. Tests with compounds affecting house fly metabolism. J. Econ. Entom., 53(5):802–805.

_____, D. W. Meifert, and C. N. Smith. 1962. Mating competitiveness of chemosterilized and normal house flies. Science, 136(3514): 388–389.

_____, and H. K. Gouck. 1963. Compounds affecting fertility in adult house flies. J. Econ. Entom., 56(4):476.

_____, D. W. Meifert, and H. K. Gouck. 1963. Effectiveness of three 2-methyl-1-aziridines as house fly chemosterilants. Fla. Entom., 46(1):7–10.

_____, and J. C. Keller. 1965. Advances in insect population control by the sterile-male technique. Int. Atomic Energy Agency, Tech. Rpt. Ser. No. 44., pp 1–79.

_____, P. B. Morgan, D. W. Meifert, and R. L. Fye. 1966. Effectiveness of hempa as a house fly chemosterilant. J. Med. Entom. 3(1):40–43.

_____, P. B. Morgan, D. W. Meifert and R. L. Fye. 1966. Effectiveness of hempa as a housefly chemosterilant. J. Med. Entom. 3(1): 40–43.

LaChance, L. E., and M. M. Crystal. 1963. The modification of repro-
    duction in insects treated with alkylating agents. II, Differen-
    tial sensitivity of oocyte meiotic stages to the induction of
    dominant lethals. Biol. Bull. 125(2):280-288.
Ladd Jr., T. L. 1966. Egg viability and longevity of Japanese beetles
    treated with tepa, apholate, and metepa. J. Econ. Entom.,
    59(2):422-425.
Lindquist, D. A., L. J. Gorzycki, M. S. Mayer, A. L. Scales, and T. B.
    Davich. 1964. Laboratory studies on sterilization of the boll
    weevil with apholate. J. Econ. Entom., 57(5):745-750.
Loaeza, R. M., and A. O. Corona. 1965. Esterilization de la mosca
    domestica con apholate. Folia Entomologica Mexicana, 10:1-
    28.
Lobbecke, E. A., and R. C. Von Borstel. 1962. Mutational response of
    Habrobracon oocytes in metaphase and prophase to ethyl
    methanesulfonate and nitrogen mustard. Genetics, 47(7):853-
    864.
McFadden, M. W., and R. E. P. Rubio. 1965. Compounds affecting the
    reproductive capacity of the Mexican fruit fly. U.S. Dept. of
    Agr., ARS, 33-108. pp 1-5.
Meifert, D. W., R. L. Fye, and G. C. LaBrecque. 1963. Effect on house
    flies of exposure to residual applications of chemosterilants.
    Fla. Entom., 46(2):161-168.
_____, P. B. Morgan, and G. C. LaBrecque. Infertility of male house
    flies induced by sterilant-bearing females. J. Econ. Entom. In
    press.
_____, G. C. LaBrecque, C. N. Smith, and P. B. Morgan. 1967. Control
    of house flies (Musca domestica L.) on some West Indies
    islands with metepa, apholate and trichlorfon baits. J. Econ.
    Entom. 60(2):480-485.
Meltzer, J. 1956. Acaricidal properties of 2,4,5,4'-tetrachlorodiphenyl
    sulfone (Tedion). Proc. 10th Int. Cong. Entom. (Montreal),
    3:347-351.
Millar, E. S. 1965. Chemical sterilization of the green sheep blow fly
    Lucilia sericata Meigen with apholate. New Zeal. J. Agr. Res.,
    8(2):295-301.
Mitlin, N., B. A. Butt, and T. J. Shortino. 1957. Effect of mitotic
    poisons on house fly oviposition. Phys. Zool., 30(2):133-136.
_____, and A. M. Boroody. 1958a. Use of the house fly as a screening
    agent for tumor inhibiting agents. Cancer Res., 18(6):708-710.
_____, and A. M. Boroody. 1958b. The effect of some biologically ac-
    tive compounds on growth of house fly ovaries. J. Econ. En-
    tom., 51(3):384-385.
Morgan, P. B., and G. C. LaBrecque. 1964. Studies of the effect of
    meat exposed to gamma radiation or chemosterilants on the
    reproductive capacity of a blow fly Phaenicia cuprina (Wiede-
    mann). Fla. Entom., 47(1):31-33.
_____, G. C. LaBrecque, C. N. Smith, D. W. Meifert, and C. M. Mur-
    vosh. 1967. Cumulative effect of substerilizing dosages of

apholate on laboratory populations of the house fly (*Musca domestica* L.) J. Econ. Entom. In press.

_____ . Booby-trapped female house flies as sterilant carriers. J. Econ. Entom. 60(2):612–613.

Mukherjee, M. C. 1961. Sterility in *Drosophila melanogaster* consequent on using a mammalian oral contraceptive. Science and Culture, 27(10):497–498.

Mulla, M. S. 1964. Chemosterilization of the mosquito *Culex P. quinquefasciatus*. Mosq. News, 24(2):212–217.

Murray, W. S., and W. E. Bickley. 1964. Effects of apholate on the southern house mosquito *Culex pipiens quinquefasciatus* Say. Univ. Md. Agr. Res. Sta. Bull., A-134, pp 1–37.

Murvosh, C. M., R. L. Fye, and G. C. LaBrecque. 1964. Studies on the mating behavior of the house fly *Musca domestica* L. Ohio J. Science, 64(4):264–271.

_____ , G. C. LaBrecque, and C. N. Smith. 1964. Effect of three chemosterilants on house fly longevity and sterility. J. Econ. Entom., 57(1):89–93.

Mustafa, M., and M. B. Naidu. 1964. Chemical sterilization of *Dysdercus cingulatus* F. (Red cotton bug) Indian J. Exp. Biol., 2(1):55–56.

Nagasawa, S., and H. Shinohara. 1964a. Sterilizing effect of apholate on the Azuki bean weevil, *Callosobruchus chinensis* L., with special reference to the hatching of the eggs deposited by the treated weevils. Jap. J. Appl. Entom. Zool., 8(4):272–276.

_____ , and H. Shinohara. 1964b. Sterilizing effect of metepa on the Azuki bean weevil *Callosobruchus chinensis* L. with special reference to the hatching of the eggs deposited by the treated weevils. Jap. J. Appl. Entom. Zool., 8(2):123–128.

_____ , and H. Shinohara. 1965. Mating competition between apholate-sterilized and normal males of the Azuki bean weevil *Callosobruchus chinensis* L. Jap. J. Appl. Entom. Zool., 9(4):271–274.

Orphanidis, P. S. 1963a. Recherches en laboratoire sur la sterilization d'adultes de *Ceratitis capitata* Wied. au moyen de substances sterilisantes. I. Experience avec l'apholate. Ext. Ann. Inst. Phytopath. Benaki. N. S., 5(3):260–287.

_____ . 1963b. Recherches en laboratoire sur la sterilization d'adultes de *Ceratitis capitata* Wied. au moyen de substances sterilisantes. II. Experiences au moyen de metaphoxide, d'aphoxide et de chlorure de cuivre. Ext. Ann. Inst. Phytopath. Benaki. N. S., 5(4):323–331.

_____ , and P. G. Patsacos. 1963. Recherches en laboratoire sur la sterilization d'adultes du *Dacus oleae* Gmel au moyen de metaphoxide et d'aphoxide. (Comparaison avec les resultats obtenus sur *Ceratitis capitata* Wied.) Ann. Inst. Phytopath. Benaki. N. S., 5(4):305–322.

Ouye, M. T., R. S. Garcia, and D. F. Martin. 1965. Sterilization of pink bollworm adults with metepa. J. Econ. Entom., 58(5): 1018-1020.

Painter, R. R., and W. W. Kilgore. 1964. Temporary and permanent sterilization of house flies with chemosterilants. J. Econ. Entom., 57(1):154-157.

_____, and W. W. Kilgore. 1965. Chemosterilant effect of 5-fluoro-orotic acid on house flies. J. Econ. Entom., 58(5):888-891.

Parish, J. C., and B. W. Arthur. 1965. Chemosterilization of house flies fed certain ethylenimine derivatives. J. Econ. Entom., 50(4):699-702.

Pickett, A. D. and N. A. Patterson. 1963. Arsenates: effect on fecundity in some diptera. Science, 140(3566):493-494.

Piquett, P. G., and J. C. Keller. 1962. A screening method for chemosterilants of the house fly. J. Econ. Entom., 55(2):261-262.

Plapp, F. W., W. S. Bigley, G. A. Chapman, and G. W. Eddy. 1962. Metabolism of methaphoxide in mosquitoes, house flies, and mice. J. Econ. Entom., 55(5):607-613.

Ratcliffe, R. H., and S. S. Ristich. 1965. Insect sterilant experiments in outdoor cages with apholate, metepa, and four bifunctional aziridine chemicals against the house fly. J. Econ. Entom., 58(6):1079-1082.

Ridgway, R. C., L. J. Gorzyki, and D. A. Lindquist. 1966. Effect of metabolite analogs on larval development and oviposition in the boll weevil. J. Econ. Entom., 59(1):143-146.

Ristich, S. S., R. H. Ratcliffe, and D. Perlman. 1965. Chemosterilant properties, cytotoxicity, and mammalian toxicity of apholate and other P-N ring chemicals. J. Econ. Entom., 58(5):929-932.

Roach, S. H., and J. A. Buxton. 1965. Apholate and tepa as chemosterilants of the plum curculio. J. Econ. Entom., 58(4):802-803.

Sacca, G., R. Magrone, and A. Scirochi. 1965. Sulla repellenza esercitata de alcuni chemosterilanti verso *Musca domestica* L. Riv. Parassit., 26(1):61-66.

_____, A. Scirocchi, E. Stella, M. L. Mastrilli, and G. M. DeMeo. 1966. Studio Sperimentale di un ceppo di *Musca domestica* L., selezionato con il chemosterilante Metepa. Atti IV° Congresso Nazionale di Parassitologia, June 26-29, 1966, Lorica (Italy); *In:* Atti della Societa Peloritana di Scienze fisiche, matematiche, e naturali, XII—fasc. I/II. 447-456.

Schwartz Jr., P. H. 1965. Effects of apholate, metepa, and tepa on reproductive tissues of *Hippelates pusio* Loew. J. Invertebr. Path., 7(2):148-151.

Shaw, J. G., and M. Sanchez Riviello. 1962. Sterility in the Mexican fruit fly caused by chemicals. Science, 137(3532):754-755.

_____, and M. Sanchez Riviello. 1965. Effectiveness of tepa-sterilized Mexican fruit flies released in mango grove. J. Econ. Entom., 58(1):26-28.

Shinohara, H., and S. Nagasawa. 1963. Sterilizing effect of apholate and metepa on adults of the Azuki bean weevil, *Callosobruchus chinensis* L. Studies of the chemosterilants of insects. I. entom. Exp. Appl., 6:263–267.

Simkover, H. G. 1964. 2-Imidazolidinone as an insect growth inhibitor and chemosterilant. J. Econ. Entom., 57(4):574–579.

Smith, F. F., A. L. Boswell, and T. J. Henneberry. 1965. Chemosterilant treatment of two greenhouse spider mites. J. Econ. Entom., 58(1):98–103.

Sugai, E., and C. Hirano. 1965. Studies on the male sterility in the silkworm *Bombyx mori* L. induced by apholate. Jap. J. Hum. Genet., 40(5–6):357–363.

Swailes, G. E. 1966. Sterilization of the cabbage maggot with apholate. J. Econ. Entom., 59(3):596–598.

Tahori, A. S., G. S. Zeidler, and A. H. Halevy. 1965a. The effect of phosphon (2, 4-dichlorobenzyltributyl phosphonium chloride) as a house fly sterilant. Naturwissenschaften, 52:1–2.

_____, A. S. Zeidler, and A. H. Halevy. 1965b. Phosphon (2, 4-dichlorobenzyltributyl phosphonium chloride) as an insect antifeeding compound. Naturwissenschaften, 52(8):191–192.

Vanderzant, E. S., C. D. Richardson, and T. B. Davich. 1959. Feeding and oviposition by the boll weevil on artificial diets. J. Econ. Entom., 52(6):1138–1143.

Vinson, S. B., and J. D. Land. 1965. The effects of aminopterin on egg development and behavior in the house spider *Theridon lepidariorum* Koch. Phys. Zool., 38(2):174–176.

Weidhaas, D. E. 1962. Chemical sterilization of mosquitoes. Nature (London), 195(4843):786–787.

_____, H. R. Ford, J. B. Gahan, and C. N. Smith. 1961. Preliminary observations on the chemosterilization of mosquitoes. Proc. 48th Ann. Mtg. N.J. Mosq. Exterm. Ass., 106–109.

_____, and C. H. Schmidt. 1963. Mating ability of male mosquitoes *Aedes aegypti* (L.), sterilized chemically or by gamma radiation. Mosq. News 23(1):32–34.

White, G. B. 1966. Chemosterilization of *Aedes aegypti* L. by pupal treatment. Nature (London), 210:1372–1373.

Yeoman, G. H., and B. C. Warren. 1965. The chemosterilization of the sheep blowfly *Lucilia sericata* (Meig.) with apholate. Vet. Rec., 32:922–928.

Young, J. R., and H. C. Cox. 1965. Evaluation of apholate and tepa as chemosterilants for the fall armyworm. J. Econ. Entom., 58(5):883–888.

4

Cytogenetic and Cellular Basis of Chemically Induced Sterility in Insects

LEO E. LA CHANCE, DAVID T. NORTH, and
WALDEMAR KLASSEN

RADIATION BIOLOGY AND INSECT GENETICS
    SECTION
METABOLISM AND RADIATION RESEARCH
    LABORATORY
ENTOMOLOGY RESEARCH DIVISION, UDSA
STATE UNIVERSITY STATION
FARGO, NORTH DAKOTA

INTRODUCTION

The inclusion of a chapter on the cytogenetic effects of chemosterilants in this volume devoted almost solely to their sterilizing effects, suggests that the cytogenetic damage produced by certain chemicals is somehow related to sterility. This is the approach we intend to develop. Thus in this chapter, we discuss the various facets of insect sterility and attempt to relate the cytogenetic and cellular effects of chemosterilants and chemical mutagens to the kinds of sterility we observe in entomological studies. We do not intend, however, to give the impression that insect sterility is caused solely by cytogenetic damage or that chemosterilants produce *only* this kind of damage. On the contrary, we will attempt to show that certain types of sterility may not be due to cytogenetic abnormalities and still be useful in controlling some insect species.

Cytogenetic effects will play an important role in the applied use of chemosterilants. If these agents damage the hereditary material of mammals as well as insects, such damage will limit (but not eliminate) their use as insect-control agents. Thus the mode of application of any chemical agent for control of an insect population will be directed both by our knowledge of its toxicological effects and also by our assessment of its genetic and cytogenetic effects.

A clear distinction should be made between mutagenic chemicals and chemosterilants. A chemosterilant is any chemical that produces sterility, regardless of the method by which the state is attained. Many chemical mutagens are chemosterilants, but not all chemosterilants can induce heritable mutations or cytogenetic changes.

Although many effective compounds are now available for chemosterilization of insects and many insect species have been sterilized (Chapter 2), much remains to be learned. For example, we usually do not know what biological event caused the sterility. Also, in some species, the production of sterility is not enough; we must learn how to sterilize without seriously reducing sexual competitiveness or longevity (see section on Somatic Effects). A start, however, has been made. The available knowledge can be expanded, new chemosterilants can be developed, and their mode of action can be delineated. It is with these points in mind that the present chapter was developed.

HISTORY OF CHEMICAL STERILIZATION RESEARCH

Intensive interest in the sterilization of insects by chemical methods was not aroused until insects sterilized by irradiation were used successfully in control and eradication programs. The sterile-male method of insect control originated in a small, isolated laboratory in Texas where Dr. E. F. Knipling was studying the biology and ecology of the screwworm fly, *Cochliomyia hominivorax* (Coquerel), and where Melvin and Bushland (1940) had developed an artificial medium for rearing these insects. (For further details on the sterile-male approach to insect control see Chapter 1.) Before the idea could be tested, a successful method of sterilizing insects was required. Many chemicals were tested as sterilants for the screwworm fly during 1947 to 1950. Since none were effective, the results were not published (R. C. Bushland, personal communication). During this same period, however, and unknown to these workers, insects had already been accidentally sterilized by chemical mutagens in the United Kingdom. Thus, while entomologists were searching for sterilizing agents, geneticists were accidentally sterilizing fruit flies with chemicals and were, in turn, unaware of the practical value of their observations—a classic example of poor scientific communication.

Current research on insect chemosterilants is a logical extension of earlier work regarding the effect of chemical mutagens and antimetabolites on insects. The discovery of chemical mutagens resulted from wartime research on mustard gas (Auerbach and Robson, 1942, 1944, 1946). The period imme-

diately following World War II was one of intense interest in the
genetic effects of chemicals on both plant and animal cells.
Prior to 1950 more than 265 papers reporting the effects of 240
different chemicals on genetic material were published (Herskowitz, 1951). None of these studies, however, dealt specifically
with insect sterility or dominant lethal mutations. Because the
major emphasis was on basic studies of the process of mutation,
insect sterility, if it resulted, was generally regarded as a simple effect of overdose (and quite without scientific or applied
value).

Many of the pioneer investigators of chemical mutagenesis did observe insect sterility. Auerbach and Robson (1942)
observed that mustard gas produced sterility in *Drosophila
melanogaster* Meigen and a reduction in egg hatchability. Also,
Battacharya (1949) observed sterility in males of *Drosophila*
reared on food containing ethylene glycol, and Demerec et al.
(1949) and Wallace (1951) observed the induction of partial sterility in *Drosophila* by nitrogen mustard. Bird (1950) too noted
chemically induced sterility in *Drosophila* after the males had
been fed on food treated with four alkylating agents. Finally,
Auerbach, in 1951, listed a number of chemicals that induced
dominant lethal mutations (one type of sterility), Auerbach and
Moser (1953) reported the induction of dominant lethal mutations in *Drosophila* grown on media treated with formaldehyde,
and Fahmy and Fahmy (1954) studied the induction of dominant
lethal mutations in mature sperm of *Drosophila* by tretamine.

Much of the early entomological work (1950 to 1960) on
chemically induced insect sterility per se was done with antimetabolites that induced sterility in females by inhibiting the
production of eggs (see section on Infecundity), but, in general,
were not effective male sterilants. Still, the early results
(Goldsmith and Frank, 1952, Mitlin et al., 1957, Ascher, 1957,
Mitlin and Baroody, 1958) provided sufficient impetus to en-
courage others to seek chemicals that would sterilize males. By
the late 1950's, the genetic, cytogenetic, and sterilizing effects
of several radiomimetic chemicals were well known enough so
that a number of related compounds were available for consideration as insect chemosterilants.

During the period 1958 to 1960, the U.S. Department of
Agriculture initiated an extensive screening program to dis-
cover chemicals that would sterilize insects. Attention was soon
redirected to the alkylating agents and several were tested. In
a relatively short time, a large number of compounds were found

that could effectively sterilize insects without adverse side effects. (Further information on the screening and historical aspects of this work is found in Chapters 1 and 2.)

COMPONENTS OF CHEMICALLY INDUCED STERILITY IN INSECTS AND THEIR CYTOGENETIC BASIS

Sterility is a condition that can be produced in several ways. In males, sterility may be caused by dominant lethal mutations in the sperm (see Section on Dominant Lethal Mutations), aspermia (see Section on Aspermia), or sperm inactivation (see Section on Sperm Inactivation). In females, sterility may be the result of infecundity (see Section on Infecundity) or of dominant lethal mutations in the eggs that are produced. In either sex, the sterile state may be merely a reflection of the inability to mate because of treatment or some change in mating behavior (see Section on Somatic Damage). Before attempting to discuss how each type of sterility results from chemical treatments, a brief resumé of the normal progress of fertility and reproduction in male insects will be useful. Later, when we come to consider infecundity, we will attempt the same outline for the female.

Since the male reproductive system has been studied definitively in several species, we need here only a composite description. Reproduction in male insects appears to be less dependent on hormones than in mammals. For example, the male's mating drive appears to be unaffected by castration (Riemann et al., 1967); yet secretions from cells in the frontal ganglion (Clark and Langley, 1963) and from the prothoracic gland (Schmidt and Williams, 1953) control spermatogenesis to an unknown extent. The paired testes become visible in the early instars, and in many species mature sperm are produced before adult emergence (Table 1). The development of the germ cells, however, is only loosely correlated with morphogenesis, so the degree of sex-cell maturation cannot be accurately estimated from the life stage. In some insects, all types of germ cells are present in the late immature instars and adults. In others, only one or two types of germ cells (Table 2) are present at a given life stage, e.g., the silkworm, *Bombyx mori* (L.), (Sado, 1961) and very likely other Lepidoptera (Chaudhury and Raun, 1966). The spermatozoa pass from the testis through the vasa deferentia into paired seminal

TABLE 1

TYPES OF GERM CELLS PRESENT IN THE TESTES OF
MANY MALE INSECTS AT A GIVEN LIFE STAGE

Life stage	Cell stage in testes
Hatching to penultimate larval instar	Spermatogonia
Prepupa	Spermatogonia, primary and secondary spermatocytes
Pupa and adult	Spermatogonia, primary and secondary spermatocytes, spermatids, and mature sperm

vesicles for temporary storage. Usually a pair of accessory glands flanks the seminal vesicles, and their secretions are transferred with the sperm during copulation.

Each testis consists of tubules or follicles, and each tubule is divided into a number of zones. Most distal in the tubule lies the germarium which contains primary spermatogonia. One or more spermatogonia detach from the germarium and become enclosed by cyst cells. The spermatogonium then undergoes mitotic divisions to form up to 256 primary spermatocytes (Depdolla, 1928). In the zone of maturation and reduction, each of these primary spermatocytes divides into two haploid secondary spermatocytes; then the secondary sperma-

TABLE 2

TYPES OF GERM CELLS PRESENT AT GIVEN LIFE STAGES
OF THE SILKWORM (SADO 1961)

Life stage	Cell stage in testes
Hatching to first instar	Primary spermatogonia
Second to third instar	Secondary spermatogonia
Third to fourth instar	Spermatocytes in early meiotic prophase
Fourth to fifth instar	Spermatocytes in early- and late-meiotic prophase
Fifth instar to spinning	Same as fourth instar, with a few early spermatids
Pupa	Spermatids and fully formed spermatozoa
Emerged adult	Only full formed spermatozoa

tocytes divide again to produce two spermatids. In the zone of transformation, the spermatids (still enclosed in the cyst) elongate to form the sperm. These finally rupture the cyst and accumulate in the seminal vesicle as densely packed bundles. From here they are transferred to the female in semen (i.e., in Diptera) or in a spermatophore (i.e., in Lepidoptera).

In the boll weevil, *Anthonomus grandis* Boheman, 10 days are required for an early primary spermatocyte to develop into four mature sperm (T. H. Chang and J. G. Riemann, unpublished). In adult *Drosophila*, at least 5 to 6 days at 25°C are required for the development of spermatogonia into sperm (Martin, 1965); the schedule is roughly as follows:

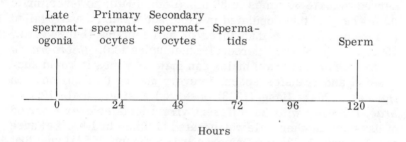

Hours

The development of spermatogonia to primary spermatocytes, however, requires 24 hr longer in *Drosophila* larvae than in adults, and treatment with mutagenic agents may lengthen the period between primary and secondary spermatocytes by 24 hr. In male *Aedes aegypti* (L.), Schwartz (1961) believed that maturation of spermatozoa was accelerated by sexual activity. Evidently in *Drosophila*, mature sperm are not transferred to the female until the sperm are 2 days old (Chandley and Bateman, 1962); also, newly formed sperm continuously enter the elastic seminal vesicle to increase its volume (in the absence of frequent copulation), and to mix with sperm that have matured previously (LeFevre and Jonsson, 1962).

The number of sperm produced by male insects is much less than that produced by mammals. *Miastor* males produce exactly 1,024 sperm per life-span (Depdolla, 1928), but males of other species produce more. An inseminated *Drosophila* female can store from 500 to 700 sperm (though considerably more sperm are transferred during copulation), and the excess are wasted (LeFevre and Jonsson, 1962). Practically all the stored sperm are utilized (Hildreth and Lucchesi, 1963) since a female may lay in excess of 500 viable eggs. When the female *Drosophila* remates, the sperm from the second male may displace the majority of the stored sperm (LeFevre and Jonsson, 1962). When the female boll weevil remates, the sperm received in a second mating are used much more frequently than those received in the first mating; this pattern was true whether or not the males were treated with apholate (Lindquist and House, 1967).

The frequency of copulation by males varies between species; for example, boll weevils mate 2.55 ± 1.50 times per day (Mayer and Brazzel, 1963), *Aedes aegypti* have been observed to mate 30 times in 30 min (Roth, 1948); however, male *Aedes aegypti* that copulated in rapid succession usually failed to inseminate more than three or four females (Baker et al., 1962, G. B. White, personal communication). *Habrobracon* (= *Bracon hebetor* Say) males can mate 14 times in rapid succession and transfer sperm in every mating (Whiting and von Borstel, 1954). Hase (1923) observed a single male *Habrobracon* mating with 28 different virgin females over a period of days and another male which mated 11 times in 1 hr. LeFevre and Jonsson (1962) and Demerec and Kaufmann (1961) found that *Drosophila* transfer progressively less sperm after the second or third mating; thus, by the fourth or fifth mating, few (if any) sperm are transferred. LeFevre and Jonsson found that the inability to transfer sperm in successive matings derived not from the lack of sperm in the seminal vesicles, but from the exhaustion of the accessory gland secretion without which sperm transfer was impossible. Once exhausted, more than 2 hr are required for its full regeneration. In male *Aedes aegypti*, sexual depletion lasts at least 24 hr (Jones, 1961).

DOMINANT LETHAL MUTATIONS

Of the several types of induced sterility in insects, the most widely used and, to date, the most successful has been dominant lethal mutations. This type of sterility is the basis for the sterile-male technique of insect control originated by Bushland and Hopkins (1951, 1953) and Knipling (1955, 1959).

Dominant lethal mutations were first reported by Hertwig (1911) when he observed that amphibian eggs fertilized by irradiated sperm often failed to hatch. Muller (1927), in his classical paper on the mutagenicity of x-rays, also observed dominant lethal mutations and presented evidence of their genetic, rather than their physiological basis. Also, in a 1940 paper, Muller discussed the relationship between radiation-induced dominant lethal mutations and structural changes in chromosomes.

Dominant lethals are nuclear alterations that can effect the death of the zygote, even though they are introduced by only one of the germ cells which unite at fertilization (Sonnenblick and Henshaw, 1941). This induction of dominant lethal mutations in insect reproductive cells usually does not hinder the maturation of the treated cell into a gamete or the participation of the gamete in the formation of a zygote; it does prevent the zygote from developing to maturity. In essence, lethal mutations are lethal to the descendants of the treated cell—the zygote it forms.

Although we are concerned here with the cytogenetic basis for dominant lethal mutations induced by various chemicals, most of our background information is obtained from radiation studies since less is known about the cytogenetic effects of chemosterilants. A dominant lethal mutation induced by a chemical may or may not be similar to a mutation induced by irradiation, the gross effect (and certainly the end effect—death of the individual) is the same. Direct comparison, however, of radiation and chemically induced genetic damage is hazardous; therefore, reference to radiation-induced dominant lethal mutations should be construed as illustrative, not comparative.

What are these chromosome alterations that are associated with dominant lethal mutations? First, we can consider what kind of chromosomal changes would be lethal and why they would produce this effect, and then we can consider the evidence that such damage is produced by chemosterilants.

Some of the ways in which chemicals can alter chromosomes are shown in Fig. 1. Many variations of the initial event at the molecular level are possible. For our purpose, we consider mainly the gross effects. During cell division, the chromosomes replicate and then separate so each cell receives one of these units. Chemosterilants can react with either one chromatid or with the whole chromosome. If a single break is produced in a chromosome in interphase (before replication) and the break fails to restitute, the lesion will be reproduced when the chromosome replicates and will appear at metaphase as a break in each chromatid (Fig. 1). When more than one break is present, they may rejoin to produce dicentric chromosomes plus acentric fragments. A dicentric chromosome implies that the rejoined chromosomes both contain the centromeres of the original two chromosomes and that the acentric fragment is without a centromere.

During anaphase, the acentric fragment is usually lost because it is not connected to a spindle fiber, and it fails to be included in either daughter nucleus. The two centromeres of the dicentric chromosome separate at random during anaphase. Therefore, in half of the divisions, the two centromeres will be attracted to the same pole; in the other half, they will be attracted to opposite poles. When the two centromeres are attracted toward opposite poles of the metaphase plate, the chromatin between the two centromeres becomes stretched out to form a bridge between the daughter nuclei. If the nuclear membrane forms at this stage, the dicentric chromosomes may not be included in either nucleus. The dicentric chromosome, however, usually breaks, which allows the centric fragments to enter the daughter nuclei. The newly broken ends now present in each nucleus may then repeat this whole process—that is, replicate and the broken ends rejoin. This phenomenon is called "breakage-fusion-bridge cycle" (Fig. 1). The initial event, however, is not always the formation of a chromosome break. There are many other ways in which chemicals can affect the genetic material. One of these possibilities is also shown in Fig. 1. The chemosterilant can, for instance, react with the chromosomal material to yield a latent lesion which will fail to replicate. This type of damage would also result in chromosome bridges and unequal distribution of genic material in subsequent divisions. The most obvious effect of chromosome breakage in the sperm or egg nucleus is the production of chromosome imbalance in the cleavage divisions in the zygote. When males have been given a chemosterilant treatment that induces dominant lethal mutations in all the sperm (sterility), chromosome abnormalities are found in nearly all developing embryos. Figure 2 shows some chromosomal abnormalities observable in embryos of the house fly, *Musca domestica* L., derived from a chemosterilant-treated sperm that fertilized an untreated egg. The results of this kind of chromosome damage have been pictured and discussed elsewhere (LaChance, 1967). Embryonic death is associated with a depression in the mitotic rate in the developing embryo, and complete cessation of mitosis often occurs in the second or third

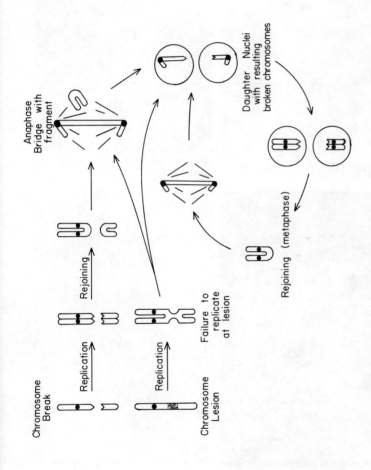

Fig. 1. Diagrammatic representation of some cytogenetic consequences of chemosterilant-induced chromosome damage.

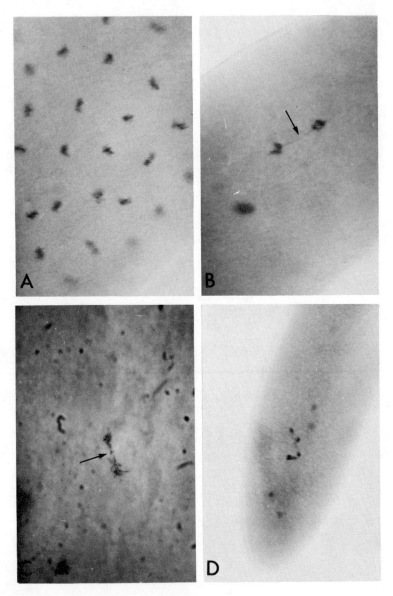

Fig. 2. Typical chromosome aberrations observed in whole mounts of developing embryos after sperm contained in the males are treated with tretamine (treated males were crossed to untreated females; developing embryos were fixed at intervals after oviposition). A. Cleavage nuclei in a control egg fixed at 66 to 71 min. B, C, C. Typical chromosome aberrations attributed to treatment of paternal sperm with tretamine. Embryos fixed at 29 to 33 min. after oviposition. Arrows indicate chromosome bridges (A, B circa 160×, C circa 320×, D circa 64×).

cleavage division. This depression in the rate of mitosis may be related to the presence of chromosome bridges (Fig. 2), but death of the embryos is not due solely to a lack of some chromosome pieces in some cleavage nuclei but perhaps to a progressive genic imbalance in the cleavage nuclei.

Time of Death of Embryos with Dominant Lethal Mutations. A dominant lethal mutation results in death of the zygote at some stage between fertilization and the mature adult. It is generally found that dominant lethal mutations cause cessation of development prior to hatching (though in some organisms, death is postponed to the larval or pupal stage). Cytogenetic studies have generally indicated that death occurs before blastoderm formation, usually during the early cleavage divisions (von Borstel, 1955, Atwood et al., 1956, Whiting et al., 1958, von Borstel and Rekemeyer, 1959, LaChance and Riemann, 1964). Under certain conditions, the time of death varies (Atwood et al., 1956); in *Bracon,* different types of dominant lethal mutations cause death at different times in development (von Borstel and Rekemeyer, 1959). Fahmy and Fahmy (1954) showed that after *Drosophila* males had been treated with tretamine and mated to untreated females, death occurred relatively early in the embryonic development, usually before blastoderm formation. The cleavage nuclei in these embryos were invariably aneuploid or polyploid. Similar findings were reported by LaChance and Riemann (1964) in their studies on screwworm embryos derived from chemosterilant-treated males. From several studies it appears that zygotic lethality is due to mitotic accidents and genetic imbalance in the developing embryo.

In a series of intricate experiments, von Borstel (1960, 1963), studied the time of death of eggs laid by virgin *Bracon* females that were heterozygous for chromosome translocations. These females lay eggs that are normally haploid. During meiosis, pairing between chromosomes heterozygous for a translocation results in an unequal distribution of the chromatin to the meiotic nuclei. Therefore, about half the gametes have nuclei that are deficient for part of a chromosome arm, and half the eggs from such a female die because certain blocks of genes are missing. In a study of 27 different translocations which were representative of a random sampling of deleted gene blocks, presumably from different parts of the chromosomes, the embryos always died about midway in development when they contained about 50,000 nuclei and embryonic differentiation was well underway. This would indicate that early embryonic development does not depend on the presence of all the genes, and that haploid insect embryos derived from a single nucleus that lacks a fairly substantial gene block can proceed to an advanced stage of differentiation. Hadorn (1961) also studied the developmental stage at which many lethal mutations become effective.

Late death of the embryo is typical of reciprocal translocations in a haploid organism and perhaps also in diploid organisms. With reciprocal translocations, chromosome bridges are not formed although nuclei lacking certain gene blocks are. The late-acting lethal mutations presumably cause death when the absent gene blocks are required for differentiation. But dominant lethal mutations usually result in death of the organisms very early in development. During cleavage divisions, the formation of dicentric chromosomes and continued bridge formation results in uncompensated gene loss in nuclei which become progressively more unbalanced in their genetic content. Therefore, the missing gene blocks found in nuclei of embryos derived from a gamete bearing a dominant lethal mutation are not comparable to the missing gene blocks among the division products of a reciprocal translocation. Death of the embryo because of dominant lethal mutations is probably the result of a series of complex cytogenetic abnormalities. These are discussed elsewhere in more detail (LaChance, 1967).

Detection of Dominant Lethal Mutations Induced in Insects. The inability of a treated gamete to produce a viable embryo has been the most widely accepted measure of dominant lethality in insects. "Dominant-lethal mutations," however, are not synonymous with inviability of the eggs. The term should be used only when the damage inflicted on the gamete is genetic in nature. Valid objection to use of the term arises when an uncertainty exists as to whether the site of damage is chromosomal, and such uncertainty often occurs when chemicals are used to treat insects, particularly females. Conceivably, many nongenetic factors could hinder the development of an organism derived from a treated gamete.

In order for a depression in egg hatchability to reflect the induction of dominant lethal mutations, only one sex should be treated, and the test should determine whether the female was mated and contained motile sperm and whether the sperm retained fertilizing capacity. Checking the spermathecae of the female after a sample of eggs has been collected for hatchability studies will reveal whether or not the female contains motile sperm, but it does not assure that the sperm retained their fertilizing capacity (see section on Sperm Inactivation).

Exposing an insect to a chemosterilant does not produce sterility via dominant-lethal mutations unless the frequency of these events closely approaches one per gamete. Dominant lethal mutations induced by chemosterilants increase proportionately with the dose (Fahmy and Fahmy, 1964, LaChance and Crystal, 1965). At very high doses, however, the rate at which dominant lethal mutations are induced often decreases so that the shape of the dose-response curve flattens out (saturation). The degree of flattening is dependent on the chemosterilant used; for example, the flattening of the dose-response curve for male house flies treated with tepa is negligible compared with that obtained when they are treated with tretamine (Fig. 3). For this reason, a dose-response curve (rather than a sampling of one or two doses) should be used to determine the best dose to use in a sterilization program, and the point just before the curve flattens out probably represents the best dose since it is at this point that the maximum number of dominant lethal mutations can be obtained with a minimum dose of chemosterilant. Such a procedure also avoids overdosage of the insect which could present other serious problems (see section on Somatic Effects).

Chemically-Induced Chromosome Aberrations. If a relationship exists between the induction of dominant lethal mutations and the production of chromosome breaks or latent lesions, which chemicals produce this effect?

The production of chromosome breaks by radiation is well documented, and though the evidence for chromosome damage by chemosterilants is not as extensive, it is nevertheless substantial and dates back several decades. For example, at the same time that the mutagenic ability of nitrogen mustard was discovered, Oehlkers (1943) showed that urethane, a nonalkylating agent, was effective in breaking the chromosomes of *Tradescantia*. Since these early studies, an astounding variety of chemicals has been found which produce breaks in chromosomes of plants and animals (Table 3). The study of chromosome breaks in insects produced by chemicals, however, has generally been limited to studies of chromosome translocations in *Drosophila* (Auerbach, 1951, 1958, Oster, 1958, Snyder and Oster, 1964). Only a limited number of studies have been conducted with economically important insects and insect

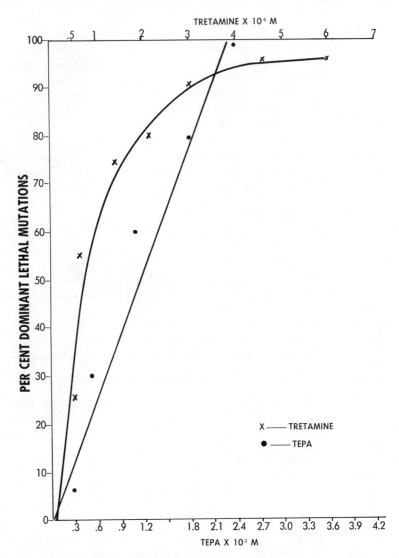

Fig. 3. Dose-response curves relating the induction of dominant-lethal mutations to the dose of chemosterilant injected in house
fly males (note differences in slopes at high doses).

chemosterilants to show that the chemosterilants tested produced chromosome aberrations (LaChance and Riemann, 1964,
Murray and Bickley, 1964, Rai, 1964a).

TABLE 3

A REPRESENTATIVE LIST OF CHEMICALS KNOWN TO
INDUCE CHROMOSOME BREAKS[a]

Name	Reference
Alkylating agents	
1. Aziridines (apholate, tepa, tretamine,	Murray and Bickley (1964) Fahmy and Fahmy (1954)[b] Michaelis and Rieger (1963)
2. Nitrogen mustards	Koller (1958) Fahmy and Fahmy (1958)[b]
3. Sulfur mustards	Koller (1958) Auerbach (1951)[b]
4. Ethylene oxide	Y. Nakao (see Auerbach, 1961 for ref.)
5. Ethyl methanesulfonate	Michaelis and Rieger (1963) Ramanna and Natarajan (1966)
6. Methyl ethanesulfonate	Ramanna and Natarajan (1966)
7. Myleran® = 1,4-Butane-diol dimethanesulfonate	Ramanna and Natarajan (1966)
8. Chloroethyl methanesulfonate	Watson (1962)
9. N-Nitroso-N-methylure-thane	Kihlman (1960)
10. β-Propiolactone	Swanson and Merz (1959) Merz et al. (1961)
11. Diepoxybutane	Auerbach (1961) Kreizinger (1960) Cohn (1961)
Chemicals other than alkylating agents	
12. N-methylated-oxypurines (8-ethoxycaffeine and 1,3,7,9-tetramethyluric acid)	Kihlman (1955)
8-ethoxycaffeine	Merz et al. (1961)
13. N-methylphenylnitro-samine	Kihlman (1961)
14. Mitomycin C	Merz (1961)
15. Streptonigrin	Kihlman (1964) Kihlman and Odmark (1965)
16. Adenine and other purine derivatives	Odmark and Kihlman (1965)
17. Maleic hydrazide	Kihlman (1956) Evans and Scott (1964) Michaelis and Rieger (1963)

TABLE 3 (CONTINUED)

Name	Reference
18. Ethyl alcohol	Michaelis and Rieger (1963)
19. Potassium cyanide	Lilly and Thoday (1956)
	Kihlman (1957)
20. Dipropoxypropyl ether	Kihlman (1956)
21. Fluorodeoxyuridine	Taylor et al. (1962)
22. Methylene Blue	Kumar and Natarajan (1965)
23. Acridine Orange	Kihlman (1959)
24. Heliotrine (alkaloid)	Clark (1963)
	Brink (1966)
25. Scopolamine (alkaloid)	Oehlkers (1953)
26. Morphine (alkaloid)	Oehlkers (1953)
27. Folic acid inhibitors	Grampa and Dustin (1953)
28. Oxygen	Conger (1952)
	Berg et al. (1965)
29. Formaldehyde	Auerbach (1951)[b]
30. Urethane	Oehlkers (1943)
	Auerbach (1951)
31. Hemel	L. E. LaChance, J. Palmquist, and D. T. North (unpublished)
	D. T. North (unpublished)[b]
32. Hempa	D. T. North (unpublished)[b]
33. N-methyl-n-nitro-n-nitroguanidine	Sax and Sax (1966)
34. Several miscellaneous chemicals	Sax and Sax (1966)

[a]Chemical names listed according to nomenclature used in reference.

[b]Induction of dominant lethal mutations.

Under certain conditions, chemicals may be even more powerful in inducing dominant lethal mutations than x-rays. Nasrat et al. (1954) compared the effect of x-rays and mustard gas at doses that produced equivalent numbers of recessive lethal mutations in the X-chromosome of *Drosophila*. They found that within the range of the more powerful doses, mustard gas was as effective in producing chromosome breaks as x-rays, but that the chances of healing were less favorable; consequently, the chromosome breaks persisted.

The majority of the successful insect chemosterilants (particularly the alkylating agents) are known to be chromosome breakers in some organisms and there is no reason to believe that they do not produce this effect in insects.

To list all of the chemicals known to produce chromosome breaks in some organisms would require considerable space. A *few* are listed in Table 3, but the list does not include all such chemicals. Rather it is intended to show the great diversity of chemicals that produce this effect. Some chemicals have been tested on plants only, but they will probably be effective in insects providing they are able to reach the critical sites. This would, of course, vary with the mode of administration. The types of chemicals are varied and include such diverse agents as pure oxygen (Conger, 1952) and aluminum chloride (Manna and Parida, 1965). Not all, of course, are insect chemosterilants, probably because they do not reach the critical sites in sufficient quantities at the proper time. A brief survey, however, of the cytogenetic effects of some chemicals that are known or potential insect chemosterilants is in order.

Alkylating agents. These compounds comprise the largest class of chemosterilants and are perhaps the most reactive. Alkylating agents possess one, two, or more alkyl groups and are generally classified as mono-, bi-, and polyfunctional. Ample evidence now exists that all three classes are capable of inducing both chromosome breaks and mutations, an indication that the changes they effect are not directly related to the ability of the agents to crosslink biologically important molecules (Snyder and Oster, 1964).

Most oncologists agree that effective carcinostatic agents carry two or more active groups, e.g., ethyleneimine or chloroethyl groups. The same is true for chromosome breakers. Yet the monofunctional compounds, ethylene oxide and ethyleneimine, also are effective chromosome breakers in barley (Ehrenberg and Gustafson, 1957, Ehrenberg et al., 1958), and in *Drosophila* (reported in Auerbach's 1961 paper as "unpublished communication" from Y. Nakao), Alexander and Glanges (1965). Loveless (1951) found that monofunctional compounds were 50 to 100 times less effective than polyfunctional agents in their mutagenic ability.

Auerbach (1961) tested the theory that cross linkage between biologically important molecules is a prerequisite for mutagenic ability, a theory which has more appeal in regard to producing point mutations than chromosome breaks. She found no evidence to support the cross-linkage theory for chromosome breakage when *Drosophila* was treated with ethylene oxide or diepoxybutane.

Kreizinger (1960) produced chromosome breaks in maize with diepoxybutane and Crystal (1966a) proved that 18 of 61 monoaziridinyl compounds applied topically to the screwworm were sterilants as were 42 of 72 compounds applied by multiple feedings.

Much work with insect sterilization has centered around the use of aziridines since it was generally believed that the alkylating action of these groups was essential to sterilization. Chang et al. (1964), however, showed that hempa and hemel, analogs of the alkylating compounds, tepa and tretamine (structurally and sterically similar except that the aziridines have been replaced by dimethyl amine groups) are effective in sterilizing house flies and possess low mammalian toxicity. Thus, even nonalkylating agents can produce sterility. Palmquist and LaChance (1966) demonstrated that hempa does induce recessive lethal mutations in *Bracon* sperm. Thus, these nonalkylating chemosterilants may possess the ability to break chromosomes, and although hempa has not yet been tested for chromosome-breakage effects, the possibility appears likely. Hemel, injected into male house flies, is also known to produce chromosome aberrations that are seen in the developing embryos derived from treated sperm (L. E. LaChance and D. T. North, unpublished data).

Evidence exists (Nilan and Konzak, 1961) that some alkylating agents, such as diethyl sulfate and ethyl methanesulfonate (EMS) produce chromosome breaks and that the majority of the rejoining is intrachromosomal. This leads to a large number of chromosome inversions rather than translocations or rearrangements.

More recently Ramanna and Natarajan (1966) showed that three mesyloxy esters [ethyl methanesulfonate (EMS), methyl ethanesulfonate (MES), and 1,4-dimethylsulfonoxybutane (Myleran®)] induced chromosome breaks in dividing cells of barley. The number of chromosomal abnormalities increased with temperature illustrating that the biological effect of these chemicals is greatly influenced by the conditions of the test.

Cells treated with alkylating agents often exhibit a marked degree of chromosome "stickiness" at division. These "sticky" bridges should not be confused with anaphase bridges resulting from illegitimate rejoining of broken chromosomes.

Alkaloids. The alkaloids are a group of compounds that have not been widely considered as insect chemosterilants although they have proved effective in producing chromosome breaks. For example, Oehlkers (1953) found that morphine and scopolamine produced chromosome rearrangements in plants, and Clark (1959, 1960) found that several alkaloids, including heliotrine, monocrotaline, and lasiocarpine, were effective mutagens in *Drosophila*. Colchicine is a widely used alkaloid that inhibits cell division by its effect on the spindle fiber. This chemical sterilizes female insects (see section on Chemosterilants directly related to nucleic acid and protein metabolism).

Peroxides. Hydrogen peroxide is mutagenic in microorganisms but is wholly ineffective in *Drosophila* because the enzyme catalase breaks it down rapidly. Organic peroxides have been reported by Altenberg (1954) and Sobels (1956) to be mutagenic in *Drosophila*, though very little is known about their efficiency as chromosome breakers.

Chemosterilants directly related to nucleic acid and protein metabolism. Many substances that act primarily by disrupting nucleic acid metabolism have been tested and found to be mutagenic (Auerbach, 1961). The great majority of these substances, however, produce point mutations and are not known chromosome breakers. Kihlman (1952) found that many purines produced both mutations and chromosomal rearrangements in plants. Novick (1955) suggested that purines, by interfering with enzymes, are concerned with nucleic acid metabolism. The ultimate fate of chromosomes broken by purines appears to depend on the species involved. Kihlman (1955) found that chromosomes broken by 8-ethoxycaffeine readily formed rearrangements in *Vicia faba* (L). But that these breaks remained open as fragments in *Allium cepa* (L). The consequent fate of these chromome breaks would influence the yield of dominant lethal mutations.

Oehlkers (1943) demonstrated the ability of urethane to break plant chromosomes, and Vogt (1948) confirmed this in *Drosophila*. Urethane is an interesting mutagen because it also has a great degree of species specificity. Rogers (1955) found that a metabolite of urethane was an active agent that produced tumors in mice but not in guinea pigs, which may explain why *Neurospora crassa* Shear and B. O. Dodge are completely unaffected by this compound (Jensen et al., 1951). Rogers (1957) found a correlation between urethane and nucleic acid metabolism in mice. As with the purines, the fate of the induced chromosome breaks varies with different species. Urethane-induced breaks in *Oenothera* (Oehlkers, 1943) form rearrangements readily, while they remain open as fragments in *Vicia* (Duefel, 1951).

Chemicals which produce chromosome breaks that do not restitute might be extremely efficient as chemosterilants. Their yield of dominant lethal mutations might be high at low doses since breaks that fail to rejoin will produce high frequencies of fragments and, consequently, higher frequencies of lethal mutations per chromosome break than when restitution is more prevalent. Chemicals affecting nucleic acid and protein metabolism, however, are effective only on chromosomes that are replicating. In the adult male insect, chromosome replication in germ cells is limited to the spermatogonia and early primary spermatocytes. For this reason, none of the purine and pyrimidine analogs have been practical as male sterilants. In the female, meiosis occurs in the fully formed egg. Thus these compounds could prevent eggs from hatching (LaBrecque et al., 1960, Crystal, 1963).

ASPERMIA

When chemosterilants are applied to insects, the effects are not limited to the mature sperm or oocytes. The entire contents of the testes and ovaries are exposed to the chemosterilant; the effect of the chemical on the various cell stages is expected to produce different effects.

Aspermia is a condition that occurs when mature sperm are not produced or the supply becomes exhausted and the continued production of sperm is inhibited. Aspermia is observed in male insects following treatments or conditions that inhibit the spermatogenic cycle. Unfortunately, we know little concerning the production of aspermia by chemosterilants. From radiation studies, however, we know that developing germ cells differ widely in their sensitivity. Such differential sensitivity was demonstrated in the limited work with chemosterilants and screwworm flies by LaChance and Crystal (1963). Also, Fahmy and Fahmy (1964) discussed in detail the variation in mutagenic response observed when different types of germ cells were sampled after the males had been treated with chemosterilants.

Treating the gonial stages in either sex yields few observable dominant-lethal mutations. This is not because gonial

cells are resistant to mutagens. Actually these cells are sensitive and exhibit a high frequency of cell death, at least after
radiation treatments. The killing of gonial cells by chemosterilants has hardly been studied but it is expected that the treated
cells will not survive to produce gametes which can be evaluated for the presence or absence of dominant lethal mutations. Cell death in gonial cell populations can lead to infecundity in the female and aspermia in the male.

Keiser et al. (1965) reported that in some species the
spermatogonia and spermatocytes were destroyed by some
chemosterilants but that spermatids beyond the last division
continued to develop and became mature spermatozoa. This
pattern is similar to that observed in radiation-sterilized
screwworm flies (Riemann, 1967).

Cantwell and Henneberry (1963) found that adult *Drosophila* fed 1 percent apholate for 24 hr ceased sperm development in the anterior portion of the testes and showed a general
necrosis of the germinal epithelium after the eighth day.

Inhibition of sperm production by chemicals might explain the observed decrease in the size of the testes of treated
males. Lindquist et al. (1964) noted that 5 days after a single
dipping of boll weevil males in apholate, the testes decrease
noticeably in overall size, and that after 10 days, the decrease
was very apparent. Likewise, Schwartz (1965) reported that
when eye gnats, *Hippelates pusio* Loew, were fed apholate,
metepa, or tepa, the testes of the treated gnats were about 23
percent smaller than those of untreated gnats. The germarial
region of the gonads was most severely affected; it was partly
collapsed and void of spermatogonia in some testes. Also in
mice, the injection of alkane sulfonic esters produced both
aspermia and dominant lethal mutations (Partington and Jackson, 1963).

Probably many alkylating agents will produce death in
gonial cells, and some antimetabolites may have the same effect. Death of the gonial cells may be related to chromosome
breakage and the subsequent mitotic difficulties, but death
may also occur without cell division. This latter type of cell
death may or may not involve DNA replication which is a
susceptible target for many chemosterilants including alkylating
agents (Herriot, 1948) and nonalkylating agents such as urethane (Rogers, 1957).

Several instances of "nonpermanent sterility" or "recovered fertility" have been reported in connection with insect

chemosterilant experiments, and these may be related to cell
death in spermatogonial cells (Keiser et al., 1965). If a chemical treatment produces a high level of dominant lethal mutations in the sperm but does not succeed in killing all the gonial
cells, the surviving gonial cells will continue to divide and repopulate the germarium section of the testes. Sperm derived
from these surviving gonial cells would probably not contain
dominant lethal mutations. When this occurs, males may "regain" or "recover" their fertility during later matings. Although this event is theoretically possible, its occurrence has
not been widely investigated with chemosterilants. The gonial
cells, however, are quite sensitive to radiation treatments;
doses that produce high frequencies of dominant lethal mutations in the mature sperm are adequate to kill all gonial cells
(Oakberg and Clark, 1961, Oakberg, 1965, Riemann, 1967). When
chemicals are used, one would expect the same relative sensitivity, but some chemicals may spare the gonial cells or fail to
reach them.

It is commonly thought that sterility based on aspermia
would be unacceptable for use with the sterile-male technique
of insect control, but this is not completely true. For species
that are polygamous or for those that require sperm to remain
monogamous, the sterile male must transmit sperm containing
dominant lethal mutations that are competitive with the sperm
contributed by normal males. In species that are monogamous,
however, males contributing immotile sperm or no sperm at
all would be quite effective, providing that the act of copulation
is sufficient to prevent the female from further mating (Riemann, 1967).

SPERM INACTIVATION

Inactivation of the sperm is another way of producing
sterility in insects. The central question then becomes—do
chemosterilants produce sperm inactivation and, if so, is this
phenomenon fairly common or restricted to a few compounds?
Accurate data on sperm inactivation are difficult to obtain. In
species that require fertilization for egg development, sperm
activity is difficult to evaluate without using special cytological
techniques. Generally it is difficult to determine whether a
treated male transmits sperm with dominant lethal mutations,
inactivated sperm, or any sperm at all. All three possibilities

are expressed as nonhatching eggs. This consideration puts serious stress on studies based solely on egg hatchability which are extrapolated to indicate cytogenetic injury.

Reliable comparisons of dominant lethal mutations and sperm inactivation are available mainly for insect species that reproduce parthenogenetically. In these species, the two effects can be separated easily and accurately; the methods used are shown in Table 4.

With radiation-induced sterility, most investigators have agreed generally that sperm inactivation does not occur until doses that induce dominant lethals in all the sperm have been administered. More recent experiments (Yanders, 1959, 1964, LeFevre and Jonsson, 1962) indicate, however, that radiation treatments within the range of doses commonly used in genetic experiments do have some effect on sperm utilization patterns and competitiveness. Moreover, Proverbs and Newton (1962) showed that doses of radiation that sterilize male codling moths, *Carpocapsa pomonella* (L.), also inactivate the sperm; they are not competitive in egg fertilization with the sperm received from untreated males.

Our knowledge of the effects of chemicals on sperm activity is more limited. Whiting and von Borstel (1954) reported that after treatments with nitrogen mustard, sperm inactivation occurred only at doses far higher than those required to induce dominant lethal mutations in all the *Bracon* sperm. Grosch and Valcovic (1964) and L. R. Valcovic (unpublished data) observed that the exposure of *Bracon* males to topical applications of apholate (0.01 to 0.1 percent) produced only a minor amount of sperm inactivation at doses that produced 40 to 80 percent dominant lethal mutations in the sperm. The level of inactivation was considered insigificant for field application.

When *Drosophila* males were injected with p-N-di(chloroethyl) amino-phenylalanine[1] and mated to untreated females, most of the eggs did not hatch (Fahmy and Fahmy, 1958). The result thus superficially resembled dominant lethality, but cytological examination of the eggs showed that only a few contained the cytogenetic abnormalities associated with dominant lethality. The majority of the eggs showed no development (no cleavage nuclei). The authors concluded that "most of the sperm

[1] 3-[p-[bis (2-chloroethyl)amino]phenyl]alanine, i.e. melphalan.

TABLE 4

EXPERIMENTAL DESIGN TO TEST FOR CHEMOSTERILANT-INDUCED SPERM INACTIVATION
AND/OR DOMINANT LETHAL MUTATIONS IN THE WASP, *Bracon*[a], COMPARED WITH THE RESULTS
EXPECTED IN OTHER INSECT SPECIES (MALES ARE TREATED AND MATED TO VIRGIN FEMALES)

Treatment which causes	Results in *Bracon*			Results in house flies, *Drosophila*, screwworms, etc.		
	Expected egg hatch (%)	Sex ratio of progeny ♀♀ : ♂♂	Percent ♂♂ progeny	Expected egg hatch (%)	Sex ratio of progeny ♀♀ : ♂♂	Percent ♂♂ progeny
Controls (no effect)	100	66 : 33	33	100	50 : 50	50
50% dominant lethals in sperm	66	33 : 33	50	50	50 : 50	50
100% dominant lethals in sperm	33	0 : 33	100	0	---	---
100% dominant lethals in sperm + 50% sperm inactivation	66	0 : 66	100	0	---	---
100% sperm inactivation	100	0 : 100	100	0	---	---

aMated females generally produce 66.6 percent diploid progeny (daughters from fertilized eggs) and 33.3 percent haploid progeny (males from unfertilized eggs).

124

of the treated father must have been killed by the compound, thus causing the eggs to be laid unfertilized.''

Bateman and Chandley (1964) also found that injection of methyl methanesulfonate into *Drosophila* males resulted in physiological inhibition of the sperm and suggested this as a major factor in the failure of the eggs to hatch.

A recent study by Simkover (1964) suggested that 2-imadazolidinone produced effects attributable to sperm inactivation. In these studies with the large milkweed bug, *Oncopeltus fasciatus* (Dallas), he found that treated males transmitted sperm but the eggs did not hatch. Actually, without cytological examination, it is impossible to ascertain whether the result was caused by dominant lethal mutations in the sperm or sperm inactivation.

More recent studies with the wasp *Bracon* (LaChance, 1966) showed that some chemosterilants do, in fact, produce a significant amount of sperm inactivation though other chemicals do not. In these studies, tarsal-contact treatments of *Bracon* males with sterilizing doses of tretamine produced no sperm inactivation; in contrast, significant amounts of inactivation were produced with tepa, and the effect was clearly detectable, even at substerilizing doses. These data clearly suggest that (1) the production of sperm inactivation by certain chemicals is not always the result of overdose, and (2) sperm inactivation occurs only with certain classes of chemosterilants.

Although it is commonly thought that a significant amount of sperm inactivation resulting from chemical treatments would cause the sterile-male technique to fail, such is not necessarily true. When the females are polygamous, sterile males with immotile sperm may be useless because future mating with fertile males might completely negate the effects of the previous sterile mating (but see also Table 5 and Lindquist and House, 1967). When the females mate only once, however, mating with a sterile male containing inactivated sperm might have the same effect as mating with a sterile male that transmits active sperm with dominant lethal mutations. The adequacy of sperm inactivation as the basis for sterility depends largely on whether sperm transmission is required to insure that females will refrain from further mating. Recent studies on the house fly (Riemann, 1967) indicate that sperm transfer is not necessary to prevent females from remating; therefore, sterility based on sperm inactivation is potentially useful for some species.

TABLE 5

COMPARISON OF DIFFERENT KINDS OF CHEMOSTERI-
LANT-INDUCED SPERM INACTIVATION AND THE
POSSIBLE EFFECTS IN VARIOUS INSECT SPECIES

Effect produced in	Treatment which produces sperm inactivation characterized by	
	Loss of motility or lack of egg penetration (types 1 and 2)	Loss of fertilizing capacity—(failure to function in syngamy) (type 3)
Parthenogenetic species (Bracon)	Eggs hatch and produce haploid males	Eggs hatch and produce haploid males
Monogamous bisexual species (house fly or mosquito)	No egg hatch (resembles dominant lethal mutations)	No egg hatch (resembles dominant lethal mutations)[b]
Polygamous bisexual species (codling moth or boll weevil)[a]	Eggs hatch, since sperm from treated males are not competitive with those from untreated males[a]	No egg hatch (resembles dominant lethal mutations); sperm from treated males probably competitive[b]

[a]May vary considerably, depending upon sperm utilization by
multimated females.
[b]The results of this kind of sperm inactivation are also affected by the incidence of polyspermy in various species.

We must be just as careful in using the term "sperm inactivation" as we are in using the term "insect sterility."
Actually, sperm inactivation can be due to three different
factors: (1) completely immotile sperm, (2) lack of egg penetration, and (3) lack of pronuclear fusion or failure to function in
syngamy. These three possibilities are distinct. The differences are not purely academic but may have a definite bearing
on the use of chemosterilants in insect-control programs. The
effect of these three types of sperm inactivation and the results
they would have on some insect species are shown in Table 5.
One kind of sperm inactivation (Type 3) could be identified as
such in parthenogenetic species but would be inseparable from
dominant lethal mutations in other insects. Unfortunately, we
do not know what kind of sperm inactivation occurs with certain
chemosterilants nor how important this kind of sterility may
be. Further studies are badly needed.

In summary, when males are treated, the sterilizing activity of any chemical can be due to: (1) chemicals that induce chromosome damage and produce dominant lethal mutations; (2) chemicals that produce cell death in premeiotic stages and produce aspermia (this effect may or may not be related to chromosome breakage); and (3) chemicals that inactivate the sperm. A single chemical might possibly produce all three effects, depending on the dose and the type of cell attacked.

Sterility in female insects can be achieved either by the production of dominant lethal mutations in their mature eggs or by the failure of eggs to be produced at all (infecundity). The induction of dominant lethal mutations in the eggs by chemicals is attributed to chromosome aberrations similar to those causing dominant lethal mutations in the sperm. Although there are some important differences between the induction of dominant lethal mutations in eggs and sperm (LaChance, 1967), the subject is outside our sphere here.

INFECUNDITY

Sterility characterized by infecundity is limited to females. Generally, male sterility is sought for insect control. In every successful application of the sterile-male technique, however, both sexes were sterilized and released together; sterility of the females was due to infecundity. Also, population suppression by the release of sterile females has been suggested (E. F. Knipling personal communication). In species with short-lived males, the release of sterile females into the target area might have a significant effect on the population trend. In fact, Husseiny and Madsen (1964) showed that the release of sterile females of the navel orangeworm, *Paramyelois transitella* (Walker), was actually more effective than release of sterile males. For these reasons, it is important to consider how chemical agents produce infecundity.

First, two terms, "fertility" and "fecundity," must be defined because they are often used interchangeably. For physiological purposes, "fertility" is defined as the percentage of eggs deposited that develop into viable progeny and "fecundity" as the number of eggs produced, regardless of their fertility. The biotic potential (reproductive capacity) is the product of fecundity and fertility.

Infecundity is probablv no more complex than the other types of sterility, but it is undoubtedly the most difficult to discuss for two reasons: Little is known about the causes of infecundity produced by chemosterilants in insects, and even less is known about their cytogenetic or cellular basis. Also, though some sort of uniformity exists among male insects in the production of sperm, no such uniformity exists in egg production.

To understand how chemicals prevent egg formation, we need to understand how eggs are produced. Oogenesis is dependent on the proper functioning of the endocrine system, but the effects of chemosterilants on this system are largely unknown.

The basic unit responsible for the production of eggs is the pair of ovaries, each of which consists of ovarioles (varying in number from one to several thousand in some insects). Beyond this, interspecific differences are vast. Insect ovarioles are classified as panoistic or meroistic, depending on the presence or absence of nurse cells. In primitive orders such as Orthoptera and Odonata, no special cells for yolk production are present in the panoistic ovarioles; yolk materials are absorbed from the haemolymph and produced by the enlarged oocyte nucleus or germinal vesicle (Telfer, 1965).

In other orders, special nutritive cells or trophocytes are provided in the meroistic ovarioles for yolk formation. The meroistic ovarioles are divided into either telotrophic or polytrophic ovarioles, depending on the location of nurse cells in relation to the oocyte. In telotrophic ovarioles, these trophocytes are distant from the oocyte, and they deliver the yolk through cytoplasmic strands. In polytrophic ovarioles, the trophocytes lie adjacent to the oocyte and form part of the egg follicle. Telotrophic ovarioles are characteristic of Coleoptera; polytrophic ovarioles are characteristic of Diptera and Hymenoptera. Since most studies on chemosterilant-produced infecundity involve Dipteran species, our discussion will necessarily be based on them. Future studies may show that the basic causes of infecundity in other insect orders are fairly similar, but that remains to be seen.

Egg production depends on the continued mitotic division of oogonial cells, these being the ultimate source of eggs. These oogonial divisions produce a cyst of interconnected cells. Generally, within the germarium, each oogonium gives rise to 1 oocyte and 1, 7, 15, 31, or more trophocytes (nutritive cells), depending on the species. Thus the essential first step in egg formation, at least in the Diptera, is the formation of the cyst of interconnected cells. King (1964) presented a detailed summary of the process of oogenesis and discussed the chromosomal events and differences in the behavior of the chromosomes of the oocytes, nurse cells, and follicle cells. Before egg maturation can get underway, important changes must first occur in the chromosomes of the nurse cells. Their major function is to nurse the growing oocyte. In preparation for this, the nurse-cell chromosomes undergo the process of endomitosis, which is common in the Diptera and many other insect orders, and prepares the trophocyte for the normal synthetic activity of oogenesis. Endomitosis entails the repeated replication of the nurse-cell chromosomes without cell division. [This polyploid nature of the nurse-cell chromosomes in the Diptera has been known for almost 30 years (Bauer, 1938).] Initially the replicated chromonemal threads remain in close association and appear as greatly thickened polyploid-polytene chromosomes. Subsequently these replicated strands separate completely to form a mass of chromatin fibrils which completely fills the nucleus. In many orders of insects, the nurse-cells simply become polyploid.

During oogenesis the volume of the nurse-cell nuclei has been estimated to increase two thousandfold. Vitellogenesis cannot proceed to completion without the normal elevated chromosomal complement in the nurse-cell nuclei (King and Sang, 1959). Once the nurse cells have completed the endomitotic process, growth of the oocyte usually proceeds rapidly, perhaps because the nurse cells are most active in the synthesis of nucleoproteins and may even transfer ribosomes to the yolk (Bier, 1963, Painter and Biesele, 1966). For example, King (1964) estimated that in *Drosophila* the volume of the oocyte increases by over 100,000 times in 3 days; and this process takes place simultaneously in many ovarioles. Then after the oocyte has matured and assimilated the necessary precursors for the developing embryo, the nurse cells degenerate and disappear. Nurse cells, however, are not alone responsible for the synthesis of yolk. Proteins and lipoproteins are also absorbed from the haemolymph. In insects lacking trophocytes, yolk is assimilated from the haemolymph and the germinal vesicle (Telfer, 1965). Also, the follicle cells are responsible for much synthetic activity; in the ovary of the cricket (Gryllidae) (Favard-Seréno and Durand, 1963), these cells secrete RNA.

After vitellogenesis is completed, the follicle cells secrete the chorion but leave an opening, the micropyle, to facilitate the entry of sperm. Finally, the egg ruptures through the follicle, passes down the vagina, receives the sperm from the spermathecae, and is laid. Evidently the presence of the sperm within the egg stimulates its nucleus to divide into four haploid nuclei. One nucleus becomes the female pronucleus and unites with the sperm nucleus to form the zygote.

From this brief account, it is evident that oogenesis is characterized by cellularly and chromosomally diverse events and is controlled by genetic, hormonal, chemical, and environmental factors. It can therefore be inhibited by: (1) treatments that cause cell death in the gonial cells to prevent them from dividing to form a normal cyst of cells; (2) conditions that prevent the nurse-cell chromosomes from attaining the proper degree of ploidy and from functioning properly in vitellogenesis; and (3) interruption of any of the complicated steps in vitellogenesis by environmental, hormonal, biochemical, or genetic factors.

Indeed, chemosterilants inhibit oogenesis in all these ways. The number and diversity of compounds that inhibit fecundity is truly astounding. The most widely tested chemicals, however, have been antimetabolites and alkylating agents, some of which are listed in Table 6 (although Table 2 in Chapter 2 contains many of these chemicals and lists many more, it does not identify them according to whether fecundity was affected or what kind of sterility was produced). All the chemicals that produce infecundity have not been listed, and we have made no attempt to list all the insects whose fecundity was affected by a given chemical. Table 6 merely illustrates the wide variety of compounds that have that effect. Too, the references were selected to introduce the reader to the vast literature on chemicals affecting fecundity, but they do not necessarily reflect the priority of discovery.

Gouck and LaBrecque (1964) listed 27 compounds which prevented oviposition in the house fly, most of them alkylating agents (13 aziridines and 6 mustards). Apholate inhibited the development of the ovaries in *Drosophila* (Cantwell and Henneberry, 1963), in the house fly (Morgan and LaBrecque, 1962), and in the eye gnat (Schwartz, 1965). Also, Mitlin and Baroody (1958) listed 15 compounds that affected fecundity of the house fly and reported that six produced complete infecundity. Of the cytostatic agents studied for their effect on the house fly ovary,

TABLE 6

SOME CHEMICALS AFFECTING FECUNDITY IN INSECTS[a]

Chemical	Organism[b]	Reference[c]
Antimetabolites		
Folic acid antagonists:		
Aminopterin	*Drosophila*	Goldsmith and Frank (1952)
Aminopterin	House fly	Mitlin et al. (1957)
Aminopterin	*Bracon hebetor*	Grosch (1963)
Aminopterin	Screwworm	Crystal (1963)
Methotrexate	*Drosophila*	Goldsmith and Frank (1952)
Methotrexate	Screwworm	Crystal (1963, 1964a)
Methotrexate	House fly	LaBrecque et al. (1960)
Methotrexate	*Bracon hebetor*	Grosch (1963)
Chloromethotrexate	Screwworm	Crystal (1964a)
Dichloromethotrexate	Screwworm	Crystal (1964a)
Glutamine antagonists:		
6-diazo-5-oxonorleucine	Screwworm	Crystal (1963)
6-diazo-5-oxonorleucine	*Bracon hebetor*	Grosch (1963)
Pyrimidine antagonists:		
5-fluorouracil	House fly	LaBrecque et al. (1960)
5-fluorouracil	Screwworm	Crystal (1963)
5-fluoroorotic acid	Screwworm	Crystal (1963)
5-fluoroorotic acid	House fly	Painter and Kilgore (1965)
5-fluorodeoxyuridine	House fly	Painter and Kilgore (1963)
Sterol antagonists:		
Sodium fluoroacetate	House fly	Monroe et al. (1963)
Halogenated deoxyuridines	*Bracon hebetor*	Grosch (1963)
Alkylating agents		
Aziridinyl derivatives: 2,5-bis(1-aziridinyl)-3,6-bis-(2-methoxyethoxy)-*p*-benzoquinone	Screwworm	Crystal and LaChance (1963)
Thiotepa	Screwworm	Crystal and LaChance (1963)
Tretamine	House fly	LaBrecque et al. (1960)

TABLE 6 (CONTINUED)

Chemical	Organism[b]	Reference[c]
Aziridinyl derivatives:		
Methyl tretamine	House fly	LaBrecque et al. (1960)
Tepa	House fly	LaBrecque (1961)
Apholate	Stable fly	Harris (1962)
Apholate	House fly	LaBrecque (1961)
Nitrogen mustards:		
Methyl bis(beta-chloroethyl)- amine hydrochloride	House fly	Mitlin et al. (1957)
Mechlorethamine	Screwworm	Crystal (1963)
Miscellaneous chemicals		
Colchicine	House fly	Mitlin et al. (1957)
Colchicine	*Drosophila*	Jacob (1958)
DDT	House fly	Beard (1965)
Chlorinated hydrocarbons:		
bis(p-chlorophenyl)- trifluoromethylcarbinol	House fly	Ascher (1957)
bis(p-chlorophenyl)- pentafluoroethylcarbinol	House fly	Ascher (1957)
Herbicides	Pea aphid	Robinson (1960, 1961)
Acaricides	House fly	Ascher and Hirsch (1961)
Arsenates	*Rhagoletis pomonella*, *Drosophila* (2 species), House fly	Pickett and Patterson (1963)
Arsenates	*Bracon hebetor*	Grosch (1963)
Antibiotics and aureomycin	Spider mite	Harries (1963)
Antibiotics and aureomycin	*Bracon hebetor*	Grosch (1963)
Antivitamins	House fly	Levinson and Bergman (1959)
Anthelminthics	Screwworm	Crystal (1964c)
Coumarin, thiourea, piperonyl butoxide, p-quinone, 1-phenyl- 2-thiourea	House fly	Mitlin and Baroody (1958)
Benzene, tetrahydrofuron, benzyl alcohol	House fly	Ascher (1965)

TABLE 6 (CONTINUED)

Chemical	Organism[b]	Reference[c]
Aziridinyl carbamates (dual antagonists):		
Uredepa	Screwworm	Crystal (1964d)
Benzodepa	Screwworm	Crystal (1964d)
Methyl [bis(1-aziridinyl)-phosphinyl] carbamate	Screwworm	Crystal (1964d)
2-imidazolidinone	House fly (ovaries develop normally) Milkweed bug	Simkover (1964)
9-oxo-trans-2-decenoic acid (queen substance)	House fly	Nayar (1963)

[a]Chemical names listed according to nomenclature used in reference.

[b]The insect named is an illustration. We have not attempted to list all insect species whose fecundity is affected by each chemical.

[c]References are given for convenience and as a starting point for further literature search, not to establish priority in the discovery of the sterilizing activity of each chemical.

Landa and Rézábóva (1965) found 12 that caused infecundity. Other chemicals affecting infecundity were listed by Crystal (1963) and Ascher (1964). Hays and Cochran (1964) found several compounds (including steroids) that prevented the production of offspring but did not report the effects on fecundity per se. Obviously, fecundity is affected by tumor-inhibiting agents, antimetabolites, alkylating agents, and a wide array of miscellaneous chemicals.

Although egg production is reduced and often eliminated by some compounds (such as alkylating agents) that also induce dominant lethal and other mutations, many chemicals that reduce fecundity are ineffective mutagens. Probably all these chemosterilants produce infecundity in a different manner; similarity of the end effect does not indicate similarity of mode of action.

For the present, we must limit ourselves to discussing the cytogenetic basis for chemically induced infecundity. Infecundity may result from severe damage to the oogonia, and chemical mutagens are known to produce cell death and inhibit cell division. Infecundity caused by oogonial death is comparable to aspermia caused by spermatogonial death. Gonial cells are the only germ cells in the larvae of most species; therefore treatment of larvae with chemosterilants may kill the gonial cells to prevent the formation of gametes. In some instances, however, the gonial cells are not killed, and infecundity is caused by other factors. For example, when Rai (1964b) reared larval *Aedes aegypti* in water containing 15 parts per million (ppm) of apholate from 2 days after hatching to pupation, the gonial cells divided, and the egg follicles eventually formed but only to undergo subsequent degeneration. Thus, infecundity was produced that proved irreversible for at least 1 month (three gonadotrophic cycles). Apholate applied to larval *Culex pipiens quinquefasciatus* Say severely damaged the germaria and reduced the size of the ovaries, and viability was reduced among the eggs that were laid (Murray and Bickley, 1964). Bing (1966) found that oriental house flies, *Musca domestica vicina* Macquart, treated with thiotepa exhibited degeneration of oogonial cells.

Insects are usually treated as pupae or adults when the ovarioles contain both gonial cells and egg chambers with nurse cells and oocytes. In radiation studies (Grosch et al., 1956, Terzian and Stahler, 1958, LaChance and Bruns, 1963), only small doses are required to inhibit egg production when the radiation treatments coincide with the peak of the endomitotic process in the nurse cells. After the nutritive cells become fully polyploid, even large doses of radiation will not affect the growth and production of outwardly normal-appearing eggs. Thus, there are two radiosensitive targets which can affect fecundity in insects: gonial cell divisions and the endomitotic replications in the nurse cells. Grosch (personal communication) considers the mitotic divisions required to set up the nest of cells equally radiosensitive to the endomitotic divisions in the nurse cells that soon follow.

In a series of investigations relating the effect of chemosterilant treatments on the fecundity and the endomitotic process in the nurse-cell nuclei of the screwworm fly (Crystal and LaChance, 1963, LaChance and Leverich, 1965), the following technique was used. The alkylating agents were administered topically to two groups of adult females. Those in the 0- to 4-hr-old group contained nurse cells in which the chromatin material was *undergoing* the process of endomitotic replication. The 24-hr-old females were treated when endomitosis had been completed, and the chromatin material in the nurse cells had completely dissociated into fine chromatin

threads that completely filled the nucleus. By using this technique, Crystal and LaChance (1963) found that the greatest inhibition of ovarian growth occurred if the chemical was administered while the nurse cells were in the endomitotic phase;
such treatments caused complete or nearly complete infecundity. The same treatment given 24 hr later had virtually no
effect on the fecundity of the females, but most of the eggs laid
did not hatch.

In later research (LaChance and Leverich, 1965, and unpublished data), this same technique was used to study the effect of 2,5-bis(1-aziridinyl)-3,6-bis-(methoxyethoxy)-p-benzo-
quinone—a chemical with two alkylating groups. The females
were sacrificed periodically after treatment to determine cytologically the progress of oogenesis and to relate any retardation
or abnormalities to the condition of nurse-cell chromosomes at
the time of treatment. Ovarioles were dissected from 4-day-
old females, and the degree of development was compared with
that of control females (Fig. 4). All the ovarioles in control
females contained a well-formed mature egg almost ready to
be oviposited, a second egg chamber with distinct nurse cells
that had differentiated completely from the germarium, and a
normal-appearing germarium. Females of the same age treated
when they were 24 hr old were retarded in egg development, but
the most severely affected ovarioles were found in the group
treated at 0 to 4 hr after emergence. Only the earlier treatment
completely prevented the formation of eggs. Apparently treatment with an alkylating agent when the nurse-cell chromosomes
are undergoing endomitotic replication completely disrupts this
process. Presumably the mutagen prevents the nurse-cell
chromosomes from attaining a degree of ploidy and a nuclear
volume sufficient to sustain the biochemical processes and all
the synthetic activities required during oogenesis.

A similar loss of fecundity by female *Aedes aegypti*
treated with thiotepa was reported by Bertram (1964). When
treatment was given shortly after emergence, oogenesis did
not proceed beyond the resting stage (Stage II). In the survivors
that did not lay eggs, the ovaries lacked organized structure
and had a cytopathology resembling that caused by antimetabolites. When the females were already 24 hr old at the time of
treatment, oogenesis was not inhibited.

Landa and Rézábóva (1965) described the cytological
changes that occur within the house fly ovariole treated with a
variety of chemosterilants. Their observations also indicate

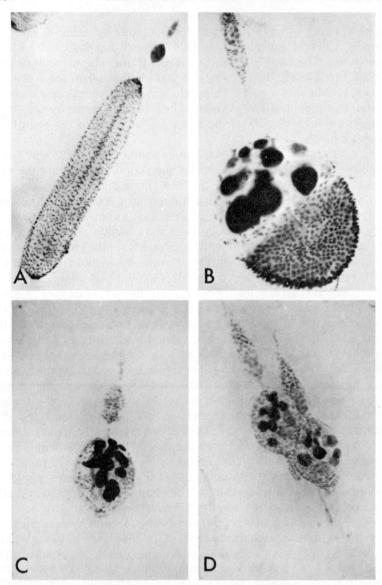

Fig. 4. Whole mounts of ovarioles dissected from 4-day old, adult screwworm females. A. Control ovarioles—fully developed egg, well-formed second egg chamber and germarium (circa 28×). B, C, D (circa 75×). Ovarioles from females treated with the chemosterilant 2,5-bis(1-aziridinyl)-3,6 bis(methoxyethoxy)-p-benzoquinone, either at 0 to 4 hr or at 24 hr after emergence. B. Ovarioles from female treated at 24 hr after emergence (note retardation in egg development and absence of second egg chamber). First egg chamber can eventually form a mature egg, C and D. Ovarioles from females treated 0 to 4 hr after emergence (note severe retardation in development). These ovarioles eventually atrophy.

that damage to the follicle cells and the nurse cells of the egg chamber, in addition to destruction of the germarium, was responsible for the infecundity of the females. Cantwell and Henneberry (1963) found a degeneration of ovarioles in *Drosophila* after apholate treatment.

Probably antimetabolites also attack the nurse-cell chromosomes though perhaps in a different manner. Folic acid antagonists inhibit the folic acid enzymes required for synthesis of nucleic acid, and this, in turn, would result in the disturbance of cell division and endomitosis. Nucleic acids undergo rapid synthesis in nurse cells of young females. DNA replication in the nurse-cell nuclei can be prevented by feeding females a medium containing 5-aminouracil (King, 1958), aminopterin (King and Sang, 1959), or sulfanilimide (Sang and King, 1961). Vitellogenesis is also retarded in flies treated with these antimetabolites.

Grosch (1963) found that when methotrexate was fed to *Bracon* females they failed to lay eggs the third and fourth days after feeding. Dissection showed that this was because of atrophy of the nurse cells and degeneration of the oocytes. In time, the effect wore off, and egg production was resumed but never reached control levels. Poor egg production from the sixth to eleventh day was traced to difficulties in mitosis and differentiation. Apparently alkylating agents and antimetabolites have similar targets in their attack on oogenesis, though they must produce their effect in largely different ways because of their vastly dissimilar chemical properties. One observation, however, has some bearing on this point. King (1964) found that the nurse-cell chromosomes in a female-sterile strain of *Drosophila* remain polytene (in bundles) and do not "fall apart" and concluded that most of their loci are quiescent. In normal flies, the chromomeres uncoil during periods of synthetic activity and concurrently lose their adhesive properties. It is possible that the nurse-cell chromosomes dissociate rather than remain polytene because so many of their loci are synthetically active or vice versa. In insects treated with chemosterilants, we do not know whether the chromosomes remain polytene and do not unravel because the loci are not synthetically active or whether vitellogenesis fails because the chromonemal threads did not unravel and, consequently, the loci are not active. These are two different causes with the same end effect.

Perhaps the most important factor governing the effect of a chemosterilant on fecundity is timing of treatment. For a treatment to reduce fecundity, it must be administered to a sensitive life stage. Many studies have shown that an egg follicle, beyond a certain stage of development, is refractory to chemosterilants and will continue to develop, even if the egg produced is inviable because of damage to the genetic material in the oocyte nucleus. Therefore, when a chemosterilant is fed, the females receive the dose over a prolonged period during which the cells and chromosomes in the ovarioles are constantly changing in sensitivity. Whether or not fecundity is reduced depends, evidently, upon the dose received by each female by the time critical events (such as endomitosis in the nurse cells) occur; i.e., some eggs might develop within certain females; other females would be infecund.

Moreover, Morgan and LaBrecque (1962, 1964) noted that when apholate, tepa, or metepa was fed to female house flies from emergence to sexual maturity, some of the egg chambers were affected but others were not. The oocytes in the first egg chamber sometimes reached maturity, but the second and third egg chambers failed to form. Similarly, when hempa was fed to adult female house flies (Morgan, 1967), they were able to develop eggs from the first egg chamber only in some ovarioles. No eggs were developed, however, from the second or third egg chambers. In insects such as the olive fruit fly, *Dacus oleae* (Gmelin), which has mature eggs at the time of emergence, production of the first clutch of eggs could not be inhibited, but further egg production could be curtailed.

As noted, many miscellaneous chemicals (some shown in Table 6) reduce fecundity. Although the ways in which they produce their effects are unknown, they are surely fundamentally different from those of antimetabolites or alkylating agents. For instance, some chemicals (arsenic, for example) only *repress* ovarian development and must be continuously present in the diet to prevent oviposition. Also when the antimitotic substances, colchicine and heparin, were fed to *Bracon* females (Grosch, 1959), fecundity was reduced in the first half of the lifespan, but the treated females laid more eggs than the controls during the latter portion of their life. The egg production pattern obtained with these agents was notably different from that obtained after treatment with enzyme inhibitors or antimetabolites. Although depression of insect fecundity by insecticides has been known for some time (Tenhet, 1947), the basis for this effect is not known. Sublethal doses of DDT in the food of house flies reduced ovarian growth (Beard, 1965) and fecundity (see reviews by Knutson, 1959, and Ascher, 1964), but sometimes insecticides also stimulate oviposition or increase fecundity. Thus far, it is not known whether any chemosterilants affect fecundity via an effect on the endocrine system. Probably in the future some will be found that mimic the effect of hormones and affect insect fecundity via this pathway.

SOMATIC EFFECTS

Thus far we have stressed the effects of chemosterilants on the gonads. Chemosterilants, however, become distributed throughout the insects' tissues, and they may damage the somatic cells. Insects can be sterilized without serious adverse effects only if (1) the germ cells are more sensitive to the chemosterilant than the somatic cells; (2) the insect can tolerate whatever somatic damage is induced without effects on lifespan or competitiveness; or (3) the chemical selectively attacks the gonads. In the absence of such clear-cut differential sensitivity between germ cells and somatic cells, we may expect damage to somatic tissues which, in turn, may lead to altered sexual competitiveness or longevity. Such changes may reduce the effectiveness of the sterile-male technique. In this section, we will consider the factors involved in harmful side effects and how these may be manipulated. But first we will sketch a working hypothesis of how somatic damage may occur.

Cytogenetic damage in somatic cells is similar to that in germ cells. Oster (1959) demonstrated the genetic basis of x-ray-induced somatic damage, and Rai (1964a) found that apholate induces chromosome breaks, deletions, ring chromosomes, dicentric chromosomes, anaphase bridges, stickiness, polyploidy, and interference in chromosome replication in the somatic cells of *Aedes aegypti*. In addition, chemically induced chromosome breaks are a major cause of cell death (Auerbach, 1958), and they are most readily induced in interphase cells that are preparing for division (Brewen, 1965, Scott and Evans, 1964, Chang and Elequin, 1967). Clearly then, the more proliferating tissue present in a treated insect, the more somatic damage will occur. Damage to the cytoplasm by alkylating agents is also a major cause of cell death, and the ensuing physiological disturbance may cause chromosomal fragmentation (Koller, 1958).

One obvious change in cells treated with alkylating agents is an increase in volume ascribed to the increased synthesis of cytoplasm. The ultrastructural cytoplasmic changes involved in fibrosarcoma cells cultured in therapeutic doses of thiotepa have been reported by Barton and Barton (1965). These include the formation of a new cell membrane, proliferation of the endoplasmic reticulum and the extrusion of large masses of cytoplasm into the extracellular space.

The effect of the somatic damage produced in an insect by chemosterilants is usually observed or measured by changes in life-span, sexual competitiveness, or vigor (Chapter 2). The measurement of the somatic effects of a chemosterilant, however, often depends on the investigator's ingenuity in devising critical tests. For example, Grosch (1956) and Baumhover (1965) showed that the longevity of irradiated males may not be an accurate measure of deleterious side effects because the life-span of treated males was extended by their reduced activity. The longevity and competitiveness of chemosterilized boll weevils was severely reduced because of somatic damage. This has delayed field studies on the eradication of this species with sterile males (Davich et al., 1965). The same is true of the tsetse fly, *Glossina morsitans* Westwood (Simpson, 1958). In measuring longevity, factors such as temperature, humidity, light, population density, and sex ratio should be rigidly standardized (Baumhover, 1965). Also, with the tsetse fly, Chadwick (1964) found that the already impaired longevity of apholate-treated females was further reduced when they were mated to treated males; untreated females mated to treated males lived much longer than when mated to untreated males. In contrast, sterilization by tepa increased the longevity of male and female oriental fruit flies, *Dacus dorsalis* Hendel, and of female Mediterranean fruit flies, *Ceratitis capitata* (Wiedemann) (I. Keiser, personal communication). House flies treated with tepa are much less likely to mate than untreated flies (Chang, 1965), and Oster (1961) found that *Drosophila* treated with quinacrine mustard[2] and the nonalkylating compounds urethane and formaldehyde aged prematurely, based on cell death and chromosomal damage. Weidhaas and Schmidt (1963) found no such effect in *Anopheles quadrimaculatus* Say, which received the minimum sterilizing dose.

[2] 9-[[4-[bis(2-chloroethyl)amino]-1-methyl butyl]amino]-6-chloro-2-methoxyacradine dihydrochloride.

FACTORS INFLUENCING SOMATIC DAMAGE BY CHEMO-STERILANTS

Undesirable effects on the somatic tissue may be reduced or avoided by considering five causal factors: (1) the chemosterilant; (2) its mode and frequency of administration; (3) the types of germ cells in the treated stage; (4) the presence of dividing somatic cells in the treated stage; and (5) nutrition.

Molecular Structure of the Chemosterilant. Safety margins ($LD_{0.01}$ — $ED_{99.99}$) were determined by Chang and Borkovec (1965) for a series of bis(1-aziridinyl)(alkylamino)phosphine oxides and for tepa, hempa, and the two intermediate analogs. These margins showed no trend up or down with structural changes. Crystal (1966a) found that toxicity to the screwworm varied widely among 200 aziridinyl chemosterilants and was largely unrelated to the number of aziridines in the molecule, to substitutions on the aziridinyl carbons, and to the sterilizing dose; it appeared to be a function of the carrier portion of the molecule.

Evidently the carrier moiety alters the pattern of chemical reactivity of the sterilant molecule by affecting its physico-chemical properties (Crystal, 1963, 1966a). Thus the carrier moiety may reduce the tendency of the functional groups to undergo those reactions with the cell constituents that lead to toxicity but do not contribute to sterility (Fahmy and Fahmy, 1964).

Mode and Frequency of Adminstration.   Chamberlain (1962) and Gouck et al. (1963) clearly showed that the mode of administration of a chemosterilant affects its induction of undesirable side effects. In the latter study, the toxic effects of topically applied chemicals overshadowed any sterilization achieved. But a margin of safety existed when these sterilants were administered as multiple oral feedings. From an analysis of the effects of 200 aziridine compounds on the screwworm, Crystal (1966a) concluded that the multiple-oral method was generally far superior for monofunctional and bifunctional compounds and for those polyfunctional compounds without substituents on the aziridinyl carbons. On the other hand, topical application proved superior to feeding for polyfunctional compounds with substituents on the aziridinyl carbon(s). All monofunctional and many bifunctional and polyfunctional chemosterilants proved to be ineffective when fed for a single day, although several days feeding was usually effective. Moreover, in a study involving the feeding of six aziridinyl chemosterilants, the house fly was sterilized more readily by the protracted feeding than by feeding for only 8 hr or 1 day (Ratcliff and Ristich, 1965). Similarly, a single feeding of apholate failed to sterilize adult male fall armyworms, *Spodoptera frugiperda* (J. E. Smith), even though the amount consumed exceeded that required to sterilize by continuous feeding (Young and Cox, 1965).

There are exceptions to these generalizations. For example, screwworm flies sterilized with tretamine show less pronounced toxic effects if the sterilant is administered topically rather than orally (Crystal, 1963). Whether multiple or protracted treatments are less deleterious for all modes of administration has not been studied thoroughly. Topical treatments with divided doses, however, may improve the survival of screwworm flies treated with tretamine (Crystal, 1964b) and of boll weevils immersed in apholate solutions (Lindquist et al., 1964). Similarly, prolonged exposure of adult gypsy moths to low concentrations of tepa or metepa was more effective than short exposures at higher concentrations (Collier and Downey, 1965).

Chemosterilization by tarsal contact may impair sexual competitiveness as occurred with adult male *Anopheles quadrimaculatus, Aedes aegypti,* and house flies exposed to surfaces treated with metepa; it does not occur when metepa is administered orally (Dame and Schmidt, 1964). Similarly, when pink boll worms, *Pectinophora gossypiella* (Saunders), were sterilized by tarsal contact with metepa, their longevity was reduced (Ouye et al., 1965a), but sterilization by topical application did not significantly affect longevity or sexual competitiveness (Ouye et al., 1965b).

Type of Germ Cell in Stage Treated. Numerous studies have shown that the immature stages are often more refractive to chemical sterilization than the adult, as in the house fly (LaBrecque et al., 1960, Gouck et al., 1963); the carmine spider mite, *Tetranychus telarius* (L.), (Smith et al., 1965); gypsy moth (Collier and Downey, 1965); the Mexican fruit fly, *Anastrepha ludens* (Loew) (Shaw and Sanchez-Riviello, 1962) the oriental fruit fly; the melon fly, *Dacus curcurbitae* Coquillett; the

Mediterranean fruit fly (Keiser et al., 1965); and *Aedes aegypti* (Weidhaas and Schmidt, 1963, Dame et al., 1964). These findings are not at all surprising because, before pupation, usually only spermatogonia are present in many insects (Table 1) such as the screwworm fly (Riemann, 1967) and the boll weevil (McLaughlin and Lusk, 1967). The larvae of some Lepidoptera, however, contain some more advanced stages of spermatogenesis, often to the exclusion of younger stages (Table 2).

Since the larval forms contain many dividing cells, they are often most sensitive to somatic damage by the chemosterilant, and large doses of chemosterilant usually kill larval forms. Keiser et al. (1965) treated three species of fruit flies with chemosterilants in the larval stage. When concentrations were high enough to affect egg laying and hatch even slightly, mortality was high; at lower concentrations at which mortality was not affected, subsequent egg deposition and hatch were normal. If a sterilizing dose of the chemical reaches the gonads without killing the larva, then the gonial cells would probably be killed and the sterility would be characterized as aspermia. If the gonial cells are not killed outright, then in order for the males to be sterile they would have to produce sperm with dominant lethal mutations. It is unlikely that many gonial cells bearing dominant lethal mutations can successfully undergo meiotic divisions and spermiogenesis to produce motile sperm. More likely the cells would probably die before reaching the sperm stage (Riemann, 1967). The result would be a sterile male but an aspermic one.

Immature forms are refractive to chemical sterilization because doses that are nontoxic probably do not cause sufficient damage in the gonial cells to produce aspermic males. Those cells surviving treatment continue to divide and to repopulate the germarium region of the testes with a store of relatively undamaged cells which can then proceed through meiosis and maturation to yield mature sperm without dominant lethal mutations. Thus the surviving male is fertile. But exceptions to these general statements exist. When diapause larvae of the European corn borer were irradiated, maturation of the treated gonial cells continued; adults with mature, but probably immotile, sperm were obtained (Earl Raun, personal communication). Furthermore, when Rai (1964b) reared *Aedes aegypti* males in water containing apholate from the second larval instar until pupation, the adult males were able to transmit motile sperm to females; but fewer sperm were produced by treated males than by control males. Possibly spreading the treatment over both the larval and pupal stages was largely responsible for the ability of treated males to produce sperm.

The susceptibility to sterilization may vary considerably in the pupal and adult stages. For example, house fly pupae dipped in ethanolic chemosterilant solutions are more readily sterilized by apholate or metepa when they are 2 days old and by tepa when they are 1 day old (Gouck, 1964). Similarly, apholate is more effective in early screwworm prepupae than in late prepupae (Chamberlain, 1962), but male *Culex pipiens* may be sterilized by metepa with increasing ease as they age (R. W. Fay, personal communication).

Presence of Dividing Somatic Cells in Treated Stage. Since a major cause of death in cells treated with alkylating agents is chromosome breakage (Auerbach, 1958), it is not surprising that chemosterilants are toxic to insects with rapidly dividing tissues. The chromosomal changes induced by apholate in dividing cells of the larval brain of *Aedes aegypti* have been described (Rai, 1964a). Of course, some tissues damaged in the immature stages undergo histolysis during morphogenesis, however, adults that emerge are sometimes deformed (LaBrecque et al., 1960, Burden and Smittle, 1963), discolored (Smith et al., 1965), or lack sexual competitiveness (Dame et al., 1964).

In normal adult insects, rapid cell division is not known to occur except in the gonads and in the midgut of some species. Damage to this organ of the boll weevil by ionizing irradiation (Riemann and Flint, 1967) and by apholate (J. G. Riemann, personal communication) has precluded sterilization without shortening lifespan and competitiveness. Also, the refractiveness of the boll weevil to sterilization by numerous alkylating agents strongly suggests that the chemosterilization of species with dividing adult tissues is one of our most formidable problems. The cause of death, however, has still not been established in other species that are refractive to chemosterilization, such as the plum curculio, *Conotrachelus nenuphar* (Herbst) (Roach and Buxton, 1965); the tsetse fly (Chadwick, 1964), the Mexican bean beetle, *Epilachna varivestis* Mulsant (Henneberry et al., 1964); the screwworm fly (Crystal, 1963); or even the house fly, whose longevity is reduced by nearly 50 percent after sterilization with apholate or metepa (Murvosh et al., 1964).

Nutrition. In applying sterilizing doses of apholate to the fourth larval instar of *Culex pipiens*, Murray and Bickley (1964) found that withholding food increased the toxicity of apholate and that fecundity and fertility were reduced. Sterility was obtained without toxicity or infecundity by withholding food during the first day of treatment and by providing food during the four subsequent days. Also, female *Culex pipiens* are more readily sterilized by metepa before they obtain a blood meal than thereafter (R. W. Fay, personal communication). Similarly, Crystal (1966b) found that starvation increased the ease with which the screwworm fly may be sterilized.

* * * * * * *

Although the in vivo reactions of chemosterilants which lead to sterility have not been satisfactorily established, we know that cytogenetic damage is the basis of the several forms of sterility that occur in insects. Presumably the genetic damage is not limited to insects. This is not cause for pessimism concerning the future of chemosterilants in insect control though chemicals that damage the genetic material must be used with care. Eventually sterility may be produced by less hazardous chemicals, and possibly some that are free of cytogenetic effects will produce aspermia or act as insect-sperm inactivators. Both types of sterility are potentially useful for some species. Also, chemicals may be devised that are tailored to produce a given physiological response, such as deterring that insect from mating or reproductive activities.

Much will be gained from studies of the chemistry and physiology of insect reproduction. For example, recent studies on house flies (Riemann et al., 1967) and mosquitoes (Craig, 1966) indicate that the monogamous reaction is chemically controlled. If future research is successful in producing chemicals that prevent mating or alter the reproduction of insects in any number of ways, then potent chemosterilants will have been added to the entomologists' arsenal.

REFERENCES

Alexander, M. L., and E. Glanges. 1965. Genetic damage induced by ethyleneimine. Proc. Nat. Acad. Sci. U.S.A., 53:282–288.

Altenberg, L. 1954. The production of mutations in *Drosophila* by tertiary-butyl hydroperoxide. Proc. Nat. Acad. Sci. U.S.A., 40: 1037–1040.

Ascher, K. R. S. 1957. Prevention of oviposition in the house fly through tarsal contact agents. Science, 125:938.

―――. 1964. A review of chemosterilants and oviposition-inhibitors in insects. World Rev. Pest Control, 3:7–26.

―――. 1965. Oviposition inhibiting agents: A screening for simple model substances. International Pest Control, 1:8–11.

―――, and I. Hirsch. 1961. Inhibition of oviposition in the house fly by ingestion of acaricides (ovicides). Riv. Malar., 40:139–145.

Atwood, K. C., R. C. von Borstel, and A. R. Whiting. 1956. An influence of ploidy on the time of expression of dominant lethal mutations in *Habrobracon*. Genetics, 41:804–813.

Auerbach, C. 1951. Problems in chemical mutagenesis. Cold Spring Harbor Symp. Quant. Biol., 16:199–213.

―――. 1958. Radiomimetic substances. Radiat. Res., 9:33–47.

―――. 1961. Chemicals and their effects. Mutation and Plant Breeding. Nat. Acad. Sci., Nat. Res. Council, 891:120–144.

―――, and H. Moser. 1953. Analysis of the mutagenic action of formaldehyde food. II. The mutagenic potentialities of the treatment. Zeit. Indukt. Abstamm. Vereb. Lehre, 85:547–563.

―――, and J. M. Robson. 1942. Experiments on the action of mustard gas in *Drosophila*. Production of sterility and of mutation. Report to Ministry of Supply, W3979. (Great Britain).

―――. 1944. Production of mutations by allyl isothiocyanate. Nature (London), 154:81.

―――. 1946. Chemical production of mutations. Nature (London), 147: 302.

Baker, R. H., W. L. French, and J. B. Kitzmiller. 1962. Induced copulation in *Anopheles* mosquitoes. Mosq. News, 22:16–17.

Barton, A. A., and M. Barton. 1965. Electron microscope studies on the effect of thiotepa on the cytoplasm of fibrosarcoma cells grown in tissue culture. Brit. J. Cancer, 19:527–530.

Bateman, A. J., and A. C. Chandley. 1964. Sensitivity of the male germ cells of *Drosophila* to methyl methanesulphonate. Heredity (London), 19:711–718.

Battacharya, S. 1949. Tests for a possible action of ethylene glycol on the chromosomes of *Drosophila melanogaster*. Proc. Roy. Soc. (Edinburgh) 63B, 17:242–248.

Bauer, H. 1938. Die polyploide Natur der Riesenchromosomen. Naturwissenschaften, 26:77.

Baumhover, A. H. 1965. Sexual aggressiveness of male screw-worm flies measured by effect on female mortality. J. Econ. Entom., 58:544–548.

Beard, R. L. 1965. Ovarian suppression by DDT and resistance in the house fly (*Musca domestica* L.). Entom. Exp. et Appl., 8:193–204.

Berg, C. C., R. A. Nilan, and C. F. Konzak. 1965. The effect of pressure and seed water content on the mutagenic action of barley seeds. Mutat. Res., 2:263–273.

Bertram, D. S. 1964. Entomological and parasitological aspects of vector chemosterilization. Trans. Roy. Soc. Trop. Med. Hyg., 58:296–317.

Bier, K. 1963. Synthese, Interzellularer Transport, und Abbau von Ribonukleinsüre in Ovar der Stubenfliege. *Musca domestica*. J. Cell Biol., 16:436–440.

Bing, T. 1966. A preliminary observation on the mechanism of sterilization of the house flies (*Musca vicinia* Macquart) treated with thiotepa. In Chinese, English summary. Acta. Ent. Sin., 14:250–256.

Bird, M. J. 1950. Production of mutations in *Drosophila* using four aryl-2-halogenoalkylamines. Nature (London), 165:491–494.

Brewen, J. G. 1965. The induction of chromatid lesions by cytosine arabinoside in post-DNA-synthetic human leukocytes. Cytogenetics, 4:28–36.

Brink, N. G. 1966. The mutagenic activity of heliotrine in *Drosophila*. Mutat. Res., 3:966–972.

Burden, G. S., and B. J. Smittle. 1963. Chemosterilant studies with the German cockroach. Florida Entom., 46:230–234.

Bushland, R. C., and D. E. Hopkins. 1951. Experiments with screwworm flies sterilized by X-rays. J. Econ. Entom., 44:725–731.

_____. 1953. Sterilization of screw-worm flies with X-rays and gamma rays. J. Econ. Entom., 46:648–656.

Cantwell, G. E., and T. J. Henneberry. 1963. The effects of gamma radiation and apholate on the reproductive tissues of *Drosophila melanogaster* Meigen. J. Insect Pathol., 5:251–264.

Chadwick, P. R. 1964. Effect of two chemosterilants on *Glossina morsitans*. Nature (London), 204:299–300.

Chamberlain, W. F. 1962. Chemical sterilization of the screw-worm. J. Econ. Entom., 55:240–249.

Chandley, A. C., and A. J. Bateman. 1962. Timing of spermatogenesis in *Drosophila melanogaster* using tritiated thymidine. Nature (London), 193:299–300.

Chang, S. C. 1965. Chemosterilization and mating behavior of male house flies. J. Econ. Entom., 58:669–671.

_____, and A. B. Borkovec. 1965. Structure-activity relationships in tepa and hempa analogs. Amer. Chem. Soc. Meeting; 26. (Abstr.)

_____, P. H. Terry, and A. B. Borkovec. 1964. Insect chemosterilants with low toxicity to mammals. Science, 144:57–58.

Chang, T. H., and F. T. Elequin. 1967. Induction of chromosome aberrations in cultured human cells by ethyleneimine and its relation to cell cycle. Mutat. Res. 4:83–89.

Chaudhury, M. F. B., and E. S. Raun. 1966. Spermatogenesis and testicular development of the European corn borer, *Ostrinia nubilalis* (Lepidoptera: Pyraustidae). Ann. Entom. Soc. Amer., 59:1157–1159.

Clark, A. M. 1959. Mutagenic activity of tne alkaloid heliotrine in *Drosophila*. Nature (London), 183:731–732.

_____. 1960. Sterilization of *Drosophila* by some pyrrolizadine alkaloids. Z. Indukt. Abstamm. Vereb. Lehre, 91:74–80.

Clark, K. U., and P. A. Langley. 1963. Effect of the removal of the frontal ganglion on the development of the gonads, *Locusta migratoria* L. Nature (London), 198:811–812.

Cohn, N. S. 1961. Production of chromatid aberrations by diepoxybutane and an iron chelator. Nature (London), 192:1093–1094.

Collier, C. W., and J. E. Downey. 1965. Laboratory evaluation of certain chemosterilants against the gypsy moth. J. Econ. Entom., 58:649–650.

Conger, A. 1952. Breakage of chromosomes by oxygen. Proc. Nat. Acad. Sci. U.S.A., 38:289–299.

Craig, G. B., Jr. 1966. Sterilization of female mosquitoes with male accessory gland substance. Bull. Entom. Soc. Amer. 12:225. (Abstr.)

Crystal, M. M. 1963. The induction of sexual sterility in the screwworm fly by antimetabolites and alkylating agents. J. Econ. Entom., 56:468–473.

_____. 1964a. Insect fertility: inhibition by folic acid derivatives. Science, 144:308–309.

_____. 1964b. Sexual sterilization of screw-worm flies by the biological alkylating agents, tretamine and thiotepa. Exp. Parasit., 15:249–259.

_____. 1964c. Antifertility effects of anthelminthics in insects. J. Econ. Entom., 57:606–607.

_____. 1964d. Chemosterilant efficiency of bis(1-aziridinyl)phosphinyl carbamates in screw-worm flies. J. Econ. Entom., 57:726–731.

_____. 1966a. Some structure-activity relationships among aziridinyl antifertility agents in screw-worm flies. J. Econ. Entom., 59:577–580.

_____. 1966b. Sexual sterilization of screw-worm flies by a peroral chemosterilant: quantitative aspects and relation to pretreatment starvation. J. Econ. Entom., 59:580–585.

_____, and L. E. LaChance. 1963. The modification of reproduction in insects treated with alkylating agents. I. Inhibition of ovarian growth and egg production and hatchability. Biol. Bull., 125:270–279.

Dame, D. A., and C. H. Schmidt. 1964. Uptake of metepa and its effect on two species of mosquitoes (*Anopheles quadrimaculatus* and *Aedes aegypti*), and house flies (*Musca domestica*). J. Econ. Entom., 57:77–81.

_____, D. B. Woodward, D. B. Ford, R. Hugh, and D. E. Weidhaas. 1964.

Field behavior of sexually sterile *Anopheles quadrimaculatus* males. Mosq. News, 24:6–14.

Davich, T. B., J. C. Keller, E. B. Mitchell, P. Huddleston, R. Hill, D. A. Lindquist, G. McKibben, and W. H. Cross. 1965. Preliminary field experiments with sterile males for eradication of the boll weevil. J. Econ. Entom., 58:127–131.

Demerec, M., and B. P. Kaufmann. 1961. Time required for *Drosophila* males to exhaust the supply of mature sperm. Amer. Natur., 75:366–379.

———, B. Wallace, E. M. Witkin, and G. Bertani. 1949. The gene. *In* Carnegie Institution Yearbook, 48:154–166.

Depdolla, P. 1928. Die Keimzellenbildung und die Befruchtung bie den Insekten. *In* Schroder, C., ed., Handbuch der Entomologie, 1:825–1116. Jena, Fischer.

Duefel, J. 1951. Untersuchungen uber den Einfluss von Chemikalien und Rontgenstrahlen auf die Mitose von *Vicia faba*. Chromosoma, 4:239–272.

Ehrenberg, L., and A. Gustafson. 1957. On the mutagenic action of ethylene oxide and diepoxybutane in barley. Hereditas, 43:594–602.

———, U. Lindquist, and G. Strom. 1958. The mutagenic action of ethyleneimine in barley. Hereditas (Lund), 44:330–336.

Evans, H. J., and D. Scott. 1964. Influence of DNA synthesis on the production of chromatid aberrations by X-rays and maleic hydrazide in *Vicia fabs*. Genetics, 49:17–38.

Fahmy, O. G., and M. J. Fahmy. 1954. Cytogenetic analysis of the action of carcinogens and tumour inhibiting in *Drosophila melanogaster*. II. The mechanism of induction of dominant lethals by 2,4,6-tri(ethyleneimine)-1,3,5-triazine. J. Genetics, 52:603–619.

———, and M. J. Fahmy. 1958. Discussion of paper, "Mutagenic effects of alkylating agents." (by C. Auerbach). Ann. N.Y. Acad. Sci., 68:736–748.

———. 1964. The chemistry and genetics of the alkylating chemosterilants. Trans. Roy. Soc. Trop. Med. Hyg., 58:318–326.

Favard-Sereno, C., and M. Durand. 1963. L'utilisation de nucleosides dans l'ovaire du Grillon et ses variations au cours de l'ovogenese. I. Incorporation dans l'RNA. Develop. Biol., 6:184–205.

Goldsmith, E. D., and I. Frank. 1952. Sterility in the female fruit fly, *Drosophila melanogaster*, produced by the feeding of a folic acid antagonist. Amer. J. Physiol., 171:726–727.

Gouck, H. K. 1964. Chemosterilization of house flies by treatment in the pupal stage. J. Econ. Entom., 57:239–241.

———, and G. C. LaBrecque. 1964. Chemicals affecting fertility in adult house flies. J. Econ. Entom., 57:663–664.

———, M. M. Crystal, A. B. Borkovec, and D. W. Meifert. 1963. A comparison of techniques for screening chemosterilants of house flies and screw-worm flies. J. Econ. Entom., 56:506–509.

Grampa, G., and P. Dustin, Jr. 1953. Associated use of aminopterin and colchicine and nuclear abnormalities. Research on the mouse intestine. Tumori, 39:63–71.

Grosch, D. S. 1956. Induced lethargy and the radiation control of insects. J. Econ. Entom., 49:629–631.

_____. 1959. The effect of feeding antimitotic substances to adult female Habrobracon [Microbracon hebetor (Say) (Hymenoptera: Braconidae)]. Ann. Entom. Soc., Amer., 52:294–298.

_____. 1963. Insect fecundity and fertility: chemically induced decrease. Science, 141:732–733.

_____, and L. R. Valcovic. 1964. Genetic analysis of the effects of apholate. Bull. Entom. Soc. Amer., 10:163. (Abstr.)

_____, R. L. Sullivan, and L. E. LaChance. 1956. The comparative effectiveness of four beta-emitting isotopes fed to Habrobracon females on production and hatchability of eggs. Radiat. Res., 5:281–289.

Hadorn, E. 1961. Developmental Genetics and Lethal Factors. New York, John Wiley & Sons.

Harries, F. H. 1963. Effects of some antibiotics and other compounds on fertility and mortality of orchard mites. J. Econ. Entom., 56:438–441.

Harris, R. L. 1962. Chemical induction of sterility in the stable fly. J. Econ. Entom., 55:882–885.

Hase, A. 1923. Beiträge zur Kenntnis des Geschlechtslebens männlicher Schlupfwespe. Arb. Biol. Reichsanst Land. u. Forstw. 12:339–346.

Hays, S. B., and J. H. Cochran. 1964. Evaluation of compounds affecting the reproductive potential of the plum curculio. J. Econ. Entom., 57:217–219.

Henneberry, T. J., F. F. Smith, and W. L. McGovern. 1964. Some effects of gamma radiation and a chemosterilant on the Mexican bean beetle. J. Econ. Entom., 57:813–815.

Herriot, R. M. 1948. Inactivation of viruses and cells by mustard gas. J. Gen. Physiol., 32:221–230.

Herskowitz, I. H. 1951. A list of chemical substances studied for effects on Drosophila. Amer. Natur., 85:181–199.

Hertwig, O. 1911. Die Radiumkrankheit tierischer Keimzellen. Ein Beitrag zur experimentellen Zeugungs- and Vererbungslehre. Arch. F. Mikr. Anat., 77:1–164.

Hildreth, P. E., and J. C. Lucchesi. 1963. Fertilization in Drosophila. I. Evidence for the regular occurrence of monospermy. Develop. Biol., 6:262–278.

Husseiny, M. M., and H. F. Madsen. 1964. Sterilization of the navel orangeworm, Paramyelois transitella (Walker) by gamma radiation (Lepidoptera: Phycitidae). Hilgardia, 36:113–137.

Jacob, J. 1958. A study of colchicine induced sterility in the female fruit fly, Drosophila melanogaster. Growth, 22:17–29.

Jensen, K. A., I. Kirk, G. Kolmark, and M. Westergaard. 1951. Chemically induced mutations in Neurospora. Cold Spring Harbor Sympos. Quant. Biol., 16:245–261.

Jones, J. C. 1961. Observations on sexually depleted male *Aedes aegypti* (L.). Amer. Zool., 1:362. (Abstr.)

Keiser, I., L. F. Steiner, and H. Kamasaki. 1965. Effect of chemosterilants against the oriental fruit fly, melon fly, and Mediterranean fruit fly. J. Econ. Entom., 58:682–685.

Kihlman, B. A. 1952. A survey of purine derivatives as inducers of chromosome changes. Hereditas, 38:115–127.

_____. 1955. Oxygen and the production of chromosome aberrations by chemicals and X-rays. Hereditas, 41:384–404.

_____. 1956. Factors affecting the production of chromosome aberrations by chemicals. J. Biophys. Biochem. Cytol., 2:543–555.

_____. 1957. Experimentally induced chromosome aberrations in plants. I. The production of chromosome aberrations by cyanide and other heavy metal complexing agents. J. Biophys. Biochem. Cytol., 3:363–380.

_____. 1959. Studies on the production of chromosomal aberrations by visible light: the effects of cupferron, nitric oxide, and wavelength. Exp. Cell Res., 17:590–593.

_____. 1960. The radiomimetic effect of N-nitroso-N-methylurethane in *Vicia faba*. Exp. Cell Res., 20:657–659.

_____. 1961. Cytological effects of phenylnitrosamines. II. Radiomimetic effects. Radiat. Bot., 1:43–50.

_____. 1964. The production of chromosomal aberrations by streptonigrin in *Vicia faba*. Mutat. Res., 1:54–62.

_____, and G. Odmark. 1965. DNA synthesis and the production of chromosomal aberrations by streptonigrin, 8-ethyoxycaffeine and 1,3,7,9-tetramethyl uric acid. Mutat. Res., 2:494–505.

King, R. C. 1958. Effect of 5-amino uracil upon oogenesis. *Drosophila* Information Service, 32:131.

_____. 1964. Studies on early stages of insect oogenesis. In Highnam, K. C., ed., Insect Reproduction, 13–25, London, Roy. Entom. Soc.

_____, and J. H. Sang. 1959. Oogenesis in adult *Drosophila melanogaster*. VIII. The role of folic acid in oogenesis. Growth, 23:37–53.

Knipling, E. F. 1955. Possibilities of insect control or eradication through the use of sexually sterile males. J. Econ. Entom., 48:459–462.

_____. 1959. Sterile male method of population control. Science, 130:902–904.

Knutson, H. 1959. Changes in reproductive potential in house flies in response to dieldrin. Entom. Soc. Amer. Misc. Publ., 1:27–32.

Koller, P. C. 1958. Comparative effects of alkylating agents on cellular morphology. Ann. N.Y. Acad. Sci., 63:783–801.

Kreizinger, J. C. 1960. Diepoxybutane as a chemical mutagen in *Zea mays*. Genetics, 45:143–154.

Kumar, S., and A. T. Natarajan. 1965. Photocynamic action and post-irradiation modifying effects of methylene blue and acridine orange in barley and *Vicia faba*. Muta. Res., 2:11–21.

LaBrecque, G. C. 1961. Studies with three alkylating agents as house fly sterilants. J. Econ. Entom., 54:684–689.

_____, P. H. Adcock, and C. N. Smith. 1960. Tests with compounds affecting house fly metabolism. J. Econ. Entom., 53:802–805.

LaChance, L. E. 1966. The induction of dominant lethal mutations and sperm inactivation by chemical mutagens in *Habrobracon*. Genetics, 54:345. (Abstr.)

LaChance, L. E. 1967. The induction of dominant lethal mutations in insects by ionizing radiation and chemicals—as related to the sterile-male technique of insect control. *In* Wright, J. and R. Pal eds., Genetics of Insect Vectors of Disease, Chap. 21, Amsterdam, Elsevier Press. In press.

_____, and S. B. Bruns. 1963. Oogenesis and radiosensitivity in *Cochliomyia hominivorax* (Diptera: Calliphoridae). Biol. Bull., 124:65–83.

_____, and M. M. Crystal. 1963. The modification of reproduction in insects treated with alkylating agents. II. Differential sensitivity of oocyte meiotic stages to the induction of dominant lethals. Biol. Bull., 125:280–288.

_____, and M. M. Crystal. 1965. Induction of dominant lethal mutations in insect oocytes and sperm by gamma rays and an alkylating agent. Genetics, 51:699–708.

_____, and A. P. Leverich. 1965. Cytogenetic studies on the effect of an alkylating agent on insect nurse cell polytene chromosomes as related to ovarian growth and fecundity. Genetics, 52:453–454. (Abstr.)

_____, and J. G. Riemann. 1964. Cytogenetic investigations on radiation and chemically induced dominant lethal mutations in oocytes and sperm of the screw-worm fly. Mutat. Res., 1:318–333.

Landa, V., and B. Rézábóva. 1965. The effect of chemosterilants on the development of reproductive organs in insects. Proc. XII Int. Congr. Entom., (London), 516–517.

LeFevre, G., Jr., and U. B. Jonsson. 1962. Sperm transfer, storage, displacement, and utilization in *Drosophila melanogaster*. Genetics, 47:1719–1736.

Levinson, Z. H., and E. D. Bergman. 1959. Vitamin deficiencies in the house fly produced by antivitamins. J. Insect Physiol., 3:293–305.

Lilly, L. J., and J. M. Thoday. 1956. Effects of cyanide on the roots of *Vicia faba*. Nature (London), 177:338–339.

Lindquist, D. A., and V. S. House. 1967. Mating studies with apholate sterilized boll weevils. J. Econ. Entom., 60:468–473.

_____, L. J. Gorzycki, M. S. Mayer, A. L. Scales, and T. B. Davich. 1964. Laboratory studies on sterilization of the boll weevil with apholate. J. Econ. Entom., 57:745–750.

Loveless, A. 1951. Qualitative aspects of the chemistry and biology of radiomimetic (mutagenic) substances. Nature (London), 167:338–342.

McLaughlin, R. E., and J. W. Lusk. 1967. Morphogenesis of testes and ovaries of the boll weevil, *Anthonomus grandis* Boheman (Coleoptera: Curculionidae). Ann. Entom. Soc. Amer., 60:120–126.

Manna, G. K., and B. B. Parida. 1965. Aluminum chloride induced meiotic chromosome aberrations in the grasshopper. *Phloeoha antennata.* Naturwissenschaften, 52:647–648.

Martin, A. O. 1965. Studies on the rate of spermatogenesis in *Drosophila.* Effects on x-rays and streptonigrin. Z. Indukt. Abstamm.-u-Vereb. Lehre, 96:28–35.

Mayer, M. S., and J. R. Brazzel. 1963. The mating behavior of the boll weevil, *Anthonomus grandis.* J. Econ. Entom., 56:605–609.

Melvin, R., and R. C. Bushland. 1940. The nutritional requirements of screw-worm larvae. J. Econ. Entom., 33:850–852.

Merz, T. 1961. Effect of mitomycin C on lateral root-tip chromosomes of *Vicia faba.* Science, 133:329.

_____, C. P. Swanson, and N. S. Cohn. 1961. Interaction of chromatid breaks produced by x-rays and radiomimetic compounds. Science, 133:703–704.

Michaelis, A., and R. Rieger. 1963. Interaction of chromatid breaks induced by three different radiomimetic compounds. Nature (London), 199:1014–1015.

Mitlin, N., and A. M. Baroody. 1958. The effect of some biologically active compounds on growth of house fly ovaries. J. Econ. Entom., 51:384–385.

_____, B. A. Butt, and T. J. Shortino. 1957. Effect of mitotic poisons on house fly oviposition. Physiol. Zool., 30:133–136.

Monroe, R. E., W. E. Robbins, D. L. Chambers, and L. A. Tabor. 1963. Sterol antagonists and house fly reproduction. Ann. Entom. Soc. Amer., 56:124–125.

Morgan, P. B. 1967. Effect of hempa on the ovarian development of house flies (*Musca domestica* L.). Ann. Entom. Soc. Amer., In press.

_____, and G. C. LaBrecque. 1962. The effect of apholate on the ovarian development of house flies. J. Econ. Entom., 55:626–628.

_____. 1964. Effect of tepa and metepa on ovarian development of house flies. J. Econ. Entom., 57:896–899.

Muller, H. J. 1927. Artificial transmutation of the gene. Science, 66:84–87.

_____. 1940. An analysis of the process of structural change in chromosomes of *Drosophila.* J. Genetics, 40:1–66.

Murray, W. S., and W. E. Bickley, 1964. Effect of apholate on the southern house mosquito, *Culex pipiens quinquefasciatus.* Univ. of Maryland Agr. Exp. Sta. Bull., A-134:1–37.

Murvosh, C. M., G. C. LaBrecque, and C. N. Smith. 1964. Effect of three chemosterilants on house fly longevity and sterility. J. Econ. Entom., 57:89–92.

Nasrat, G. E., W. D. Kaplan, and C. Auerbach. 1954. A quantitative study of mustard gas induced chromosome breaks and rearrangements in *Drosophila melanogaster.* Z. Indukt. Abstamm. Vereb. Lehre, 86:249–262.

Nayar, J. K. 1963. Effect of synthetic "queen substance" (9-oxodec-trans-2-enoic acid) on ovary development of the house fly, *Musca domestica* L. Nature (London), 197:923–924.

Nilan, R. A., and C. F. Konzak. 1961. Increasing the efficiency of mutation induction. In Mutation and plant breeding. Nat. Acad. Res. Council, 891:437–458.

Novick, A. 1955. Mutagens and anti-mutagens. Brookhaven Sympos. Biol., 8:201–214.

Oakberg, E. F. 1965. The effect of dose, dose rate, and quality of radiation on the dynamics and survival of the spermatogonial population of the mouse. Jap. J. Hum. Genet., 40(Suppl.):119–127.

_____, and E. Clark. 1961. Survival of spermatogonia of the mouse at different X- and gamma-ray dose rates. Genetics, 46:888. (Abstr.)

Odmark, G., and B. A. Kihlman. 1965. Effects of chromosome-breaking purine derivatives on nucleic acid synthesis and on levels of adenosine-5-triphosphate and deoxyadenosine 5-triphosphate in bean root types. Mutat. Res., 2:274–286.

Oehlkers, F. 1943. Die Auslosung von Chromosomenmutationen in der Meiosis durch unwirklung von Chemikalein. Z. Indukt. Abstamm. -u-Vereb. Lehre, 81:313–341.

_____. 1953. Chromosome breaks influenced by chemicals. Heredity (London), 6(Suppl.):95–106.

Oster, I. I. 1958. Interactions between ionizing radiation and chemical mutagens. Z. Indukt. Abstamm. -u-Vereb. Lehre, 89:1–6.

_____. 1959. The genetic basis of x-ray induced somatic damage. *In* Martin, J. H., ed., Radiation Biology, 268–271, London, Butterworth.

_____. 1961. Genetic aspects of mutagen-induced life-shortening. Second International Conference of Human Genetics, Rome, Italy. Excerpta Médica, Int. Congr. Series 32, (Paper #18).

Ouye, M. T., R. S. Garcia, and D. F. Martin. 1965a. Sterilization of pink bollworm adults with metepa. J. Econ. Entom., 58:1018–1020.

_____. 1965b. Comparative mating competitiveness of metepa-sterilized and normal pink bollworm males in laboratory and field cages. J. Econ. Entom., 58:927–929.

Painter, T. S., and J. J. Biesele. 1966. Endomitosis and polyribosome formation. Science, 1954:426. (Abstr.)

Painter, R. R., and W. W. Kilgore. 1963. Temporary and permanent sterilization of house flies with chemosterilants. J. Econ. Entom., 57:154–156.

_____. 1965. Chemosterilant effect of 5-fluoroorotic acid on house flies. J. Econ. Entom., 58:888–891.

Palmquist, J., and L. E. LaChance. 1966. Comparative mutagenicity of two chemosterilants, tepa and hempa, in sperm of *Bracon hebetor*. Science, 154:915–917.

Partington, M., and H. Jackson. 1963. The induction of dominant lethal mutations in rats by alkane sulphonic esters. Genet. Res., 4:333–345.

Pickett, A. D., and N. A. Patterson. 1963. Arsenates: effect on fecundity in some Diptera. Science, 140:493–494.

Proverbs, M. D., and J. R. Newton. 1962. Some effects of gamma radiation on the reproductive potential of the codling moth, *Carpocapsa pomonella* (L.) (Lepidoptera: Olethreutidae). Canad. Entom., 94:1162–1170.

Rai, K. S. 1964a. Cytogenetic effects of chemosterilants in mosquitoes. I. Apholate-induced aberrations in the somatic chromosomes of Aedes aegypti (L.). Cytologia (Tokyo), 29:346–353.

_____. 1964b. Cytogenetic effects of chemosterilants in mosquitoes. II. Mechanisms of apholate-induced changes in fecundity and fertility of *Aedes aegypti* (L.). Biol. Bull., 127:119–131.

Ramanna, M. S., and A. T. Natarjan. 1966. Chromosome breakage induced by alkyl-alkane sulfonates under different physical conditions. Chromosoma, 18:44–59.

Ratcliff, R. H., and S. S. Ristich. 1965. Insect sterilant experiments in outdoor cages with apholate, metepa, and four bifunctional aziridine chemicals against the house fly. J. Econ. Entom., 58:1079–1082.

Riemann, J. G. 1967. A cytological study of radiation effects in testes of the screwworm fly, *Cochliomyia hominivorax* (Coquerel) (Diptera: Calliphoridae). Ann. Entom. Soc. Amer., 60:308–320.

_____, and H. M. Flint. 1967. Irradiation effects on midguts and testes of the adult boll weevil *Anthonomus grandis*, determined by histological and shielding studies. Ann. Entom. Soc. Amer., 60:298–308.

_____, D. J. Moen, and B. J. Thorson. 1967. Female monogamy and its control in house flies. J. Insect Physiol., 13:407–418.

Roach, S. H., and J. A. Buxton. 1965. Apholate and tepa as chemosterilants of the plum curculio. J. Econ. Entom., 58:802–803.

Robinson, A. G. 1960. Effect of maleic hydrazide and other plant growth regulators on the pea aphid, *Acyrthosiphon pisum* (Harris), caged on broad bean, *Vicia faba* L. Canad. Entom., 92:494–499.

_____. 1961. Effects of amitrole, zytron, and other herbicides or plant growth regulators on the pea aphid, *Acyrthosiphon pisum* (Harris) caged on broad bean, *Vicia faba* L. Canad. J. Plant Sci., 41:413–417.

Rogers, S. 1955. Studies on the mechanism of action of urethane in initiating pulmonary adenomas in mice. I. The indirect nature of its oncogenic influence. J. Nat. Cancer Inst., 15:1675–1683.

_____. 1957. Studies on the mechanism of action of urethane in initiating pulmonary adenomas in mice. II. Its relation to nucleic acid synthesis. J. Exp. Med., 105:279–306.

Roth, L. M. 1948. A study of mosquito behavior. Amer. Midland Nat., 40:265–352.

Sado, T. 1961. Spermatogenesis of the silkworm and its bearing on radiation-induced sterility. Jap. J. Hum. Genet., 36(Suppl.): 136–151.

Sang, J. H., and R. C. King. 1961. The nutritional requirements of axenically cultured Drosophila melanogaster adults. J. Exp. Biol., 38:793–809.

Sax, K., and H. J. Sax. 1966. Radiomimetic beverages, drugs, and mutagens. Proc. Nat. Acad. Sci. U.S.A., 55:1431–1435.

Schmidt, E. L., and C. M. Williams. 1953. Physiology of insect diapause. V. Assay of the growth and differentiation hormone of Lepidoptera by the method of tissue culture. Biol. Bull., 105:174–187.

Schwartz, P. H., Jr. 1961. Behavior of spermatozoa of Aedes aegypti (L.). M.S. Thesis, Univ. of Maryland, 45 pp.

_____. 1965. Effects of apholate, metepa, and tepa on reproductive tissues of Hippelates pusio. J. Invertebr. Path., 7:148–151.

Scott, D., and H. J. Evans. 1964. On the non-requirement for deoxyribonucleic acid synthesis in the production of chromosome aberrations by 8-ethoxycaffeine. Mutat. Res., 1:146–156.

Shaw, J. G., and M. Sanchez-Riviello. 1962. Investigations on the use of chemical products as sexual sterilants for the fruit fly. Ciencia, 22:17–20.

Simkover, H. G. 1964. 2-Imidazolidinone as an insect growth inhibitor and chemosterilant. J. Econ. Entom., 57:574–579.

Simpson, H. R. 1958. The effect of sterilized males on a natural tsetse fly population. Biometrics, 14:159–173.

Smith, F. F., A. L. Boswell, and T. J. Henneberry. 1965. Chemosterilant treatment of two greenhouse spider mites. J. Econ. Entom., 58:98–103.

Snyder, L. A., and I. I. Oster. 1964. A comparison of genetic changes induced by a monofunctional and a polyfunctional alkylating agent in Drosophila melanogaster. Mutat. Res., 1:437–445.

Sobels, F. 1956. Mutagenicity of dihydroxy dimethyl peroxide and the mutagenic effects of formaldehyde. Nature (London), 177:979–980.

Sonnenblick, B. P., and P. S. Henshaw. 1941. Influence on development of certain dominant lethals induced by X-rays in Drosophila germ cells. Proc. Soc. Exp. Biol. Med., 48:74–79.

Swanson, C. P., and T. Merz. 1959. Factors influencing the effect of beta-proprio lactone on chromosomes of Vicia faba. Science, 129:1364.

Taylor, J. H., W. F. Huat, and J. Tung. 1962. Effects of fluorodeoxyuridine on DNA replication, chromosome breakage, and reunion. Proc. Nat. Acad. Sci. U.S.A., 48:190–198.

Telfer, W. H. 1965. The mechanism of yolk formation in insects. Ann. Rev. Entom., 10:161–184.

Tenhet, J. N. 1947. Effect of pyrethrum on oviposition of the cigarette beetle. J. Econ. Entom., 40:910–911.

Terzian, L. A., and N. Stahler. 1958. A study of some effects of gamma radiation on the adults and eggs of *Aedes aegypti*. Biol. Bull., 115:536–550.

Vogt, M. 1948. Mutations auslosung bei *Drosophila* durch Athylurethan. Experientia, 4:68–69.

von Borstel, R. C. 1955. Differential response of meiotic stages in *Habrobracon* eggs to nitrogen mustard. Genetics, 40:107–115.

_____. 1960. Nature of the dominant lethality induced by radiation (in Italian) English summary. Atti. Ass. Genet. Ital., 5:35–50.

_____. 1963. Eytogenetics and developmental genetics course—a postscript. Amer. Zool., 3:87–95.

_____, and M. L. Rekemeyer. 1959. Radiation induced and genetically contrived dominant lethality in *Habrobracon* and *Drosophila*. Genetics, 44:1053–1074.

Wallace, B. 1951. Dominant lethals and sex-linked lethals induced by nitrogen mustard. Genetics, 36:364–373.

Watson, W. A. F. 1962. The production of translocations in spermatogonial cells of *Drosophila* by chloroethyl methanesulphonate. Genet. Res., 3:467–471.

Weidhaas, D. E., and C. H. Schmidt. 1963. Mating ability of male mosquitoes, *Aedes aegypti* (L.), sterilized chemically or by gamma radiation. Mosq. News, 23:32–34.

Whiting, A. R., and R. C. von Borstel. 1954. Dominant lethal and inactivation effects of nitrogen mustard on *Habrobracon* sperm. Genetics, 39:317–325.

_____, S. Caspari, M. Koukides, and P. Kao. 1958. Stages at death of X-ray-induced embryo lethals in haploids and in heterozygotes of *Habrobracon*. Radiat. Res., 8:195–202.

Yanders, A. F. 1959. The effect of x-rays on sperm activity in *Drosophila*. Genetics, 44:545–546. (Abstr.).

_____. 1964. The effects of x-rays on insemination and sperm retention in *Drosophila*. Genetics, 49:309–317.

Young, J. R., and H. C. Cox. 1965. Evaluation of apholate and tepa as chemosterilants for the fall armyworm. J. Econ. Entom., 58:883–888.

5

Chemistry of Insect Chemosterilants

RALPH B. TURNER

PESTICIDE CHEMICALS RESEARCH BRANCH
ENTOMOLOGY RESEARCH DIVISION
U.S. DEPARTMENT OF AGRICULTURE
GAINESVILLE, FLORIDA

INTRODUCTION

The purpose of this chapter is to present a concise summary of the physical and chemical properties of a few compounds representative of several classes of chemicals which are insect chemosterilants and to discuss the biochemical interactions that may be related to antifertility effects. For the latter purpose it was necessary to draw heavily from the literature of cancer chemotherapy, a field in which biochemical effects often parallel those of chemosterilization. These data are presented with the hope that the researcher will be encouraged to investigate these effects with relation to the phenomenon of sterilization, and that further study will ultimately lead to an explanation of the cause of sterility.

Despite the efforts directed toward elucidation of the mode of action of chemosterilants, little progress has been made, and a molecular basis for sterilization has not been established. Investigations of the mechanism of action of biologically active materials is extremely difficult, requiring extensive study and experimentation. Results are slow in forthcoming and generally pose as many questions as they answer. Successful application of the sterile-male concept of insect eradication with chemicals would be greatly facilitated by the elucidation of the mode of action of known chemosterilants. Chemicals can then be designed and synthesized for this specific purpose. A program of random molecular manipulation of chemical groups can not be expected to solve a problem of such complexity.

A useful chemosterilant must show a wide safety margin between sterilizing doses and doses which cause excessive behavioral variance or mortality. In order to evaluate the safety margin, mathematical models have been proposed which include the ratio, LD_{50}/ED_{50} (Chang et al., 1964) and more recently, $LD_{0.01} - ED_{99.99}$ (Chang and Borkovec, 1965), where LD values are the lethal doses for the percentage of insects indicated by the subscript and ED values are sterilizing doses.[1] The first index can be misleading since for some compounds the antifertility effects increase slowly with increasing dosage, e.g., apholate; while for others the effectiveness increases sharply, e.g., tepa (Chang and Borkovec, 1964). The second index will

[1]The abbreviation ED will be used throughout this chapter to denote sterilizing dose, sometimes referred to as SD.

indicate that a safety margin exists but does not tell by how many fold (W. Klassen, personal communication). In addition, the use of such extreme values requires the accumulation of an extensive amount of data to establish reasonable reliability. The value of the use of a ratio in evaluating safety margins is obvious. Such an index can provide additional information, e.g., the degree of selectivity of the compound for gonadal tissues. The ratio LD_{50}/ED_{90}, which has been used for some time in cancer chemotherapy research to evaluate selectivity for neoplastic tissue, is particularly practical and suitable for this type of appraisal. The usefulness of this ratio in biochemical evaluations of chemosterilants will be illustrated later as the individual chemicals are discussed. The use of any mathematical model to establish safety margins, or the degree of selectivity of a compound, must be tempered with a knowledge of the limitations of that model.

ALKYLATING AGENTS

Alkylation may be defined as the replacement of a hydrogen atom of a molecule by an alkyl group. The chemicals which are capable of performing this reaction are of extremely varied composition and structure. Indeed, the ability to combine with electron-rich centers represents the only chemical property which all members of this structurally heterogenous group of chemicals possess in common.

Alkylating agents are electrophiles (electron loving), i.e., reagents which function by accepting an electron pair from carbon in an organic reaction. The nucleophiles, with which they react, are polar compounds that donate an electron pair to the carbon in an organic molecule. Alkylation is, then, a substitution of an alkyl group for a hydrogen atom on a nucleophile and the process is called *nucleophilic substitution*.

The transfer of the electrophile (R^+), called a carbonium ion, is generally recognized as occurring by either of two mechanisms presented here in their simplest forms. The type of mechanism by which a chemical undergoes reaction is very important in a biological system where a limited amount of agent passes through regions in which the concentration of reacting groups varies. In the first mechanism, ($S_N 1$) (substitution, nucleophilic, unimolecular), the rate of the reaction depends upon the concentration of one species, R^+, and is independent of the concentration of the nucleophile, X^-, for example:

$$RY \xrightarrow{\text{slow}} R^+ + Y^-$$

$$R^+ + X^- \xrightarrow{\text{rapid}} RX$$

$$\text{Rate} = k_1 \, [RY]$$

The driving force which causes the separation of charges R^+ and Y^- is created by the attack of polar solvent molecules on the intact alkylating agent. The energy requirement for the initial splitting is high, and is partly compensated for by the energy of solvation of the newly formed ions. Once it is formed, the carbonium ion reacts rapidly with any nucleophile present. Factors which influence the rate of S_N1 type alkylation include the ease of carbonium-ion formation, reactivity of the leaving group, and ionizing power of the solvent.

By the other mechanism, S_N2 (substitution, nucleophilic, bimolecular), the ionization of the alkylating agent occurs at the same time as the formation of the bond with the nucleophile, i.e., by a one-step process:

$$RY + HX \longrightarrow Y^{\delta-}\text{---}R^{\delta+}\text{---}X^{\delta-}\text{---}H^{\delta+}$$

In this case, the rate depends upon the concentration of both the alkylating agent and the target molecule, i.e., rate = $k_2\,[RY][HX]$. Attachment of bulky alkyl groups will obviously be difficult because of *steric hindrance*, the fundamental factor in determining the reaction rate in the one-step displacement.

The biological alkylating agents selected for discussion in this chapter include aziridines, methane sulfonates, and mustards. Antifertility effects caused by these agents are believed to be the result of alkylation of some target nucleophile(s), thereby preventing its utilization in the process of insect reproduction. The specific molecule(s) involved is not known.

Although it is generally assumed that the target molecule is the same for the several different classes of alkylating agents, a recent report has cast some doubt upon this assumption (Ruddon, 1964). Nitrogen mustard was the only one of several alkylating agents which, at physiologically effective levels, altered DNA in vitro. It thus appears that each particular class of alkylating agents may exert the same biological effect through different molecular events.

The few reports of in vivo alkylation of cellular constituents indicate that DNA, RNA, and protein are alkylated to about the same extent on a weight basis (Brookes and Lawley, 1961). Since the molecular weight of DNA is so much greater than that of protein, the extent of alkylation per molecule is greater in the nucleic acid. It has been suggested that since the degree of alkylation of protein in vivo is low, little biological damage may occur unless considerable selectivity of protein sites is exerted by the alkylating agent (Brookes and Lawley, 1964). Although the site of alkylation of protein in vivo is not known, reports on myleran metabolism (Roberts and Warwick, 1961a, b) and on sulfur-mustard metabolism (Davison et al., 1961) have indicated that the thiol group of glutathione is readily alkylated. These reports indicate that some degree of selectivity may be expected in the alkylation of proteins.

It seems worthy of note that the concept of nonclassical antimetabolites (Dr. Bernard R. Baker) is based upon selective and irreversible alkylation of an enzyme at a point adjacent to or at the active site. Since sterilization by alkylating agents is generally irreversible, his studies on active-site-directed inhibitors are worthy of study by those engaged in chemosterilant research.

Methods of Determination.

Several colorimetric methods based upon the method of Epstein et al. (1955) have been developed (cf. Klatt et al., 1960, Friedman and Boyer, 1961, Ausman et al., 1961, Truhaut et al., 1963, and Tan and Cole, 1965). These methods are based upon the reaction of the alkylating agent with 4-(p-nitrobenzylpyridine) under acidic conditions and subsequent formation of the colored product upon addition of alkali. The method which has been routinely used in the author's laboratory is described below.

Preparation of a standard curve:

1. Make up a series of aqueous solutions of the compound

to be tested. (A good range of concentration is 0.01–0.10 mg/ml).

2. To a 3-ml sample of any given solution in the above concentration range, add 1 ml of 0.1 N potassium acid phthalate and 1 ml of a 5 percent solution of 4-(p-nitrobenzyl) pyridine in reagent-grade acetone.

3. Add a boiling chip, shake, and heat in boiling water for 20 min.

4. Cool in an ice bath, and adjust volume to 5 ml with water.

5. To the cooled mixture add sufficient reagent-grade acetone to make a volume of 9.0 ml and shake.

6. Add 1 ml of 1 M K_2CO_3 solution, mix well by shaking, and read absorption *immediately* at 600 mμ. The color developed is extremely unstable and rapid fading imposes a severe limitation on this method. To determine concentration of any unknown solution, follow steps 1 to 6 and compare to standard curve. Using a Beckman DU or Model B spectrophotometer, results are normally reproducible within two percent.

Thiosulfate titration. The thiosulfate titration (Allen and Seaman, 1955) has also been extensively used to determine alkylating agents.

Recommended procedure:
Add 5 ml of sample (ca. 0.3 $m$equivalents aziridine) to 5 ml of a 20 percent aqueous $Na_2S_2O_3$ solution while a stream of nitrogen blankets the solution. The mixture stirred constantly and titrated with 0.1 N H_2SO_4 until pH 4.0 is reached and holds unchanged for 15 sec. This can be determined with pH meter or methyl orange indicator. The solution should be allowed to stand 30 min without any treatment. Stirring and addition of nitrogen is then resumed and the titration is completed by adding 0.05 ml increments of 0.05 N NaOH until pH 11 is reached. The pH is recorded after each addition and the volume of NaOH needed to neutralize the excess acid is determined by plotting the pH change per increment of NaOH titrant vs. volume of NaOH. Then: % aziridine function = $100 \times \dfrac{(\text{ml } H_2SO_4)(0.1) - (\text{ml NaOH})(0.05)}{m \text{ equivalents of sample}}$
(This titration procedure does not always give values that agree with theoretical results.)

4-Picoline methal. Another colorimetric method for determination of alkylating agents was recently reported (Bender et al., 1965). It involves alkylation of 4-picoline at 100°C in 2-methoxyethanol (or 2-phenylethanol), followed by production of the chromogen by reaction of the 4-picolinium cation with 0-dinitrobenzene in the presence of alkali. This method, using 2-methoxyethanol, is particularly useful in the analysis of alkanesulfonates. Additional investigation of the method is suggested before its value in analysis of other kinds of alkylating agents can be adequately assessed.

Gas chromatographic method. As this was being written, a gas chromatographic method for the analysis of the phosphorous-containing chemosterilants was developed (Bowman and Beroza, 1966). The method is capable of detecting nanogram quantities of chemosterilant in crude insect extracts and is specific for the intact molecule since tepa, metepa, apholate, methiotepa, and hempa all show different retention times.

1,3,5,2,4,6 - TRIAZATRIPHOSPHORINE, 2,2,4,4,6,6-HEXAKIS - (1-AZIRIDINYL)-2,2,4,4,6,6-HEXAHYDRO-

Synonyms

Apholate
APN
Olin No. 2174
SQ 8,388
NSC 26812
ENT 26316

Structure

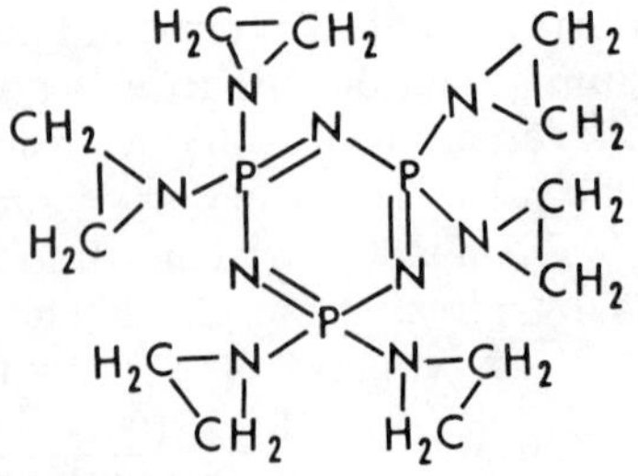

$C_{12}H_{24}N_9P_3$ Mol. Wt. 387

Physical Properties

Physical form	Crystalline solid
Color	White
Odor	Odorless
Melting point	155° C (Mendoza, 1964)

(The tendency of apholate to polymerize at high temperature makes it difficult to establish a precise melting point (Olin Mathiesen Bulletin, 1962).

Solubility. In water, 20 percent; in 70 percent ethanol, 15 percent; in chloroform, 20 percent; in methanol or acetone, only slightly. Some samples may contain as much as 5 percent water-insoluble material which forms a fine dispersion. The insoluble material, however, has the same sterilizing capacity as apholate (Olin Mathiesen Bulletin, 1962).

Stability. Since moisture and high temperatures do cause polymerization, the crystalline material should be stored in a dry cool place. Polymers of apholate have high melting points, are insoluble in both water and chloroform, and have low sterilant activity compared to the soluble material (Ristich et al., 1965). Aqueous solutions have been stored at 0° C for as long as two months without any apparent loss of sterilizing activity.

The hydrolysis and acid-catalyzed polymerization of apholate would be expected to follow the scheme outlined on pg. 000 (Mendoza, 1964).

Methods of Determination and Purification

Apholate can be purified by recrystallization from ethyl acetate or from chloroform. It should then be dried in vacuo and stored at 0° C in a dry atmosphere (Chang and Borkovec, 1964). Purity can be assessed by visualizing with iodine vapors after thin-layer chromatography on silica gel-G; when developed in methanol, the R_f of apholate is 0.50 to 0.55.

A micromethod has been developed for the detection of 5 μg of apholate per drop (100 μg per ml) of a column eluate using methanol as the eluant (Beroza and Borkovec, 1964). Add one drop of sodium thiosulfate and one drop of mixed indicator (0.05 percent methyl red plus 0.07 percent bromocresol green in 95 percent ethanol) to one drop of the solution to be tested.

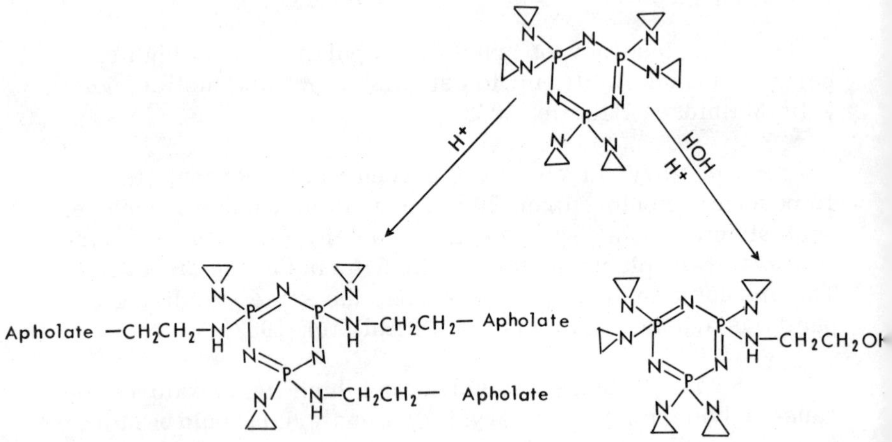

After stirring, the mixture turns deep blue or blue-green. When 2 μl of 0.1 N H$_2$SO$_4$ is added, the color turns to bright red. A positive test is indicated by the reappearance of the original blue or blue-green color within three min.

Biochemistry

The distribution and fate of apholate have not been investigated, probably because of its complex structure as compared to other aziridine chemosterilants, e.g., tepa and metepa. There is no reason to believe the metabolic fate of the ethyleneimine groups of apholate is any different from that of other aziridine chemosterilants, although steric effects will certainly alter the rate of the biological alkylation reactions.

The ED$_{50}$ for male-adult house flies has been determined by injection to be 0.404 μg per fly (Chang and Borkovec, 1964).

By comparison, it appears that tepa has four times the sterilant activity of apholate. But, on a molar basis, tepa is only 1.8 times as effective as apholate, notwithstanding the fact that apholate has twice as many aziridine groups per molecule.

The alkylation reaction by apholate proceeds via S_N^2 type mechanism, as can be demonstrated by the reaction with nitro-benzyl pyridine and with a thiol compound, cysteine.

In a series of P-N ring compounds related to apholate, a positive correlation was established between percent aziridine in the molecule, water solubility, and chemosterilant activity in the house fly (Ristich et al., 1965). Among 14 analogs containing chlorine or dimethylamino substituents in the P-N ring, those having 32 percent aziridine (or at least three ethyleneimine groups) or higher, manifested higher sterilant activity and the water soluble chemicals were more active than the insoluble ones. Additional information about the relationship between structure and sterilant activity might be obtained through the use of a method which makes it possible to disentangle three of the most important parameters governing biological activity of organic compounds; steric, electronic, and rate of penetration (cf. Hansch et al., 1963).

At the time of oviposition, house fly eggs have a low concentration of DNA and lactic dehydrogenase (LDH) (Kilgore and Painter, 1964). During embryonic development, the DNA content and LDH activity increased at about the same rate. In nonviable eggs, oviposited by flies which had fed on apholate mixed with fly food, synthesis of DNA and LDH did not occur. It was suggested that the effect of apholate on DNA synthesis may be direct by transfer of the chemical from the ovary into the egg; or indirect, by "ovarian damage, hormonal imbalance," or other "metabolic abnormalities."

Resistance to apholate has been developed in the mosquito, *Aedes aegypti* (L.) (Hazard et al., 1964). Since the mechanism of resistance may be related to the mode of action of the sterilant, biochemical characteristics of the resistant strain have been investigated in the author's laboratory.

The ratio, discussed previously, LD_{50}/ED_{90}, indicates a higher degree of selectivity of apholate for gonadal tissue in the susceptible (7.7) than in the resistant larvae (1.6) (Dr. R. S. Patterson, personal communication). One explanation for this difference might be a decreased reactivity of the target site in the resistant larvae. This could occur as a result of simple chemical or physical masking, and this would allow more apholate to react with essential metabolites other than those involved in reproductive fertility.

It has been suggested that apholate is absorbed along with other nutrients through the anal papillae of the mosquito larvae (Murray and Bickley, 1964). A reduced permeability of anal papillae in resistant larvae might thus decrease the absorption of apholate and result in the manifestation of resistance. In order to study this possible contribution to resistance, larvae of both strains were caused to drop their anal papillae by a technique described by Wigglesworth (1933). The papillae-less larvae were then treated with apholate, and no change in susceptibility was noted in either strain. On this basis, it was concluded that absorption of apholate must occur at some site other than the anal papillae. The relative amounts of chemical absorbed by the larvae is still not known.

Histological studies have shown that vacuolation and a decrease in the periodic acid-Schiff (PAS) positive material occurs in the ovaries of susceptible adults following treatment in the larval stage with a sterilizing dose of apholate (E. I. Hazard, personal communication). Treatment of the resistant larvae with the same dose caused little or no change in the appearance of ovaries.

Since nucleic acids and proteins represent prime targets for alkylation by these agents, the content and intracellular distribution was investigated in the author's laboratory and found to be the same in both strains of mosquito larvae. In addition, no alteration of nucleic acid or protein metabolism was detected in larvae which had been sterilized by apholate. Since the amount of chemical participating in the molecular reaction responsible for loss of fertility is undoubtedly extremely small, it should be emphasized that our inability to detect subtle changes in the large macromolecular structures does not preclude the existence of such alterations.

The radioprotective effect of sulfhydryl compounds has been well established, although the mechanism of action has not been clearly elucidated. Recently, similar protective effects against the toxicity of "radiomimetic" alkylating agents have been attributed to thiol compounds (Connors and Elson, 1962, and Connors et al., 1964a). Studies in our laboratory have shown that the sterilizing effect of apholate can be significantly reduced by pretreatment of mosquito (*A. aegypti*) larvae with cysteine 24 hr before exposure to apholate.

Calcutt and his co-workers (1963) demonstrated a correlation between "the degree of protection afforded by cysteine and (a) the chemical reactivity of the nitrogen mustard and (b) the amount by which cysteine raises the intracellular protein free-SH level of spleen, liver and thymus." We have also found that an "SH reagent," p-chloromercuribenzoate, will exert anti-fertility effects on *A. aegypti* larvae. Mazia (1960) has shown that SH compounds are required for the formation of the mitotic apparatus. Others have shown an effect of thiols on viability of sea urchin eggs. Even though the relative affinity of aziridines for SH at physiological pH is believed to be low compared to that for other nucleophiles (e.g., NH_2, OH, COOH), the low concentration of SH in the insect may thus represent a particularly sensitive class of essential nucleophiles. Since sulfhydryl compounds are essential to such a wide variety of biosynthetic and bioenergetic processes, the relationship of SH compounds to fertility in the insect should be investigated.

Administration of as little as 40 μg (0.104 μmoles) of alpholate to the southern corn rootworm (Diabrotica undecimpunctata, howardi) caused a decrease in the alkaline phosphatase activity of the gonads in both males and females (Mendoza, 1964). Phosphatases are generally found in the cytoplasm of growing cells in which protein synthesis is taking place although they are important participants in the metabolism of lipids, carbohydrates, nucleic acids, and nucleotides. The term "alkaline phosphatase" includes several enzymes which have similar although not identical properties. The alkaline phosphatases studied in this report showed a remarkable specificity for DNA. It was also noted that the same dose of apholate visibly weakened and inactivated sperm.

PHOSPHINE OXIDE, TRIS(1-AZIRIDINYL)-

Synonyms

Tepa
TEP
APO
Aphoxide
Triethylenephosphoramide
SK 3818
NSC 9717
ENT 24915

Structure

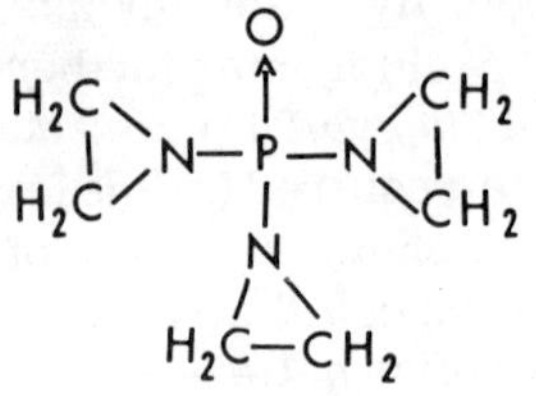

$$H_2C\begin{matrix} \\ | \\ \end{matrix}N-P-N\begin{matrix} /CH_2 \\ | \\ \end{matrix}$$

$C_6H_{12}N_3OP$ Mol. wt. 173.16

Physical Properties

Physical form	Crystalline solid
Color	Colorless
Odor	Odorless
Melting point	$41°$ C
Boiling point	(0.3 mm Hg) 90 to $91°$ C

Solubility. Extremely soluble in water; very soluble in alcohol, ether, and acetone (Crossley et al., 1953, and Sykes et al., 1953).

Stability. In the preparation of P^{32}-labeled tepa, the material was found to undergo violent decomposition if heated above $130°$ C (Craig and Jackson, 1955). Tepa is very hygroscopic and unstable in aqueous solutions.

Certain therapeutic imine derivatives, including tepa, have been stabilized for as long as 12 months in liquid anhydrous polyethylene glycols (Sumitomo Chemical Co., Ltd. British Patent 845,823). The compositions were reported to be stable to heat and to be of low toxicity. Only 1.5 percent of the effectiveness was lost from preparations stabilized in this manner after storage at room temperature for 6 months.

The stability of tepa and thiotepa at concentrations of 1 μg/ml in biological fluids and aqueous buffers has been determined by incubation in a Dubnoff apparatus at $38°$ C for 30 min. (Mellett and Woods, 1960). The results shown in Table 1 indicate the extreme sensitivity of tepa to acidic conditions and the reactivity with components of the blood. In this report,

TABLE 1

STABILITY OF CONCENTRATIONS OF 1.0
μg/ml TEPA INCUBATED AT 38°C IN A
DUBNOFF APPARATUS FOR 30 MIN.

Medium	% Tepa lost in 30 min
Whole blood, pH 7.8	60
Plasma, pH 7.8	30
0.15 M NaHCO$_3$, pH 8.4	0
0.1 M Acetate buffer, pH 4.2	95
0.1 M Phosphate buffer, pH 7.4	72

(From Mellet and Woods, 1960).

tepa was determined by a method which is specific for the intact molecule (cf. Methods of Determination).

Beroza and Borkovec (1964) investigated the effects of temperature and pH on the stability of tepa and some other aziridine chemosterilants. The effect of temperature on the decomposition of a 0.3 percent aqueous solution of tepa is shown in Fig. 1. The time for decomposition of 50 percent of tepa at the various temperatures was estimated (in days) to be greater than 200 at 3°C, 31 at 25°C, 7 at 50°C, and less than 0.1 at 100°C. As decomposition progressed, the pH increased, and the rate of decomposition was slowed.

Using thin-layer chromatography, it was shown that at pH 4 in 1 N H$_2$SO$_4$, 3.1 percent solution of tepa had completely decomposed after 1.5 hr, but an aziridine function was detected for 24 hr. The authors noted that the total amount of acid present seems to be far more significant than the initial pH of the solution.

Figure 2 shows the effect of pH on the rate of tepa degradation. Nuclear magnetic resonance (N.M.R.) spectra were used in studying the effect of pH on the decomposition of tepa in D$_2$O buffers. The aziridine decomposition product was thus identified as ethyleneimine and the structures of the other products, involving C–N bond cleavage were suggested. Tepa deterioration in aqueous solutions is accompanied by liberation of inorganic phosphate (Craig and Jackson, 1955, and Beroza and Borkovec, 1964). Based on N.M.R. data, it was suggested that the decomposition of tepa in D$_2$O can be represented schematically as shown on p. 176.

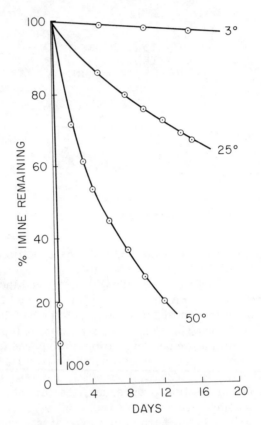

FIG. 1. Decomposition of 0.3 percent aqueous solutions of tepa as determined by titrimetric and colorimetric procedures. (From Beroza and Borkovec, 1964, J. Med. Chem., 7(1):44–49. Copyright 1964 by the American Chemical Society. Reprinted by permission of the copyright owner.)

Recognition of the effect of pH on decomposition of aziridine chemosterilants led to modification of insect diets to be used in screening tests. Replacement of an acidic diet with a neutral one for the Mexican fruit fly resulted in excellent antifertility effects of some aziridines previously considered to be ineffective.

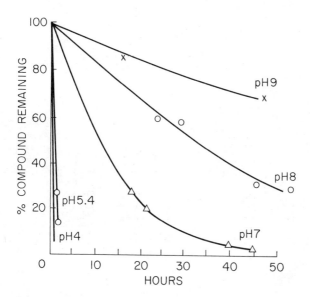

FIG. 2. Stability of 2.5 percent tepa in D_2O buffered at different pH values as determined from N. M. R. spectra. (From Beroza and Borkovec, 1964, J. Med. Chem., 7(1):44–49. Copyright 1964 by the American Chemical Society. Reprinted by permission of the copyright owner.)

Methods of Determination and Purification

Tepa can be purified by passage through silic acid (Beroza and Borkovec, 1964) or recrystallization two times from cyclohexane, then dried in vacuo (Chang and Borkovec, 1964). Purity can be determined by ascending-paper or thin-layer chromatography and R_f values for several solvent systems are given in Table 2.

Since ethyleneimine, a product of acidic degradation of tepa, shows no sterilant activity in the house fly, the sterilizing activity of solutions of tepa can be assessed in terms of aziridine content only when the purity of the material is established and the sterilizing activity of all aziridine-containing compounds known (Borkovec et al., 1964).

The micromethod described in the section on apholate can detect as little as 1 μg tepa in one drop of methanol (or approximately 20 μg/ml) (Beroza and Borkovec, 1964).

A sensitive photofluorometric method for the estima-

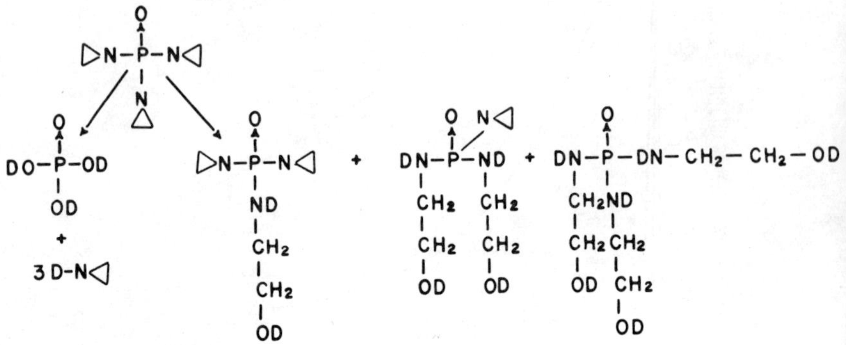

(Adapted from Beroza and Borkovec, 1964.)

TABLE 2

SOLVENT SYSTEMS USEFUL FOR PAPER AND THIN-
LAYER CHROMATOGRAPHY OF TEPA

Type	Solvent system	R_f
Paper	n–Butanol saturated with water	0.57[a]
Paper	80% Ethanol	0.80
Paper	n–Butanol saturated with 1% NH_4OH	0.55[b]
Paper	Acetone:water (3:2 v/v)	0.86
TLC (Silica gel)	Methanol	0.53[c]

[a]Craig and Jackson (1955).
[b]Nadkarni et al., (1957).
[c]Beroza and Borkovec (1964).

tion of tepa in biological fluids has been developed by Mellett and Woods (1960). Unlike the common aziridine assays, this method appears to be specific for the intact molecule and can be used for determining tepa and thiotepa separately or in the presence of each other. When both are to be determined simultaneously, aliquots of the sample are carried through each of the procedures for tepa and thiotepa. The procedure described for tepa determines both, and therefore represents total alkylating agent. The other procedure is specific for thiotepa and thus the difference between the two values gives the tepa content. Briefly, the method for tepa consists of an initial extraction with 10 percent methanol (by volume) in chloroform, reaction with β-naphthol, followed by serial extractions with aqueous and organic solvents and determination of the fluorescence of the final acid extract. Recovery of tepa added to urine and plasma was 88 ± 15 percent.

Biochemistry

Most of the studies on the distribution and fate of tepa have been done using P^{32}-labeled material and, since it has been shown that the carrier portion of the molecule is rapidly separated from the aziridine portion in mammals (Smith et al., 1958), the conclusions which can be drawn from such data are limited. Similar limitations may apply to data obtained using C^{14}-labeled tepa since ethyleneimine itself is not effective as a male house fly sterilant. Distribution of only the aziridine moiety, or its degradation products, reveals little information about the distribution of intact tepa which, at the present time, is considered necessary for antifertility activity. The correct interpretation of such data depends upon the acquisition of additional information concerning the reason for the loss of sterilant activity when ethyleneimine is separated from the carrier.

In the rat, 80 percent of the P^{32}-labeled material was excreted within 24 hr, the majority of which was intact (Craig and Jackson, 1955). The remaining activity was distributed rather evenly between trichloroacetic acid(TCA)-soluble material, 32 percent; lipids, 23 percent; nucleic acids, 25 percent; and proteins, 20 percent. It was suggested that although tepa is a potent antitumor agent, it is not very reactive chemically in vivo.

In the mouse, virtually all the tepa was rapidly metabolized to inorganic phosphate and very little excreted intact (Nadkarni et al., 1957). The findings of Mellett and Woods (1960) in the dog were similar to those of Craig and Jackson (1955).

It had been stated that the excretion of such large proportions of unchanged tepa by the rat "is incongruous in view of the postulated high degree of chemical and biological reactivity of this group of alkylating drugs" (Smith et al., 1958). Subsequently, Craig et al. (1959) found significant differences in the rate of metabolism of thiotepa in the mouse, rat, dog, and rabbit and thus showed that the rate of metabolic degradation of the aziridine is largely dependent upon the species investigated.

Nadkarni et al. (1959) suggested that the alkylating portion of P^{32}-labeled tepa was detached from the carrier portion in humans. Subsequently, it was shown that 25 to 30 percent of the P^{32}-labeled tepa was excreted in the urine of cancer patients within 48 hr after administration (Nadkarni et al., 1961).

Intravenous injection of tepa into the dog resulted in high levels in plasma immediately, followed by a rapid decline during the first 30 min, and a progressive decline in the rate of loss up to 5 hr after injection (Mellett and Woods, 1960). The urinary recovery during this period ranged from 24 to 34 percent. Tepa had a marked affinity for bone marrow as compared with other tissues. No radiolabel was used in these studies since the recovered material was determined by the assay specific for the intact molecule. Application of this method of determination in insect sterilization research should provide significant information in mode of action studies.

Chang and his co-workers (1966) found that 50 percent of the C^{14}-labeled tepa injected into male house flies was excreted as nonaziridinyl metabolites after 5 hr of normal activity. By the use of radiometric and colorimetric determinations, the radioactivity retained in the fly was shown to be tepa or aziridinyl functions, whereas the radioactivity in the excreta was of a nonaziridinyl nature. The treated male fly retained 9 percent of the radioactivity and 5 percent of the aziridinyl content for as long as 72 hr. It was shown that the male fly passed approximately 1 percent of the radioactivity into the body of the female during copulation, but the transfer evidently was not via the sperm. The radioactivity in the female was found distributed throughout the body, not concentrated in the

spermathecae or the abdominal tip. This would seem to indicate that tepa, or radiolabeled metabolite had been bound to
some soluble small molecule, or was itself free in the seminal
fluid and, after transfer to the female, had rapidly diffused from
the spermathecae throughout the general area of the body. Reaction of tepa with low molecular weight compounds seems
quite probable since Hedin et al. (1966a) found that over 85 percent of the radioactivity from C^{14}-labeled tepa was associated
with low molecular weight constituents in the boll weevil.
Selective concentration was found to occur in the testes, fore-
gut, and wings when weevils were injected with C^{14}-labeled tepa.
Labeling of sperm and/or seminal fluid was indicated by the
finding of radioactivity in the spermathecae of females which
had mated with treated males.

In a related study (Hedin et al., 1966b), it was shown
that in weevils treated with C^{14}-tepa, the radioactivity was
reduced to 50 percent in 6 to 48 hr, depending upon the diet.
During the first day following injection, weevils fed cotton buds
were able to excrete the radioactivity more rapidly than those
fed an artificial diet, but some 10 to 20 percent of the radioactivity was retained for at least 10 days. Obvious reduction in
the number of sperm was noticed in weevils dissected 14 days
after treatment, but no effect on the sperm numbers was
noticed in earlier samples although the weevils were sterile.
The effect of a sterilizing dose of tepa on the testes was manifested by chromatin clumping at the anaphase stage two days
after injection and in the later stages (14 days), a general
necrosis of the dividing cells became apparent.

Although ethyleneimine per se is not effective as a
chemosterilant (Borkovec et al., 1964), it is mutagenic (Alexander and Glanges, 1965), possesses oncolytic activity, and is
detected by the usual aziridine assays. The loss of sterilizing
activity which occurs when the alkylating moiety is separated
from the carrier portion of the molecule may be the result of
altered transport, enhanced detoxication, decreased affinity
for the site of sterilization, or some combination of these or
other unrecognized factors.

In consideration of the effect of pH on tepa decomposition and the failure of ethyleneimine to show sterilant activity
when injected into male house flies, an attempt was made to
influence the effectiveness of the chemosterilant by injection
of a buffered solution of the drug (Borkovec et al., 1964). Adult
male house flies were injected with 0.1 μg of tepa in 0.85 μl of

0.5 M phosphate buffer of pH values ranging from 6 to 8. No significant difference in the sterilizing activity of the chemical in this pH range was detected. It should be noted that hemolymph is generally quite well buffered and the pH of fly hemolymph is normally 7.2 to 7.6 (Glaser, 1925).

While the sensitivity of aziridines to acidic conditions is recognized, the effectiveness of certain aziridine-containing chemicals against tumors has been enhanced by administration of glucose prior to treatment with the drug (Connors et al., 1964b). The effect was attributed to a localized highly acidic condition in the tumor which effectively increased the reactivity of the aziridine at the site. The design and synthesis of drugs which will be relatively inactive except in the presence of high acidity is currently an important aspect of cancer chemotherapy. Similarly, an investigation of the pH of insect gonadal tissues might prove to be of value in research on chemosterilants.

The ED_{50} for male adult house flies has been determined by injection to be 0.100 μg (0.578×10^{-3} μmoles) per fly (Chang and Borkovec, 1964). Chang (1965) found that when tepa was injected into the fly, full effectiveness of the dosage was not realized until approximately 3.5 hr later.

The degree of selectivity of tepa and some analogs for gonadal tissue was determined (using data computed from regression equations generously supplied by Dr. S. C. Chang) by the ratio LD_{50}/ED_{90} and are presented in Table 3. It seems noteworthy that in changing from the bifunctional to the monofunctional derivative, the chemical becomes more toxic, tenfold at LD_{50}; less effective as a sterilant, sevenfold at ED_{90}; and yet more selective by almost one hundredfold. In cancer chemotherapy, it has frequently been noted that such a change in structure of aziridines results in decreased oncolytic activity by fifty- to one hundredfold.

Ratios (LD_{50}/ED_{90}) in excess of nine are considered as indicative of significant selectivity for tumorous tissue, and the degree of selectivity of tepa has been reported to be 2.9 (Bardos et al., 1965). In the house fly, the ratio is 426, indicating a high degree of selectivity and high metabolic activity in the gonads. In the immature insect, i.e., $A.$ $aegypti$ mosquito larvae, the selectivity of tepa is only 1.8 (Dr. R. S. Patterson, personal communication). This is undoubtedly a reflection of the high metabolic activity of somatic tissues in developing larvae.

TABLE 3

STERILIZATION AND TOXICITY OF VARIOUS ALKYLAMI-
NOBIS (1-AZIRIDINYL)PHOSPHINE OXIDES IN MALE
HOUSE FLIES

R	μmoles $\times 10^{-2}$/male fly		LD_{50}/ED_{90}
	LD_{50}	ED_{90}	
$-CH_3$	15.27	0.174	87.9
$-C^2H_5$	32.46	0.274	118.5
$-nC_3H_7$	1.13	0.846	1.3
$-isoC_3H_7$	44.89	0.365	123.1
$-nC_4H_9$	9.42	0.950	9.9
$-nC_8H_{17}$	3.80	5.549	0.68

Effect of replacement of aziridinyl groups of tepa
by dimethylamino groups

	57.75	0.139	416.7
	43.04	0.354	121.6
	3.05	2.25	1.36
	56.26	7.92	7.18

(From Chang and Borkovec, 1966. Generously supplied by
Dr. S. C. Chang.)

The replacement of one ethyleneimine group of tepa
with a piperidyl, morpholino, or azetidyl group did not affect
the antitumor activity, bud did significantly reduce the effect
on the testes of rats (Crossley et al., 1953). In feeding experiments with house flies, the replacement with a morpholino

group did not alter antifertility effects either, but did significantly increase the toxicity (Dr. G. C. LaBrecque, personal communication). The nature of the replacement group may be quite important since the replacement of one ethyleneimine group with $-NHCO_2C_2H_5$ reduced oncolytic activity and toxic effects although selectivity increased threefold (Bardos et al., 1965). Such effects are also seen in the data on alkylaminobis (1-aziridinyl) phosphine oxides presented in Table 3.

Dame and Ford (1964) have reported that gravid female mosquitoes (*A. aegypti*) could be sterilized by only one tenth the dosage required for virgin females. It was suggested that the effect of tepa was on the sperm in the spermathecae.

Tepa has been reported to interfere with nucleic acid metabolism in tumor-bearing rats by increasing the depolymerase activity and by inhibiting biosynthesis (Chernov and Presnova, 1963). It also acts like x-rays in reducing the concentration of RNA and DNA in a variety of malignant tissues (Grushina, 1955, and Chernov and Zakharova, 1957).

It is well known that the response of tumors to x-irradiation is influenced by dietary protein (Elson and Lamerton, 1949). The results of Crossley et al. (1953) suggest that ethyleneimines may have a specific effect on the utilization of food and protein. In the rat, tepa reduced body growth as well as tumor growth, reducing the utilization of food and possibly altering protein anabolism (Allison et al., 1954). Subsequently, it was found that supplementing the casein diet of sarcoma-bearing rats with methionine or feeding high protein diets, favored the development of the body even in the presence of tepa (Allison et al., 1956). The protective effect of methionine suggests that this amino acid may play some specific role in the relation between growth of the body and tepa. The effect of diet in altering the role of metabolism of the chemosterilant in the boll weevil mentioned previously (Hedin et al., 1966b) may be related to these effects.

Effects of tepa on glycolysis are confusing. Treatment of Yoshida sarcoma cells increased glycolysis (Hori et al., 1963) whereas in Ehrlich ascites tumor cells, glycolysis was inhibited and alkaline phosphatase activity was stimulated by tepa (Maruyama and Uchida, 1960). The latter effect occurred only after the solution had been stored at 2°C for two weeks and is thus difficult to evaluate.

PHOSPHINE OXIDE, TRIS(2-METHYL-1-AZIRIDINYL)-

Synonyms

Metepa
MAPO
Methaphoxide
ENT 50003

Structure

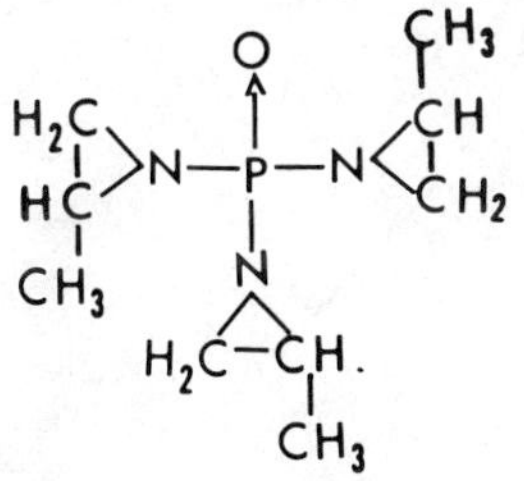

Physical properties

(Obtained from Interchemical Corporation, New Product Bulletin, MAPO, unless otherwise indicated.)

Physical form	Liquid
Color	Straw-colored
Odor	High-boiling amine
Boiling point	(1 mm) 118 to 125° C
	(760 mm) polymerizes
Specific gravity	25° C/25° C 1.079
Refractive index	n_D^{25} 1.4798

Solubility. Completely soluble in water and all common organic solvents.

Stability. Samples have been stored at room temperature in metal containers for 2 years with loss of less than 1 percent of its active imine content.

The effect of temperature on the decomposition of a 0.3 percent aqueous solution of metepa is shown in Fig. 3 (Beroza and Borkovec, 1964).

Metepa is as sensitive as the other aziridine chemosterilants to acidic conditions, and degradation in acidic media is complete within 120 min (Borkovec et al., 1964). Plapp et al. (1962) found that degradation of metepa in 1 N NaOH was very slow, requiring more than 100 hr for 50 percent hydrolysis, whereas in 1 N HCl 50 percent hydrolysis

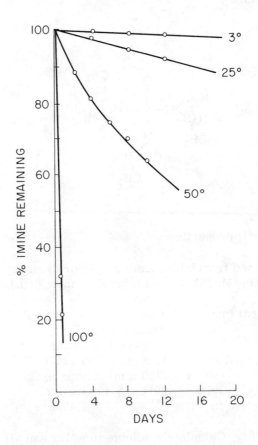

FIG. 3. Decomposition of 0.3 percent aqueous solutions of metepa at different temperatures as determined by titrimetric and colorimetric procedures. (From Beroza and Borkovec, 1964, J. Med. Chem., 7(1):44–49. Copyright 1964 by the American Chemical Society. Reprinted by permission of the copyright owner.)

occurred in less than 1 min. The major hydrolytic product was inorganic phosphate in both acidic and basic solutions.

Methods of Determination and Purification

Metepa can be purified by fractional distillation at 30 μ Hg, and collection of the fraction boiling at 86 to 88°C (Chang and Borkovec, 1964).

Purity of metepa can be assessed by ascending paper chromatography in acetonitrile:water:ammonium hydroxide (80:20:2) in which the R_f of metepa is 0.75 (Plapp et al., 1962). Metepa can be detected on paper chromatograms by the method of Hanes and Isherwood (1949).

Using the procedure described in the section on apholate (Beroza and Borkovec, 1964), it is possible to detect as little as 5 μg metepa in one drop of methanol (or approximately 100 μg/ml).

Biochemistry

The distribution and fate of P^{32}-metepa were studied by paper chromatography of chloroform extracts of house flies, mosquitoes, and mice (Plapp et al., 1962). When applied topically to house flies, the material was rapidly absorbed, 50 percent in 1.5 hr; and rapidly detoxified following absorption, 50 percent in 2 hr. After the material was injected, 50 percent degradation occurred in slightly more than 1 hr; more than 95 percent being degraded after 24 hr. The rate of degradation in two strains of house flies resistant to organophosphorous insecticides was the same as that in the susceptible strain. It was concluded that degradation of the sterilant proceeded via a pathway different from that responsible for insecticide detoxication. The amount of metepa in the ovaries of the female house fly reached a maximum approximately 1 hr after injection, and declined rapidly thereafter as shown in Table 4. The increased accumulation of P^{32} in the ovary may be the result of utilization in ovarian metabolism of the inorganic phosphate produced by degradation of P^{32}-metepa; this is indicated by the steady decrease in the amount partitioning as metepa. There was no indication of selective accumulation of metepa in ovarian tissue. The bulk of radioactive material was excreted within eight hr, and much of the extreted radioactivity was found to be intact metepa.

TABLE 4

FATE OF P^{32} METHAPHOXIDE IN OVARIES OF HOUSE
FLIES INJECTED WITH THE CHEMICAL AT A DOSAGE
OF 2 μg PER FLY

Time after treatment, hr	P^{32}/ovary, mμg-equiv.	P^{32}/ovary Partitioning as methaphoxide, %	Methaphoxide per ovary, mμg
0.25	23.0	76	17
.5	34.3	59	19.9
1	44.0	57	24.6
2	31.0	26	7.8
4	41.0	8	3.4
8	51.0	5	2.3
24	66.0	3	1.9

(From Plapp et al., 1962. Reprinted from the J. Econ. Entom. 55 (5) 611, 1962, by permission of the copyright owner, Entomological Society of America.)

In mosquito larvae, degradation occurred rapidly and was virtually complete within 48 hr after treatment was terminated. An amount of P^{32} remained through pupal and adult stages, but very little of the radioactivity behaved like metepa. In the adults, which were fed sugar solutions of metepa, the degradation was even more rapid, being complete within 24 hr after the sterilant solution was removed. A similar rate of degradation was observed in adult mosquitoes after feeding on mice which had been treated with metepa.

Values of ED_{50} for male house flies, as determined by injection, is 1.310 μg/fly or 6.1×10^{-3} μmoles/fly (Chang and Borkovec, 1964). The lower sterilant activity of this compound compared to tepa is consistent with the observations of Borkovec (1962), Borkovec and Woods (1963), and Crystal (1963) concerning decreased activity of C-methyl substituted aziridine compounds compared to the unsubstituted compound.

Resistance to metepa has been developed in *A. aegypti* larvae and the metepa-resistant strain was shown to detoxify the chemosterilant in vitro more rapidly than the susceptible strain (Klassen and Matsumura, 1966).

PHOSPHINE SULFIDE, TRIS(1-AZIRIDINYL)-

Synonyms

Thiotepa
Triethylene thiophosphoramide
STEPA
TESPA
Tiofosyl
TSPA
APS
NSC 6396
ENT 24916 (formerly 25295)

Structure

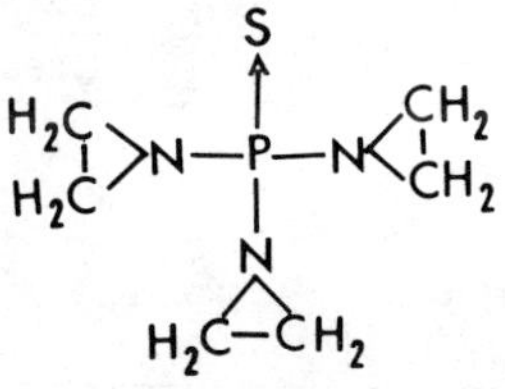

$C_6H_{12}N_3SP$ Mol. wt. 189

Physical Properties

Physical form	Crystalline solid (moderately hygroscopic)
Color	White
Odor	Odorless
Melting point	51.5 C (Crossley et al., 1953)

Solubility. Soluble in water (19 percent at room temperature), in benzene, acetone, warm petroleum ether, and warm diethyl ether (Crossley et al., 1953). (Some slight turbidity is frequently observed in aqueous solutions.)

Stability. Thiotepa, like most of the aziridine chemosterilants, tends to polymerize in aqueous solutions, or in the presence of moisture, especially at acidic pH. Stock solutions of thiotepa prepared in sodium bicarbonate solutions were more suitable for use than bulk thiotepa which underwent changes in solubility over a period of several months even though it was kept cold and desiccated (Mellett and Woods, 1960).

The stability of thiotepa in various media incubated in a Dubnoff apparatus at 38° C is shown in Table 5 (Mellett and Woods, 1960). Since the values shown were obtained using a method of determination specific for thiotepa (Mellett and Woods, 1960), the rate of degradation should correspond well with a decrease in sterilizing activity.

TABLE 5

STABILITY OF CONCENTRATIONS OF 1.0 μg/ml
THIOTEPA INCUBATED AT 38° C IN A DUBNOFF
APPARATUS FOR 30 MIN

Medium	Loss in 30 min, %
Whole blood, pH 7.8	60
Plasma, pH 7.8	45
0.16 M NaHCO$_3$, pH 8.4	0
0.1 M Acetate buffer, pH 4.2	95
0.1 M Phosphate buffer, pH 7.4	68

(From Mellett and Woods, 1960.)

Degradation of thiotepa produces ethyleneimine and sulfur (as SO) and since ethyleneimine is not effective as a sterilant, the precautions previously mentioned should be observed in relating alkylating activity, as determined by the commonly used aziridine assays, to its effectiveness as a chemosterilant.

Some of the solvent systems which have been used for paper chromatography of thiotepa are listed below.

Solvent	Rf
n-Butanol saturated with 1 percent NH$_3$	0.84
Acetone: water (80:20 v/v)	0.80[a]
Butanol: dioxane: 2N NH$_3$	0.90[b]

[a]Mellett and Woods, 1960.
[b]Craig et al., 1959.

Methods of Determination

A photofluorometric method, specific for unchanged thiotepa has been described by Mellett and Woods (1960). The procedure for thiotepa is the same as that discussed previously for tepa, except the initial extraction is done with benzene. In the concentration range of 0.05 to 0.2 μg/ml, recovery from aqueous solutions was 95 percent ($\pm$20 percent), and at levels of 0.2 to 2.0 μg/ml, 90 percent ($\pm$12 percent).

Biochemistry

Thiotepa was found to be rapidly converted to tepa in the rat, rabbit, and dog (Craig et al., 1959, and Mellet and Woods, 1960), and in several insect species (Parish and Arthur, 1965). The in vivo conversion seems to occur at a rate faster than the drug can be metabolized. The first stage of degradation of thiotepa is the rapid conversion to tepa in the rat, rabbit, and dog, whereas in the mouse, although degradation apparently proceeds via tepa, inorganic phosphate is the main metabolite excreted (Craig et al., 1959). Tepa was the main metabolite extreted by the rat and larger amounts of three additional metabolites were excreted by the rabbit and dog.

Mellett and Woods (1960) were unable adequately to recover added thiotepa from tissues even though the tissues were chilled and processed rapidly. The addition of a number of enzyme inhibitors to the system failed to improve the recovery and it was concluded that thiotepa reacted "chemically and almost instantaneously" with materials from intracellular sources.

Parish and Arthur (1965) studied the metabolism of P[32]-labeled thiotepa by topical application to the German cockroach (*Blatella germanica*), house fly (*Musca domestica*), stable fly (*Stomoxys calcitrans*), and boll weevil (*Anthonomus grandis*), and by oral and dermal administration to white rats. The results obtained with the rat were essentially the same as those of Craig et al. (1959). In the insects studied, maximum absorption had occurred within 4 hr after application in all species except the boll weevil, in which absorption increased steadily during 24 hr. The amount of the radioactive material present as thiotepa in the insect decreased rapidly due to its conversion to tepa as shown in Table 6. In the boll weevil, after 24 hr, tepa appeared to be undergoing conversion back to thiotepa.

TABLE 6

PERCENTAGE OF P^{32}-THIOTEPA ABSORBED AND THE
FRACTIONATION BY SILICA GEL CHROMATOGRAPHY OF
THE INTERNAL EXTRACTS RECOVERED FROM INSECTS
TREATED TOPICALLY AT 100 mg/kg

Insect	Time after treatment, hr	% Absorbed	% Internal extracts present	
			Thiotepa	Tepa
German cockroach	0	18.8	—	—
	1	43.6	65.1	34.9
	4	85.0	49.3	50.7
	24	69.1	17.9	82.1
House fly	0	15.2	—	—
	1	81.6	50.2	49.8
	4	87.8	24.3	75.7
	24	75.7	18.0	82.0
Stable fly	0	8.6	—	—
	1	75.6	64.2	35.8
	4	81.2	66.5	33.5
	24	40.7	52.9	47.1
Boll weevil	0	1.5	—	—
	1	41.2	37.2	62.8
	4	60.7	37.7	62.3
	24	73.5	62.8	37.2

(From Parish and Arthur, 1965.)

Wheeler and Alexander (1964a) reported that there was
no difference in the amount of C^{14}-thiotepa fixed in resistant
and susceptible tumors. In addition, the intracellular distribution of C^{14}-thiotepa was the same in both types of tumors and
no selectivity for tumor tissue was observed.

Electrophoretic patterns indicated that all of the radiolabeled thiotepa found in the blood serum of treated cancer
patients was associated with the protein (Bateman et al.,
1960). It was suggested that a "loose chemical association"
or some other adsorption phenomenon was involved.

When rats were treated with C^{14}-thiotepa, a substantial amount of radioactivity was bound to the nuclear fraction and most of it was not removed by washing (Ruddon and
Mellett, 1964). No selectivity for a particular tissue or organ
was noted.

Several reports have indicated that in vivo effects of

thiotepa cause an alteration of sulfhydryl metabolism. Intraperitoneal injection of thiotepa caused increased urinary excretion of taurine by rats (Schuberth and Sorbo, 1963). The level of taurine excretion is similar to that caused by a dosage of 500 r of x-rays.

Connors and Elson (1962) found that thiol compounds did not reduce the toxicity of thiotepa in rats although some protection against other "radiomimetic" alkylating agents was observed. The ability of thiol compounds to reduce toxicity may be the result of detoxication by combination with the alkylating agent or of protection by chemical masking of a susceptible site as in disulfide formation. The former is favored.

Administration of thiotepa caused a decrease in the concentration of SH groups in the blood serum and in tumor tissue of rats. In rats with sarcoma 45, a correlation was established between the antitumor activity of the chemical and a decrease in SH groups of the blood serum (Kulik, 1963).

In addition, thiotepa inhibited dehydrogenase activity in Ehrlich ascites tumor cells (Di Paola, 1963a, b). Dehydrogenase activity and growth inhibition in vitro have been correlated with in vivo growth inhibition through the use of four different types of dehydrogenase assays. The methods include in vitro cells; monolayer agar diffusion, using defined and semidefined medium; and a coverslip test.

These tests could be used to investigate the possible correlation between effects on dehydrogenase activity and antifertility activity of chemosterilants. If such a correlation is found to exist, the use of these tests would greatly facilitate preliminary screening of chemicals for sterilant activity. In addition, it could provide information about in vivo effects.

Exposure of dividing cells in tissue culture to thiotepa during prophase causes a prolongation of metaphase although cell division is not stopped (Oishi, 1961). The administration of higher doses of thiotepa at prophase or metaphase caused chromosomal clumping and resultant cell damage. There appears to be a period between prophase and metaphase which is particularly sensitive to the chemical. This effect may be a consequence of reaction with thiol compounds, since the SH-rich mitotic apparatus is being assembled during these stages of cell division which are particularly sensitive to the chemical. Binding of thiol compounds by thiotepa, or its metabolite tepa, could prolong metaphase by interfering with either the assembly or function of the mitotic apparatus.

The observed effects of intraperitoneal injection of thiotepa appear to resemble those of x-rays in that chromosomes appear sticky and condensed in metaphase, and chromosome bridges are subsequently detected in anaphase (Umemo, 1959). Combination of x-ray therapy and thiotepa showed that each exerted its own effect independently since no synergism was noted.

Several reports indicate the effect of thiotepa on nucleic acid metabolism. Only slight change in the DNase activity of both normal and tumorous tissue occurred following the administration of a therapeutic dose of thiotepa to rats (Chernov and Presnova, 1963). The RNase activity of the tumor increased, however, while that of the spleen decreased.

Depression of incorporation of H^3-thimidine into DNA has been correlated with the in vivo inhibition of tumor growth by thiotepa (MacDonald et al., 1963). A slight depression of RNA synthesis was indicated by reduced incorporation of H^3-uridine.

In vitro treatment of an aqueous solution of salmon sperm DNA with thiotepa caused the formation of larger molecular aggregates as determined by the ultracentrifuge pattern (Klemm and Obrecht, 1962).

The effects of thiotepa upon growth, fixation of C^{14} from C^{14} formate and adenine-8-C^{14} are similar to those of cyclophosphamide on cyclophosphamide-sensitive and cyclophosphamide-resistant tumors grown bilaterally in the hamster (Wheeler and Alexander, 1964b). The incorporation of C^{14} from formate into the purines of RNA and DNA was inhibited by thiotepa in the sensitive, but not in the resistant tumor. Incorporation of adenine-8-C^{14} into DNA of the sensitive tumor was also inhibited, but incorporation into RNA was not affected. In the resistant tumor, there was no inhibition of adenine-8-C^{14} incorporation into either RNA or DNA. It was concluded that thiotepa inhibited nucleic acid synthesis in two ways, i.e., by inhibition of de novo synthesis of purine ribonucleotides and by inhibition of the conversion of purine ribonucleotides to deoxy components of DNA. Schematically:

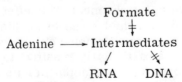

Formate
Adenine ⟶ Intermediates
RNA   DNA

(From Wheeler and Alexander 1964b, Cancer Res. 24:1338–1346.)

Effects of thiotepa on protein metabolism have also been noted in several reports. Thiotepa has been shown to cause an increase in serum albumin when it caused improvement in patients with malignant tumors (Shimizu, 1961). Total serum protein, which had undergone alterations in the course of carcinogenesis, showed a tendency to return to normal in response to treatment with thiotepa.

Pradhan and West (1964) found thiotepa caused an initial increase, followed by a decline, in the incorporation of radio-labeled glycine into both histone and nonhistone fractions of nuclear protein in tumor-bearing mice. On the other hand, the incorporation of glycine into cytoplasmic proteins was definitely inhibited by the administration of a single dose (5 mg/kg) intraperitoneally. Maximum inhibition occurred within the first 24 to 30 hr after injection. On the basis of these data is was suggested that the primary site of action of thiotepa is on cytoplasmic protein.

The serum properdin level of rabbits was decreased when an LD_{50} dosage of thiotepa was administered (Blumberg and Bass-Shadkin, 1964).

Thiotepa acted like x-rays, or Cobalt 60 treatment, in causing a reduction of the level of total and fraction III protein in the liver of the rat (Kaji, 1962). A probable relationship to sulfhydryl and to carbohydrate metabolism is indicated by the observation that the decreased level could be restored by treatment with lipoic acid. Lipoic acid functions in the oxidative decarboxylation of pyruvate and α-ketoglutarate, in sulfite oxidation and as electron carrier in biological oxidations.

Daily injections of thiotepa (2 mg/kg) prevented a decrease of β- and γ-globulin in the serum which usually develops in rats with experimental sarcoma M-1. Thiotepa, however, seems to potentiate the development of the pathological hypoalbuminenia (Beslekoev and Surodeikina, 1964).

When Ehrlich ascites cells were incubated in vitro with C^{14}-glycine, the presence of 0.15 M thiotepa caused decreased incorporation of the amino acid into cellular protein (Perevoshchikova, 1964).

An effect of thiotepa on carbohydrate metabolism has been reported in ascitic carcinoma (Burdzhanadze et al., 1965). Ascitic cells commonly contain an abnormally high amount of glycogen, and treatment with thiotepa reduced the glycogen content and simultaneously increased the glucose concentration in the ascitic fluid.

Respiration of human cancer cells is inhibited in vitro by thiotepa (5.3 mM or above); whereas, aerobic metabolism was stimulated (Katchman et al., 1963).

Thiotepa, 10^{-5} M, administered in vitro to liver cell homogenates and to liver carcinoma ascites cells, inhibited anaerobic glycolysis of the cancer cells but had very little effect on normal cells (Tsukagoshi et al., 1959). Aerobic glycolysis was affected only slightly in both the malignant and nonmalignant cells. In the normal cells, the P:O ratio was markedly lowered in the mitochondria, while in the cancer cells it was not affected. The oxygen consumption was depressed in normal cells but only slightly so in the tumor cells.

Thiotepa markedly inhibits the oxidation of α-keto-glutarate by mitochondria prepared from Ehrlich ascites cells (Maruyama, 1962). It is proposed that the inhibition, involving the NAD-linked oxidase systems, may be a general reaction of alkylating agents. This effect may be related to the finding of Kaji (1962) previously mentioned.

In mice, metabolism of 5-aminolevulinic acid, which is disturbed by tumors, can be restored to normal by treatment with thiotepa (Hano and Akashi, 1964). The biosynthesis of 5-aminolevulinic acid involves cellular constituents of several classes, i.e., succinyl CoA, pyridoxalphosphate, glycine, and an enzyme which may contain an essential SH group. Thiotepa has been found to alter the metabolism directly or indirectly of all these except B_6. The role of 5-aminolevulinic acid in porphyrin biosynthesis led to the establishment of its participation in the biosynthesis of vitamin B_{12} by microorganisms. Since the requirement for vitamin B_{12} has not been established in insects, other roles of 5-aminolevulinic acid might well be considered in relating this report to the chemosterilant activity of thiotepa, e.g. the porphyrins as cytochromes.

Certain furocoumarins (hydropencedanin, imperatonin, and bergapten) have little activity against Ehrlich ascites tumor cell, but have been found to increase the therapeutic effect of thiotepa (Vermel, 1964). The synergistic effect was noted even when the furocoumarin was administered by stomach tube and thiotepa by intraperitoneal injection (Vermel and Tsetlin, 1964). The furocoumarins may exert similar effects on the antifertility action of thiotepa in the sterilization of insects.

The effects of thiotepa on the reproductive capacity of mammalian cells have been compared by Berry (1964) to those of x-rays and the radiomimetic characteristics. Thiotepa produced a dose-response curve truly of the x-ray type in which the shoulder region is very sharp and resembles a true threshold below which no effect on cell survival is seen, but above which the survival decreases exponentially with dosage.

PHOSPHINE SULFIDE, BIS(1-AZIRIDINYL)MORPHOLINO

Synonyms

OPSPA
Morzid
OSPA
CL 14899
MSPA
N-(3-oxapentamethylene)-N',N-diethylene-thio-
   phosphoramide.
NSC 10429
ENT 25301

Structure

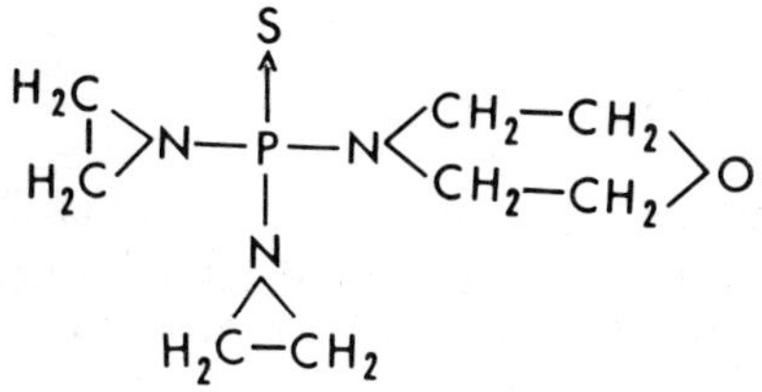

$C_8H_{16}N_3OPS$ Mol. wt. 245.11

Physical Properties

Physical form	Crystalline solid
Color	White
Odor	Garlic-like
Melting point	75 to 77°C

Solubility. Slightly soluble in water ($\leq$ 0.7 mg per ml at room temperature, J. S. Bowman, personal communication, American Cyanamide); very soluble in benzene, toluene, and hot petroleum ether (Crossley et al., 1953).

Stability. The extreme sensitivity of OSPA to acidic conditions, even in the cold, precludes the use of the common acidic reagents used for precipitation of protein (Maller and Heidelberger, 1957a). Neutral solutions appear to be fairly stable since it was shown, by thiosulfate titration, a solution of 10 mg/ml in saline contained 90 percent OPSPA after one month at room temperature (Heidelberger and Baumann, 1957). A solution in corn oil, kept refrigerated, was stable for the same period of time. It should be noted that these data are based upon the determination of the intact ethyleneimine ring and thus may not reflect the actual concentration of intact OPSPA.

Methods of Determination

Purity of OPSPA can be assessed by descending paper chromatography using n-butanol saturated with water as the developing solvent; the R_f of OPSPA is 0.87 (Maller and Heidelberger, 1957a). The high volatility of OPSPA when plated in thin layers makes it necessary to conduct assays for radiolabeled OPSPA by the wet combustion method (Maller and Heidelberger, 1957a).

Biochemistry

Following intraperitoneal injection of C^{14}-morpholino-labeled OPSPA in rats, the principal route of excretion was via the urine, 73 percent of the total injected radioactivity being passed during the first 24 hr, and only an additional 4 percent during the next 5 days (Maller and Heidelberger, 1957a). The maximum blood level was attained 1 hr after intratumoral injection but occurred 8 hr after intraperitoneal injection. The difference in time for maximum blood levels is probably a reflection of the high degree of vascularization of the tumor. Virtually all of the radioactivity in the blood was found to be water soluble, and only very little was bound to protein. In all tissues examined there was relatively low accumulation and no selective concentration was noted even in tumor tissue. Among the tissue fractions, distribution of P^{32}-labeled OPSPA was essentially the same as that of C^{14}-labeled OPSPA, the major portion being found in the aqueous and lipid fractions with only small amounts found in the protein and nucleic acid fractions. The amount of radiolabeled material in the aqueous and lipis fractions was less after 24 hr than at 2 hr; whereas the nucleic acid fraction radioactivity was greatest at 24 hr. The time required for maximum accumulation of radio-activity in the nucleic acid fraction indicates that OPSPA reacts, not directly with the nucleic acids, but rather with some pre-cursor involved in nucleic acid biosynthesis. These results are extremely interesting and indicate the value of a similar study of distribution of radioactive tepa, C^{14} and P^{32}-labeled (or both), injected into the male adult house fly or another suitable insect species. The tissue distribution and rate of excretion reported above are in agreement with those ob-served by Crossley et al. (1953) and Craig and Jackson (1955), who were using P^{32}-tepa. It was concluded that the tumor-inhibitory effects of the ethyleneimines must be caused by a minute amount of the chemical or of some metabolite.

The metabolic reations of OPSPA have been sum-marized by Maller and Heidelberger (1957b) as follows:

$$H_3PO_4 \xleftarrow{} OPSPA \xrightarrow{} O{\Big\langle}\begin{smallmatrix}CH_2-CH_2\\CH_2-CH_2\end{smallmatrix}{\Big\rangle}NH$$
$$\downarrow$$
$$MEPA$$

The formation of MEPA is analogous to the in vivo conversion of thiotepa to tepa. Although MEPA generally appears to be the principal metabolite, the extent of formation of each of these metabolites depends upon the species in which the reac-tions are being studied.

It has been shown that SKF525A (the diethylamino ester of diphenylpropyl acetic acid) significantly protects OPSPA from metabolic degradation in the rat (Maller and Heidelberger, 1957b). This ester, SKF-525A, had been shown previously to inhibit the microsomal desulfuration by which parathion is converted to an active cholinesterase inhibitor in mammalian liver (Davison, 1955). It would be interesting to study the effect of SKF-525A on the sterilant activity of OPSPA as well as on thiotepa.

Heidelberger and Baumann (1957) have reported that MEPA has better antineoplastic activity than tepa. Crossley and his co-workers (1953), however, reported that replacement of one of the ethyleneimine groups of tepa or morpholino, azetidyl or piperidyl group, did not alter oncolytic properties but did cause a marked reduction in the effect on testes. The activity of OPSPA against animal tumors was approximately equal to that of thiotepa (Crossley et al., 1953). As mentioned previously, the sterilant activity of OPSPA in the house fly is about equal to that of thiotepa, while the toxicity is greater (G. C. LaBrecque, personal communication).

The only reported effect of OPSPA on protein metabolism appears to be a reduction of albumins and an increase of the α-globulins in hepatectomized rats (Leonardi et al., 1959).

S-TRIAZINE, 2,4,6-TRIS(1-AZIRIDINYL)-

Synonyms

TEM
TET
Tretamine
Triamelin
Triethylenemelamine   (1Lederle)
Ppesistol Ho 1/193
M 9500
SK 1133
NSC 9706
R-246
ENT 25296

Structure

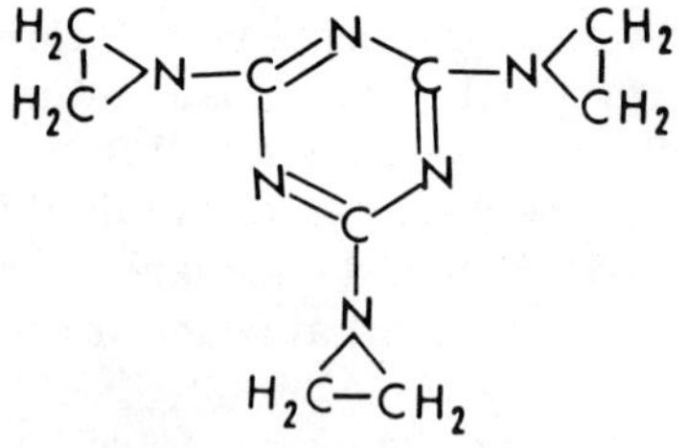

$C_9H_{12}N_6$ Mol. wt. 204.23

Physical Properties

Physical form	Crystalline solid
Color	White
Odor	None (or slight amine-line)
Melting point	160°C (polymerizes) (Goldenthal et al., 1958)
	139°C (decomp.) (Beroza and Borkovec, 1964)

Solubility. Freely soluble in water and chloroform; soluble in alcohol, acetone, benzene, and carbon tetrachloride.

Stability. Like all aziridine chemosterilants, TEM is extremely susceptible to moisture and acidic conditions. Beroza and Borkovec (1964) studied the degradation at 25 C in buffered solutions at pH 3, 5, and 7.5. Degradation at pH 3.0 was complete almost immediately and occurred more rapidly at pH 5.0 than at pH 7.5; very little degradation had occurred after 24 hr in either unbuffered solutions or buffer at pH 7.5. The degradation products remained at the origin of silica gel plates developed in chloroform:acetone (1:1) whereas the R value for TEM was 0.34.

Crystalline TEM, stored at room temperatures, polymerize forming an inactive material.

TEM has been stabilized by preparing solutions in aliphatic saturated alcohols containing from one to four carbon atoms (Maeda et al., 1964). A solution of 5 percent TEM in methanol was sealed in a tube and stored at 25 C without any loss for 3 months.

TEM may also be stabilized by adding 99 to 95 parts of anhydrous polyethylene glycols, average molecular weight of 200 to 600, to 1 to 5 parts TEM (Nakabayashi, 1958). Samples prepared in this manner were stable for at least 12 months and were completely soluble in water.

Methods of Determination and Purification

TEM may be purified by recrystallization from ethyl acetate (Beroza and Borkovec, 1964) or from chloroform and then determined by the common alkylating agent determinations.

Biochemistry

More than 90 percent of the radioactivity was lost from the blood within a few minutes following injection of tri-C - ethyleneimine-s-triazine into mice and rats (Goldenthal et al., 1958). The amount of radioactivity in feces and exhaled CO was comparatively small. Within 24 hr after injection, 68 to 73 percent of the labeled material was excreted in the urine; during the next 24 hr only 4 to 6 percent was found in the urine. Sixteen metabolites were detected when urine samples were chromatographed on an ion exchange column. The majority of the radioactivity (74 percent) was distributed among five major radioactive compounds in the eluant. One of these was identified as creatinine, indicating that the ethyleneimine moiety of TEM had been converted to 2-carbon fragments. The principle metabolite gave a positive test with ninhydrin after treatment with sodium hydroxide and is believed to be a conjugate or alkylated product of an amino acid or an amine. The major urinary metabolites showed no absorption peaks when examined in ultraviolet light, thus eliminating the possibility of these metabolites being purines, pyrimidines, or derivatives. Glycine, ethanolamine, and aminoacetaldehyde were all ruled out as possible metabolites and it was postulated that most of the urinary constituents represented alkylated normal metabolites (Smith et al., 1958).

Similar distribution and excretion of TEM was noted in the human (Nadkarni et al., 1959). The urinary excretion pattern indicated that the alkylating portion of the molecule was separated from the carrier. No unchanged drug was detected in the urine and the R values of radioactive metabolites did not correlate with those of amino acids commonly found in urine. Subsequently, it was found that within a few minutes after administration of C -labeled TEM to human patients, the level of radioactivity declined rapidly to a low level which then remained constant for 48 hr (Nadkarni et al., 1961). During the first 48 hr following administration of the chemical, 25 to 30 percent of the radioactivity was excreted in the urine.

In vivo degradation of C^{14}-TEM by conversion to cyanuric acid as shown in the following scheme occurred rapidly in the mouse (Nadkarni et al., 1954).

It is well known that the pH difference between normal and neoplastic tissues can be accentuated by treatment with glucose. As a result, certain alkylating agents would be likely to have a greater cytotoxic effect on those tissues having the lowered pH. As an example of this effect, the therapeutic index of TEM was significantly increased by glucose pretreatment of rats bearing the Walker tumor (Connors et al., 1964b). It would be interesting to see if sterilizing activity might be similarly enhanced by a "pretreatment" of insects with glucose.

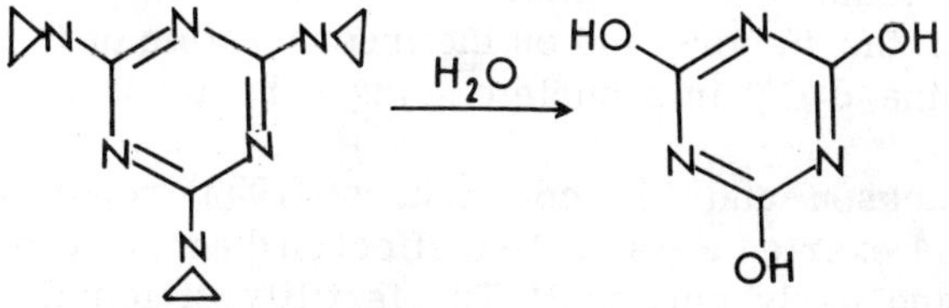

The administration of cysteine (150 mg/kg) to rats just prior to treatment with TEM reduced the cytostatic effects of the alkylating agent (Pliess, 1960). Administration of cysteine 30 min earlier, however, actually enhanced the cytostatic effects of TEM. Treatment with serotonin, either before or after administration of TEM, also enhanced the cytostatic effects. It was concluded that the protective effect of different compounds against the cytostatic drugs is achieved through a general nonspecific reaction within the organism or by cell-specific reactions which are accomplished through preferential protection of specific tissues.

Pre-incubation of TEM with L-cysteine or sodium thiosulfate eliminated the inactivation of bacteriophage T3 usually caused by TEM (Uecker, 1962). In addition, cysteine and sodium thiosulfate showed some ability to facilitate reactivation of the phage after inactivation by TEM. The in vitro alkylation of the thiol group of cysteine by TEM has been shown to form a nontoxic product having the following structure (Goldenthal et al., 1959).

The effects of TEM on cyclophosphamide-sensitive and resistant tumors are similar to the effect of thiotepa on the growth of the tumors and on the incorporation of C^{14}-formate and adenine-8-C^{14} into nucleic acids (Wheeler and Alexander, 1964a).

Jackson and his co-workers (1955) reported that in rats, TEM exerted a "selective effect on the male reproductive system and early embryo." The fertility of female rats was not affected by four times the daily dosage effective in males. Subsequently, it was shown that the principal action of TEM was exerted on spermatocytes and spermatids. With increased amounts of TEM, however, the effects became more general and even affected mature sperm (Jackson et al., 1959). It was also shown that a variety of ethyleneimino compounds exerted antifertility effects. Trifunctional compounds were the most effective while monofunctional compounds were the least; although the latter were very destructive to the seminiferous epithelium.

In an elegant study, the selective effect of di- and poly-functional ethyleneimines on spermatogenesis and fertility was demonstrated (Jackson, 1964). The apparent sensitivity of the spermatids and spermatozoa to genetic damage by TEM was difficult to understand in view of the fact that "premeiotic spermatocytes in the same physical environment" were unaffected. The need for additional studies was pointed out by the author.

During the course of normal spermatic development in the rat, the solubility of spermatid DNA in strong salt solutions decreases after the completion of the acrosome phase, becoming completely insoluble by the end of the maturation phase when the spermatozoa are formed (Berenbaum, 1962a). Treatment of the rat with TEM caused a definite loss of extractability of the DNA superimposed on the normal changes, beginning almost immediately after intraperitoneal injection and becoming most evident in spermatids during the late acrosome and early midmaturation phases. It is noteworthy that monofunctional alkylating agents did not show this effect. The naturally occurring changes in extractability appear to be the result of development of an insoluble protein sheath in the spermatid, and the loss of solubility superimposed by treatment with TEM may be the result of cross-linking of the DNA to the protein sheath.

It has been suggested by Berenbaum and Calley (1962)

that changes which occur in the cell during differentiation may alter the susceptibility of the cell; the later stages of differentiation being especially susceptible to mustards and ethyleneimines and not so susceptible to radiation. Mustards and ethyleneimines damage differentiating cells, megakaryocytes, spermatids, and spermatozoa, even though they are not dividing. Berenbaum and Calley stated: "It is often assumed that tumor inhibitory agents differentially damage tumors because they are particularly noxious to rapidly proliferating cells. This does not explain their therapeutic effect in acute leukemias, in which the neoplastic cells may divide less frequently than normal cells (Gavosto et al., 1960)." Similarly, reaction with dividing cells does not explain the ability of ethyleneimines to cause rapid loss of fertility in mature adult insects regardless of their age. It thus appears that the antifertility effect of ethyleneimines may also be on the process of differentiation or on some susceptible stage in the differentiation of the sperm, egg, or zygote. The proposed susceptibility of differentiating cells may be related to the effect of TEM upon maturation and release of hematopoietic cells as well as on proliferation of these cells in rats (Pliess, 1961).

Effects of TEM on the different stages of spermatogenesis have been demonstrated by several workers. In rabbits, aspermia developed during the tenth and eleventh weeks following administration of TEM (Fox et al., 1963a). TEM has been shown to act on the early stages of spermatid development and on spermatogonia in the sea urchin (Fox et al., 1963b). The effect of low concentrations of TEM on ova caused a significant increase in the number of abnormalities which were presumably due to polyspermic fertilizations. The role of sulfhydryl compounds in the processes which accompany cell division (Bolognari, 1952, and Sakai and Dan, 1959) and the requirement for thiol compounds in the formation of the mitotic apparatus (Mazia, 1960) are well known. The effects on spermatogenesis may be the result of in vivo reaction of TEM with sulfhydryl compounds in a manner analogous to the in vitro reaction with cysteine which has already been discussed.

TEM was found to exert a specific effect in the testicular germinal epithelium on the early generations of type A spermatogonia in rats (Steinberger, 1962). Repeated administration of TEM caused only a minimum effect on the primary spermatocytes.

The mustards and ethyleneimines have been called "radiomimetic" principally because the gross physiological changes caused by these chemicals are similar to those induced by radiation. Upon examination of the details of specific reactions, however, it becomes apparent that the term "radiomimetic" is in some respects inaccurate in describing the biological activity of these chemicals. Some differences between the biological effects of radiation and of "radiomimetic" chemicals as noted by Berenbaum and Calley (1962) are shown in Table 7.

TABLE 7

COMPARISON OF PHYSIOLOGICAL EFFECTS OF RADIATION TO THOSE OF MUSTARDS AND ETHYLENEIMINES

Mustards and ethyleneimines	Radiation and mylerans
1. Cause crosslinking in significant amount of DNA in living cells (Alexander and Lett, 1960), (Berenbaum, 1962a).	1. No significant degree of crosslinking occurs (Alexander and Lett, 1960).
2. In tissue culture of mouse lymphoblasts mitosis is stopped immediately (Alexander and Mikulski, 1961).	2. Mitosis is stopped in tissue culture of mouse lymphoblasts only after some delay (Alexander and Mikulski, 1961).
3. Antibody production is inhibited even if given after the antigen (Berenbaum, 1961, 1962b).	3. Antibody production is inhibited only if radiation occurs before the antigen is administered (Berenbaum, 1961, 1962b, and Dixon et al., 1952).
4. Cause early onset of sterility in the male rat, probably by damage to spermatids and spermatozoa (nondividing cells) (Berenbaum, 1962a, Craig et al., 1958, Block and Jackson, 1957, and Sherman and Steinberger, 1960).	4. Onset of sterility occurs late (Craig et al., 1958).

(Adapted from Berenbaum and Calley, 1962.

TEM has been shown to alter protein synthesis as indicated by two reports of depressed antibody formation. Berenbaum (1962b) found that administration of TEM 2 days after injection of T.A.B. vaccine actually suppressed antibody formation for some weeks in mice. The development of the antibody titer was found to be delayed for several days when TEM was administered with human erythrocytes (Cassi et al., 1962). In addition, TEM caused reduction in the albumin and an increase in the α-globulin fractions in hepatectomized rats (Leonardi et al., 1959).

Alteration of purine metabolism was indicated by a marked increase in the urinary excretion of allantoin and by a slight increase in the uric acid content of the animal following the administration of TEM to rats bearing the Yoshida sarcoma (Takemasa, 1958). This effect of TEM seems to be related to the neoplasm because practically no change was noted in the normal rats similarly treated.

Effects of TEM on nucleic acid metabolism include the formation of large molecular aggregates by the in vitro reaction of TEM with solutions of herring sperm DNA (Klemm and Obrecht, 1962) and the depression of the uptake of P^{32} into cells of Ehrlich ascites carcinoma by TEM (Krepsz et al., 1964). The in vivo incorporation of C^{14}-TEM into DNA was estimated to be of the order of one mole per mole of DNA (Trams et al., 1961). Since there appeared to be no correlation between tumor susceptibility and the amount of labeled material incorporated into the DNA, it was concluded that the attack of DNA does not necessarily represent the mode of action of TEM in causing cytostatic and cytotoxic effects.

In rats and guinea pigs, treatment with TEM caused a decrease in glycogen content and alkaline phosphatase activity of the cells in the marrow and peripheral blood (Squadrito et al., 1961). A large number of compounds of biological interest (e.g., nicotinamide, pyridoxine, adenine, thiamine, riboflavin, folic acid, methionine, and lysine) were alkylated in vitro by TEM and several other alkylating agents (Duntze et al., 1962).

ETHANOL, 2-CHLORO-METHANESULFONATE-

Synonyms

2-Chloroethylmethanesulfonate
Methane sulfonic acid, 2-chloroethyl ester
β-Chloroethylmethanesulfonate
CB 1506
NSC 18016
ENT 26395

Structure

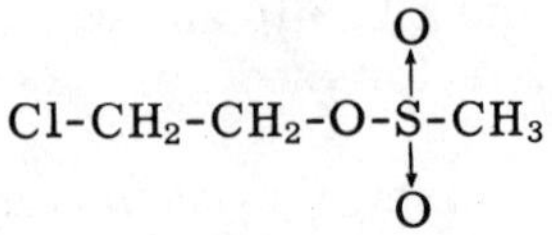

$$Cl-CH_2-CH_2-O-\overset{\overset{\displaystyle O}{\uparrow}}{\underset{\underset{\displaystyle O}{\downarrow}}{S}}-CH_3$$

$C_3H_7ClO_3S$ Mol. wt. 158.6

Physical Properties

Physical form	Oily liquid
Color	Colorless
Odor	Odorless
Melting point	5 to 6°C (Ross and Davis, 1957)
Boiling point	(11.5 mm) 130°C (Pattison and Millington, 1956)
	(11 mm) 130°C (Ross and Davis, 1957)
	(17 mm) 138 to 142°C (Ross, 1958a)
	(10 mm) 126°C (Kostova and Leontéva, 1960)
	(14 mm) 134 to 135°C (Haddow and Ross, 1956)
Refractive index	n_D^{25} 1.4545 (Pattison and Millington, 1956)
	n_D^{19} 1.4570 (Ross and Davis, 1957)
	n_D^{17} 1.4571 (Haddow and Ross, 1956)
Density	d_{20} 1.420 (Pattison and Millington, 1956)
	d_{20} 1.3837 (Kostova and Leontéva, 1960)

Solubility. Soluble in approximately 50 times its volume of water (equivalent to 2.8 percent); in saline at 1.25 percent or greater (Papac et al., 1958) but less than 5 percent (Duvall, 1961).

Stability. Extent of hydrolysis was < 2 percent after two hr at 37.5°C, and 20 percent after 10 days at 37°C (Briggs, 1960). Liberation of the sulfonoxy group occurs at a greater rate than the loss of the chlorine atom on boiling water (Haddow and Ross, 1956). The sulfonoxy group is replaced preferentially in chemical substitution reactions (Pattison and Millington, 1956). The chemical is sensitive to light which causes autocatalytic degradation involving acid production. Samples should be stored in a dark bottle containing a few pieces of potassium carbonate.

Biochemistry

The sulfonic esters react by the $S_N 2$ type mechanism in which the rate is dependent upon the concentration of the reacting centers (Ross, 1958b). Chloroethylmethanesulfonates and other sulfonic esters are believed to react via the formation of a carbonium ion. The reaction of the positively charged carbonium ion occurs with electron-rich centers which, in biological systems, include organic and inorganic anions, amino and sulfide groups. Since the reaction proceeds via $S_N 2$ mechanism, the concentrations of both the alkylating agent and the target molecule determine the rate of reaction. Schematically:

$$Cl\text{-}CH_2CH_2\text{-}O\text{-}SO_2\text{-}CH_3 + A^- \longrightarrow (Cl\text{-}CH_2CH_2 \overset{\delta-}{-\,-\,-}O\text{-}SO_2\text{-}CH_3) \longrightarrow$$
$$\overset{\big\backslash}{\underset{A^{\delta-}}{}}$$

$$Cl\text{-}CH_2CH_2\text{-}A + {}^-OSO_2CH_3$$

In a biological system the reactivity of a particular group depends upon the degree of dissociation as well as the concentration of the group. The alkyl methanesulfonates are believed to react in vivo by combination with sulfhydryl groups (Roberts and Warwick, 1958a). The products of such an in vivo reaction were isolated from rats treated with alkane sulfonates (Roberts and Warwick, 1958b, 1959a).

Chloroethylmethanesulfonate is rather unique among esters of methanesulfonate in that it shows striking activity against lymphoma 8, whether the tumor is well established or recently innoculated (Schmidt, 1960).

Anaerobic glycolysis of ascites tumor cells was found to be initially stimulated but subsequently inhibited by 2-chloroethylmethanesulfonate as shown in Table 8 (Briggs, 1960). In addition, respiration was inhibited in vivo but the

TABLE 8

ANAEROBIC GLYCOLYSIS OF EHRLICH ASCITES-TUMOUR
CELLS IN THE PRESENCE OF VARYING QUANTITIES OF
β-CHLOROETHYL METHANESULFONATE

| Time | $Q_G^{N_2}$ values and % control (see Dixon, 1952) | | | |
	0	43 mM	85 mM	128 mM
5	41.5 (100%)	43.4 (105%)	48.7 (118%)	55.8 (135%)
60	41.5 (100%)	43.5 (105%)	48.7 (118%)	23.9 (58%)
120	41.5 (100%)	43.4 (105%)	21.9 (53%)	17.5 (42%)
180	36.7 (100%)	38.7 (106%)	7.0 (19%)	5.2 (14%)

(From Briggs 1960.)

pure hydrolysis products of 2-chloroethylmethanesulfonate,
sodium methanesulfonate, and 2-chloroethanol, had no effect
on respiration. Administration of lipoic acid, nicotinamide, or
thiamine failed to reverse the inhibition. Effects of L-cysteine
were complicated and were interpreted to mean that this
compound did not protect respiration from 2-chloroethyl-
methanesulfonate, but caused an initial increase in oxygen
uptake due to auto-oxidation and inhibition of respiration possibly due to destruction of a respiratory factor (Slater, 1949).
The degree of inhibition of respiration was found to be dependent upon the substrate being used, i.e., endogenous DL-
malate, citrate, pyruvate, succinate, or glucose. Reversal of
the inhibition was accomplished by washing the cells free of
the drug, complete reversal being achieved when low concentrations of the drug had been used. The drug inhibited soluble
succinic dehydrogenase, succinoxidase-cytochrome C reductase preparation, and a pyruvate-dismutation system, but did
not inhibit fumarase, L-malic dehydrogenase, lactic dehydrogenase, aconitase, or L-glutamic dehydrogenase.

The inhibition of rat-liver succinoxidase-cytochrome
c-reductase is shown in Fig. 4. Based upon the kinetic evidence
and enzymic studies, it was proposed that the inhibition of
respiration by 2-chloroethylmethanesulfonate is caused by
physical effects of the alkylating agent on the hydrogen transport chain of the cell.

The molecular basis for the mutagenic effect of 2-
chloroethylmethanesulfonate on D. melanogaster has been pro-

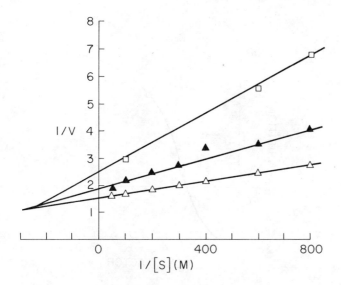

FIG. 4. Inhibition of rat-liver succinoxidase-cytochrome c reductase by β-chloroethyl methanesulfonate. Lineweaver and Burk plot of $1/v$ against $1/[S]$, where reaction velocity v is $+\Delta E_{550}$ mμ/10 min, $[S]$, succinate concentration (M). Drug was in contact with enzyme for 10 min at room temperature, 22°C, before assay. Medium contained mM-EDTA and 16 6 mM phosphate buffer, pH 7.0. $\triangle$, Controls; $\blacktriangle$, 10 0 mM β-chloroethyl methanesulfonate; $\square$, 25 1 mM β-chloroethyl methanesulfonate. (From Briggs, 1960.)

posed to be a result of reaction with the thiol group of cysteine to form S-chloroethyl-N-acetyl-cysteine, a sulfur mustard (Fahmy and Fahmy, 1957). Roberts and Warwick (1957) indicated that such a reaction would be analogous to the reported reaction of ethyl methanesulfonate with cysteine. The finding that S-chloroethylcysteine has the same characteristic high mutagenic effects as 2-chloroethylmethanesulfonate upon the early germ cells of *D. melanogaster* supports this proposal (Fahmy and Fahmy, 1957).

N. W. Coles and his co-workers (1960) have reported that in relatively short-term experiments, the incorporation of glycine-1-C^{14} into the ethanol-acetone insoluble fraction of Ehrlich ascites cells is inhibited in tumors, embryos, and normal adult tissue. The susceptibility of various tissues differs and is explained as related to "different rates of entry"

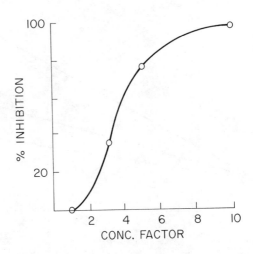

FIG. 5. Inhibition of glycine-1-C[14] incorporation into Ehrlich ascites cell proteins as a function of the concentration of the alkylating agent, 2-chloroethyl methanesulfonate. Concentration factor, $10 \equiv 42$ mM. Incubation with 2 mM glycine-1-C[14] for 60 min after 30 min pre-incubation with the alkylating agent in Krebs-Ringer phosphate medium, 37° C; gas phase is air. (From Coles et al., 1960.)

into the tissue or to "different affinities for receptor substances within the tissue." The extent of inhibition of incorporation increases with concentration of the chemical as shown in Fig. 5.

The stage of incorporation inhibited by the alkylating agent cannot be determined from the data available. Energy production from respiration does appear to be affected, but some direct effect on the process of incorporation is evident from studies conducted under anaerobic conditions.

ETHANOL, 2-FLUORO-METHANESULFONATE-

Synonyms

Fluoroethylmethanesulfonate
Methane sulfonic acid, 2-fluoroethyl ester
ENT 50191

Structure

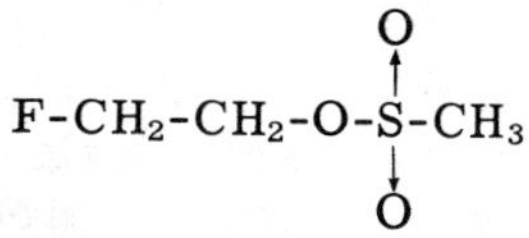

$$F-CH_2-CH_2-O-\overset{\displaystyle O}{\underset{\displaystyle O}{\overset{\uparrow}{\underset{\downarrow}{S}}}}-CH_3$$

$C_3H_7FO_3S$ Mol. wt. 142.06

Physical Properties

Physical form	Liquid
Color	Colorless
Odor	Odorless
Boiling point	(12 mm Hg) 118 to 119°C (Pattison and Millington, 1956)
	(18 mm Hg) 130°C (Haddow and Ross, 1956)
Refractive index	n_D^{25} 1.4145 (Pattison and Millington, 1956)
	n_D^{21} 1.4150 (Haddow and Ross, 1956)

Stability. Similar to that of 2-chloroethylmethanesulfonate.

Biochemistry

Fluoroethylmethanesulfonate possesses the same chemical reactivity as the chloro-derivative, but would not be expected to form a highly reactive mustard in vivo (Fahmy and Fahmy, 1957).

Treatment of neoplasms with fluoroethylmethanesulfonate causes lesions of the nucleus and cytoplasm indicating an effect on nucleic acid synthesis (Ricciardi et al., 1959). The effects appear to be a result of interference with polymerization in which the electrophilic center of the methanesulfonate active radical reacts with the nucleophiles of the biological system.

In a study of toxicities of ω-fluoroalkyl esters, it was noted with some surprise that 2-fluoroethylmethanesulfonate was relatively low in toxicity (Millington and Pattison, 1956). Since the parent alcohol, 2-fluoroethanol, had a toxicity of 10 mg/kg, it was concluded that the sulfonate ester was not readily hydrolyzed in vivo, whereas hydrolysis of the higher members of the series did occur. The toxic effects of the ω-fluorine atom of fluoroethanol appear to be considerably less than the higher even carbon-number members of a series. The reason for this anomaly is not known, but it was proposed that the intra-molecular electronic influence of the 2-fluorine atom on the other functional groups interferes with metabolic degradation and thus probably outweighs steric and solubility effects.

BUTANOL, 4-FLUORO-METHANESULFONATE-

Synonyms

Fluorobutylmethanesulfonate
Methanesulfonic acid, 4-fluorobutyl ester
ENT 50430

Structure

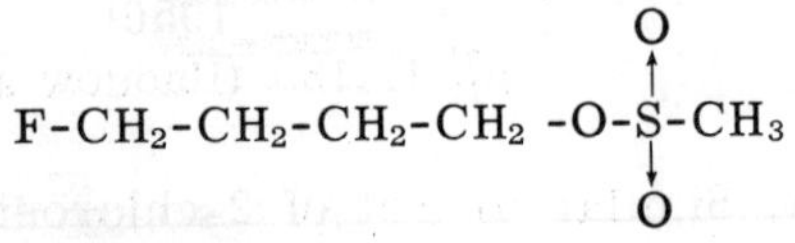

$$F-CH_2-CH_2-CH_2-CH_2-O-\overset{\displaystyle O}{\underset{\displaystyle O}{\overset{\displaystyle \uparrow}{\underset{\displaystyle \downarrow}{S}}}}-CH_3$$

$C_5H_{11}FO_3S$ Mol. wt. 170.08

Physical Properties

Physical form	Liquid
Color	Pale straw color
Odor	Odorless
Boiling point	(0.5 mm Hg) 89 to 90°C (Millington and Pattison, 1956)
Refractive index	n_D^{25} 1.4242 (Millington and Pattison, 1956)

Solubility. Soluble in alcohol, slightly soluble in acetone, insoluble in water.

Stability. This material should be stored at refrigerator temperatures.

Biochemistry

It has been pointed out that for ω-fluorinated compounds the ω-fluoro group acts as a unique indicator of the metabolism of the whole molecule. The members of an ascending homologous series of ω-fluorinated compounds showed a unique alternation of toxicity. The more toxic members containing an even number of carbon atoms were believed to undergo β-oxidation to form fluoroacetic acid while the less toxic members produced the "innocuous" fluoropropionic acid. Fluoroacetate causes the accumulation of citric acid in various tissues (Buffa and Peters, 1939). Peters (1953) has proposed that the citrate accumulation is a result of the conversion of fluoroacetate to fluorocitrate which acts as a competitive inhibition of aconitase, the enzyme responsible for the conversion of citrate to cis-aconitate and isocitrate. It was demonstrated that toxic members of a series of ω-fluoro compounds did indeed cause accumulation of citric acid in the kidney and brain of mice 20 min after treatment (Parker and Walker, 1957).

2,5-HEXANEDIOL, DIMETHANESULFONATE

Synonyms

Dimethylmyleran
Methanesulfonic acid, 1,4-dimethyltetramethylene ester
CB 2348
ENT 50858
Meso-2, 5-dimethanesulfonoxyhexane

Structure

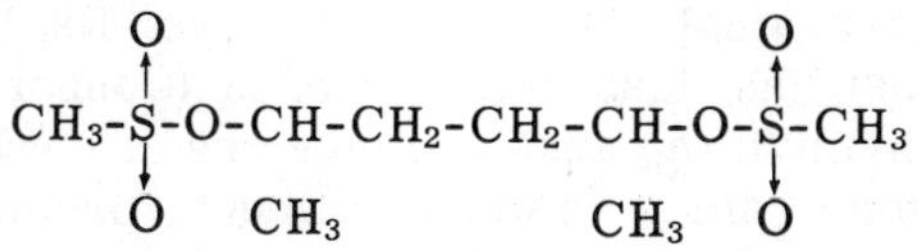

$$CH_3-\underset{\underset{O}{\parallel}}{\overset{\overset{O}{\parallel}}{S}}-O-CH-CH_2-CH_2-CH-O-\underset{\underset{O}{\parallel}}{\overset{\overset{O}{\parallel}}{S}}-CH_3$$
$$\qquad\qquad\quad CH_3 \qquad\qquad CH_3$$

$C_8H_{18}O_6S_2$ Mol. wt. 274.14

Physical Properties

Physical form	Crystalline solid
Color	White
Odor	Odorless
Melting point	97.5°C (Timmis et al., 1962)

Solubility. Sparingly soluble in water; soluble in ethanol.

Stability. Unstable in aqueous solutions.

Biochemistry

In brain tissue of female rats, dimethylmyleran caused a slight reduction in acid-soluble SH values which lasted for 24 hr but was followed by a rise to normal levels (Calcutt, 1965). No significant variation in the protein-bound SH values was noted, but marked fluctuations in acid-soluble SH levels were observed. In lympoid tissue, dimethylmyleran also caused erratic fluctuations in acid-soluble and protein-bound SH values. Calcutt and Connors (1963) have proposed that a high ratio of protein-bound SH: nonprotein-bound SH indicates a high degree of sensitivity to alkylating agents in general.

Administration of dimethylmyleran to patients having chronic granulocytic leukemia caused a decrease of glutamic acid, aspartic acid, and taurine in the free amino acids of plasma of erythrocytes and of leukocytes (Rouser et al., 1962). It is suggested that reaction of myleran, and hence dimethylmyleran, with sulfhydryl groups plays an important role in the mode of action of these drugs. This hypothesis is supported by the observation that administration of the drug altered the concentration of sulfur containing amino compounds in the free amino acid pool.

Thiol compounds have been reported to exert a protective effect against the more reactive alkylating agents but not against the less reactive ones (Connors and Elson, 1962). Dimethylmyleran appears to be one of the less reactive alkylating agents since cysteine failed to protect rats from the toxic effects of the drug. Roberts and Warwick (1959a, b), however, found that myleran reacted with sulfhydryl compounds in the rat.

Details of metabolic degradation of dimethylmyleran

have not been reported, but it has been shown that myleran, structurally quite similar to dimethylmyleran, was not metabolized via the butanediol route, as was expected, but rather formed one major urinary metabolite in rats (Roberts and Warwick, 1959a). It was concluded that the predominant reaction of myleran in the rat is alkylation of the sulfhydryl group, probably that of cysteine or cysteine-containing compounds, thus forming a cyclic sulfonium salt, the precursor of the major urinary metabolite. The sulfonium ions may cause profound effects by altering the structure and function of macromolecules.

Dimethylmyleran appears to be truly radiomimetic, killing cells by a mechanism similar to that of x-rays (Alexander, 1961). It was suggested that the probable mode of action of alkylating agents was by cross-linking different molecules of DNA, although it was recognized that alkylation of DNA in some other fashion may also occur. In addition, it should be noted that esterification of phosphate or carboxyl groups may lead to altered membrane permeability.

Dimethylmyleran and nitrogen mustard have been shown to elicit different patterns of response in leukemia cells growing in tissue culture (Alexander and Mikulski, 1961). The relation between log survivors and dose showed a marked threshold with dimethylmyleran, whereas with nitrogen mustard the relation was nearly linear. Cells were able to divide at least once after treatment with dimethylmyleran, while nitrogen mustard stopped cell division at once. The cells differed in appearance depending upon which agent had been administered. It was suggested that the initial chemical reactions responsible for the effects on growth are different because different sites are alkylated. The effects of dimethylmyleran resemble more closely those of x-rays than do those of nitrogen mustard.

Antifertility effects of several simple alkane sulfonic esters were assessed in the male rat by a combination of histological examinations of the testes and serial matings of treated animals (Jackson et al., 1961). When compared to those obtained with dimethylmyleran and derivatives of ethyleneimine, the results were difficult to reconcile with a common mode of action due to alkylation of cellular components.

BUTYRIC ACID, 4-{*p*-[BIS(2-CHLOROETHYL)AMINO]-PHENYL}-

Synonyms

Chlorambucil
Leukeran[R]
CB 1348
ENT 26083

Structure

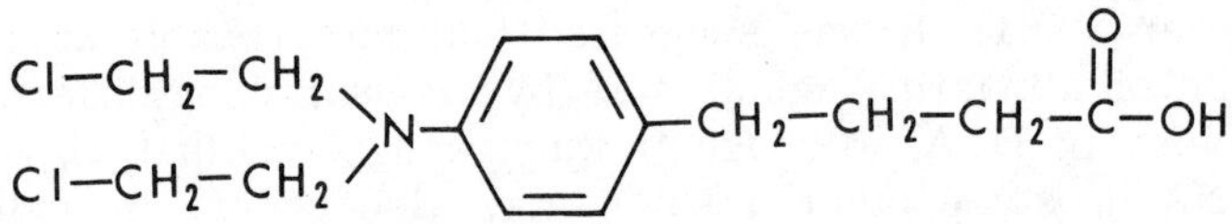

$C_{14}H_{19}N\ Cl_2O_2$ Mol. wt. 304.22

Physical Properties

Physical form	Flattened needles
Color	Off-white
Odor	Odorless
Melting point	64 to 66°C

Ultraviolet absorption spectra in different solvents have been reported by Linford (1962a) and λ max (at 30 μg/ml in H_2O (pH 9.5) is 1.55 at 256 mμ; in alcohol, 1.85.

Solubility. Very soluble in water; soluble in dilute alkali; and in acetone (50 percent) and ether. Crystallizes from petroleum ether. Details for preparing solutions of reactive (chloro) or inactive (hydroxyl) form of chlorambucil in alkaline or acidic medium are described by Linford (1962a).

Stability. Hydrolysis of the salt of chlorambucil occurs rapidly in alkaline solution, the chlorine atoms being replaced with hydroxyl groups creating an inactive form (Linford, 1962a). The hydrolytic reaction in aqueous bicarbonate or sodium hydroxide at 37°C is complete in 2 hr.

Methods of Determination

The photofluorometric method of Mellet and Woods (1960), while useful for detection of ethyleneimino and chloroethylamino groups, requires an involved procedure and laborious manipulations. A spectrophotometric assay has been developed which can detect as little as 2 μg/ml (Linford, 1962b). This method was used in studying the condensation reactions of chloroambucil with human and dog serum, and also with dog plasma, in vitro.

Petering and Van Giessen (1963) modified the method of Klatt et al. (1960) and developed a colorimetric method for uracil- and aliphatic-nitrogen mustards. The absorbancy at 60 mμ of a solution of chloroambucil was 0.199 (± .006) per 10 μg and 0.605 per 0.1 μmole.

Various types of nitrogen mustards have been studied with respect to their rate of in vitro alkylation of 4-(p-nitrobenzyl) pyridine, their rates of hydrolysis, and their anti-tumor activity (Bardos et al., 1965). Among the aromatic-nitrogen mustards, alkylation and hydrolysis rates are both dependent upon the basicity of the nitrogen. The reactivities are dramatically decreased by electron-attracting ring substituents para to the nitrogen and increased by electron-releasing substituents. The results of correlations between antitumor activities and percent hydrolysis, or alklylating activity, indicated that the biologically significant reactions of the aromatic-nitrogen mustards more closely parallel the S_N1-type solvolysis reaction than the S_N2-type alkylation reaction. Although in vitro alkylation rates of the agents would differ for each nucleophile, the relative effects of change in substituent groups on the alkylating agent would be the same provided the reaction proceeds via S_N2 mechanism. It was concluded that the rate-controlling step of the biologically significant reactions would be the formation of a transition state more closely resembling a solvated carbonium ion-nitrogen dipole (A-3) than the aziridinium ion-S_N2 complex (A-2) (Fig. 6). Since this transition state might be expected to react with the water molecules to a greater extent than with the nucleophilic groups of the cell constituents, it was proposed that alkylating agents be designed ''which would generate an A-3 type transition state only in the immediate vicinity of the desired site of action.''

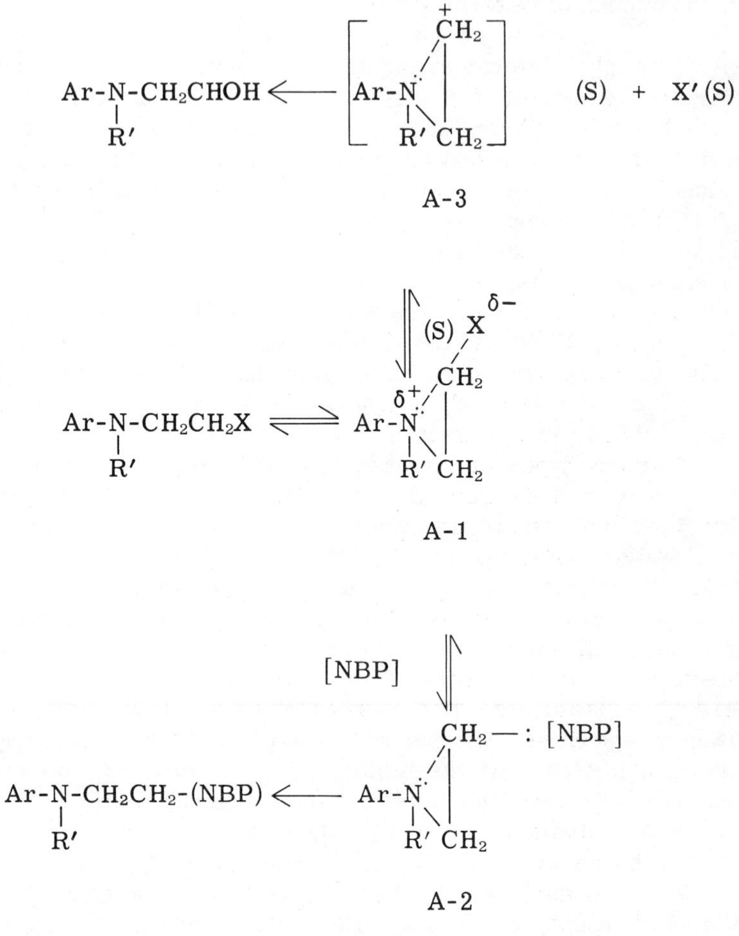

$$Ar\text{-}N\text{-}CH_2CHOH \longleftarrow \left[Ar\text{-}\overset{..}{N} \overset{\overset{+}{CH_2}}{\underset{CH_2}{\big|}} \right] \quad (S) \; + \; X'(S)$$

$$\underset{R'}{|}$$

A-3

$$Ar\text{-}N\text{-}CH_2CH_2X \; \rightleftharpoons \; Ar\text{-}\overset{\delta+}{N} \overset{\overset{(S)\; \overset{\delta-}{X}}{\underset{CH_2}{\big/}}}{\underset{CH_2}{\big|}}$$

$$\underset{R'}{|} \qquad\qquad\qquad R'$$

A-1

$$[NBP]$$

$$Ar\text{-}N\text{-}CH_2CH_2\text{-}(NBP) \longleftarrow Ar\text{-}\overset{..}{N} \overset{\overset{CH_2 - :\,[NBP]}{\big/}}{\underset{CH_2}{\big|}}$$

$$\underset{R'}{|} \qquad\qquad\qquad R'$$

A-2

FIG. 6. Reaction mechanisms for hydrolytic and alkylating reactions of aromatic nitrogen mustards. From Bardos et al., 1965, J. Med. Chem., 8(2):167–174. Copyright 1964 by the American Chemical Society. (Reprinted by permission of the copyright owner.)

Biochemistry

The results of in vitro inhibition of general glycolytic enzymes have indicated that chlorambucil may inhibit glycolysis at several different points, thus impairing utilization of glucose and energy production (Brecher and Baker, 1965). Table 9 shows the degree of inhibition of the specific enzymes caused by preincubation at 0°C for 110 min with chlorambucil.

TABLE 9

Enzyme	Chlorambucil	% Inhibition
Lactic dehydrogenase	$5 \times 10^{-4}\ M$	100
Hexokinase	$4 \times 10^{-3}\ M$	96
Enolase	$2 \times 10^{-3}\ M$	99.5
Aldolase	$2 \times 10^{-3}\ M$	100

(Adapted from Brecher and Baker, 1965.)

The reactivity of chlorambucil in aqueous solutions, as determined by the rate of the alkylation reaction with hemoglobin, decreases as the pH decreases below 7 (Linford, 1963a). Both solubility of chlorambucil and the degree of dissociation of its carboxyl group decrease at acidic pH values. In consideration of the effect of pH on these factors, it was concluded that the activation of chlorambucil to a carbonium ion form occurs as a result of the approach of the carboxyl to the chloro group. The effect of alkanoic side chains, and the points of attachment to the benzene ring, on the reactivity of members of this series of compounds can thus be explained. These considerations also help to explain the greater reactivity of the bifunctional mustards.

The rate of alkylation of hemoglobin and bovine serum albumin by chlorambucil in vitro at pH 8.4, 37°C has been studied (Linford, 1963b). Although these proteins are approximately the same molecular weight and have the same carboxyl group content, the alkylation reaction is 30 times faster with hemoglobin. The adsorption of chloroambucil by bovine serum albumin, however, is 20 times greater than that of hemoglobin. The inverse relation between the extent of adsorption and the reaction rate indicates that adsorption protects chlorambucil from undergoing activation in the solvent.

Chlorambucil-C^{14} was incorporated into the DNA fraction of regenerating liver and various other mouse ascites lymphomas (Trams et al., 1961). The extent of in vivo incorporation was estimated to be approximately one mole per mole of DNA. No correlation was observed, however,

between susceptibility of tumors and the amount of radiolabeled material incorporated into DNA. It was concluded
that the attack on DNA is not necessarily responsible for
the cytotoxic or cytostatic effects of the alkylating agents.

Incorporation of L-arginine-U-C^{14} into acid-insoluble
nuclear protein was inhibited by administration of chlorambucil
to animals bearing the Walker tumor (Busch et al., 1961).
It was concluded that the inhibition of incorporation of arginine
into nuclear protein was an intermediate stage in the overall
inhibitory action of chlorambucil.

Intraperitoneal injection of chlorambucil caused fluctuations in sulfhydryl levels of various organs and tissues
of the female rat (Calcutt, 1965).

The interactions of chlorambucil with some constituents of human serum have been investigated (Linford,
1961). The rate of hydrolysis in a number of aqueous solutions indicated that the reaction was first order and proceeded at a rate much faster than two other structurally
similar nitrogen mustards. Chlorambucil underwent a condensation reaction with serum protein; at $37°$ C, 65 percent
had condensed with protein in 24 hr and at $40°$ C, close to 80
percent had reacted. The activation energy (24 kcal) was the
same for the hydrolytic and alkylation reactions. It appears
that the reactions are accompanied by a large decrease in
standard free energy since neither the rate nor extent of
hydrolysis was affected by excess Cl$^-$ and the alkylation of
serum protein proceeds in the presence of approximately
fiftyfold excess Cl$^-$. These reactions undoubtedly represent
sources of waste of the chemical in vivo. The rate of hydrolysis
was decreased to a point of negligible consequence by the
presence of serum protein. The half-life of the condensation
reaction was about 6 hr and has such a high temperature co-
efficient that specific tissues might be favored. In addition,
serum proteins adsorb chlorambucil rapidly, and adsorption
is virtually complete at concentrations comparable to those
prevailing in vivo. Such physical binding undoubtedly limits
the extent of diffusion of chlorambucil and related drugs. Similar
studies on the interaction of various chemosterilants with
constituents of insect hemolymph should provide interesting
results.

Chlorambucil was unique in causing a profound stimulation of formate uptake by normal and chronic lymphocytic
leukemia cells (Winzler et al., 1959).

Chlorambucil inhibited incorporation of radioactive glycine and lysine into proteins, of glycine into acid-soluble nucleotides, and of glycine, formate, adenine, and orotic acid into nucleic acids of L-1 mouse tumor (Pradhan and West, 1960). The inhibition of incorporation of five different metabolites into protein and nucleic acids represents such a generalized effect that the question is raised of whether this is a cause or an effect of inhibition of some fundamental cell processes.

ORGANOTIN COMPOUNDS

Methods of determination of these compounds are presented together since they are useful for all of those under discussion.

Many researchers rely on the usual elemental analyses for carbon, hydrogen, chlorine, tin, and sulfur in the determinations of these compounds. Some alternate quantative methods include a polarographic method which detects 25 μg ($\pm$ 5 percent) (Vogel and Deshusses, 1964) and a colorimetric method which detects 0.1 to 0.6 μg/ml by measuring the absorbancy at 450 mμ of the triphenyl tin-dithiozone complex in chloroform (Hardon et al., 1960). The reaction of triphenyltins with hydrogen releases benzene which can then be determined by the method of Hancock and Laws (1956). Additional methods of analysis have been reported by Bock et al., (1958) and by Kroller (1960).

The organotins can be detected on paper chromatographs by spraying with 0.1 percent pyrocatechol in ethanol (Williams and Price, 1960). Another method employs reversed phase chromatography with 1-bromonaphthalene as the stationary phase and 50 to 70 percent acetic acid as the mobile phase; after development, the tin compounds are detected by spraying with dithiozone (Gasparic and Cee, 1962).

The herbicidal, fungicidal, bactericidal, nematocidal, molluscicidal, and insecticidal activities of these compounds have been studied to a limited extent, but only very little of the knowledge gained appears pertinent to the antifertility effects.

The physical properties of the compounds were generously furnished by Dr. Alexander Ross, M & T Chemical, Inc. unless otherwise indicated.

TIN, CHLOROTRIPHENYL

Synonyms

Triphenyl tin chloride
Tin compound, triphenyl-chloride
TPTC
ENT 25207

Structure

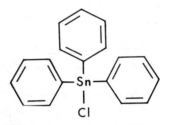

C$_{18}$H$_{15}$ClSn   Mol. wt. 385.27

Physical Properties

Physical form	Crystalline solid
Color	White
Odor	Odorless
Melting point	106°C (Schmidt and Ruf, 1963)
Boiling point	240°C (13.5 mm Hg) (Allied Chemical Bull.)

Solubility. Soluble in aromatic hydrocarbons, acetone, and ether. It has a low order of solubility in isopropanol and in aliphatic hydrocarbons from which it can be recrystallized for purification.

Stability. Hydrolyzes at 22 to 50°C.

Biochemistry

Correlations between structure and insecticidal activity showed that maximum toxicity was obtained with tri-substituted organotin compounds (Blum and Pratt, 1960). The anionic species was found to contribute little to the toxicities of the trisubstituted compounds.

Triphenyl tin chloride acted as an uncompetitive inhibitor of ATPase (Pieper and Casida, 1965). Several other
trisubstituted tin compounds were active as inhibitors of this
enzyme and a good correlation was noted between the potency
of in vitro ATPase inhibition and toxicity for female house
flies.

TIN, ACETOXYTRIPHENYL-

Synonyms

Triphenyl tin acetate
Tin compound, triphenyl—acetate
Brestan
TPTA
ENT 25208

Structure

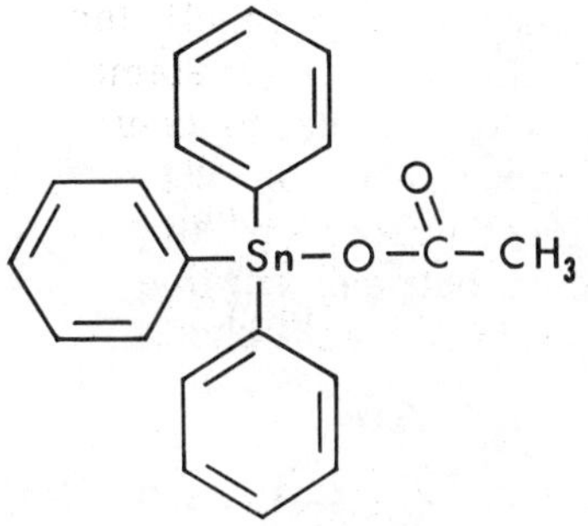

$C_{20}H_{18}O_2Sn$ Mol. wt. 408.8

Physical Properties

Physical form	Crystalline solid
Color	White
Odor	Odorless
Melting point	122 to 124°C

Solubility. Insoluble in water, ether, and hexane; soluble in acetone, chloroform, tetrahydrofuran, methanol, carbon
tetrachloride, and benzene.

Biochemistry

In mammals the radioactivity of triphenyl tin[113]-acetate was rapidly excreted almost exclusively in the feces and the small amounts which were absorbed were partly discharged in the urine and partly distributed throughout the whole body (Herok and Goette, 1963). Unchanged compound, or its hydroxide, was excreted in a biological half-life of approximately 20 hr, whereas the metabolic products had a half-life of 70 days, corresponding to the tin of inorganic compounds.

It has been proposed that the antifungal and antibacterial activities of trialkyl- and triphenyl- substituted tin, lead, and germamium compounds are a result of inhibition of oxidative phosphorylation (A. Kaars Sijesteijn et al., 1962).

ANTIMETABOLITES

Biochemical effects and mode of action of many antimetabolites have been extensively studied in microbial and mammalian systems and, as a result, the molecular basis for inhibition of particular enzyme systems is well established. Although it seems quite logical to assume that the antimetabolites exert similar effects on the enzymes of the various insect species, direct proof is lacking in many instances, and a direct relationship between enzyme inhibition and antifertility effects has not been established.

GLUTAMIC ACID, N-{p-{ [2,4-DIAMINO-6-PTERIDYL)-METHYL]-AMINO}-BENZOYL}-

Synonyms

Aminopterin
APGA
4-amino folic acid
NSC 739
ENT 26079

Structure

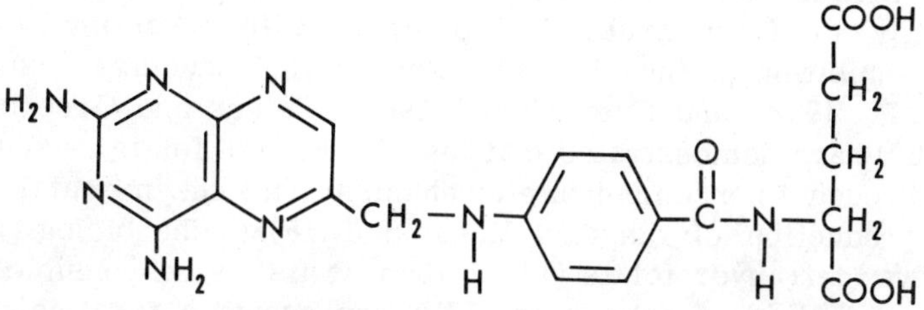

$C_{19}H_{20}N_8O_5$ Mol. wt. 440.1

Physical Properties

Physical form	Clusters of needles
Color	Yellow
Odor	Odorless
Melting point	260°C (decomp.)

Ultraviolet spectrum in 0.1 N NaOH shows λ max. at 260, 284, 370 mμ and λ min. at 239, 271, 333 mμ.

Solubility. Soluble in aqueous sodium hydroxide solutions.

Stability. Aminopterin should be protected from light and stored at refrigeration temperatures.

Methods of Determination and Purification

Aminopterin can be purified by a series of recrystallizations and filtrations described in detail by Waller et al. (1948).

The ultraviolet spectrum has been used to establish the purity of aminopterin and it may also be the basis of quantitative determinations of purified preparations. Microbiological assays are by far the most widely used methods of determination.

Biochemistry

Aminopterin has been studied intensively in relation to its antimicrobial and carcinostatic effects. It resembles the folic acid molecule and is transported across cell membranes by the same mechanism which transports folic acid. Thus it can inhibit only those organisms which require an exogenous supply of folic acid. The principle site of action lies in the inhibition of the enzyme, dihydrofolic reductase (Osborn et al., 1958, and Huennekens, 1963). Peters and Greenburg (1959) have demonstrated that the inhibition of folate reduction is through a noncompetitive mechanism. This enzyme catalyzes the reduction of dihydrofolic acid (DHF) to the biologically active, tetrahydrofolate (THF) form; it also is responsible for the reduction of folic acid. THF represents a focal point of coenzyme forms which participate in single-carbon unit metabolism.

The accompanying scheme (Fig. 7) represents a composite of most of the known interconversions of folic acid coenzymes and is not intended to imply that all of these conversions occur in all cells. It does, however, include the areas in which aminopterin has been shown to exert its cytotoxic effect. The enzyme, thymidylate synthetase, converts deoxyuridylate into thymidylate for subsequent use in DNA synthesis. The coenzyme form of folic acid, N^{5-10}-methylene THF, is converted to DHF in the process of methylation and oxidation. DHF reductase then catalyzes the conversion back to THF and other enzymes complete the recycling process. Aminopterin, and methotrexate, bind DHF reductase extremely tight (10^4 to 10^5 times as tightly as the substrate) and appear to show little discrimination for enzymes from different sources (Bertino, 1963, and Werkheiser, 1963). An induction of DHF reductase seems to occur as the result of aminopterin binding, since the cell usually responds by increased synthesis of the enzyme. In numerous instances, it has been shown that resistance to this folate analogue is accompanied by a corresponding increase in the amount of DHF reductase.

Recent studies of folic acid metabolism in insects have led to the development of a method for isolation of N^5-formyltetrahydrofolate from house flies (Miller and Perry, 1965). It has also been shown that dietary folic acid is converted to a compound at the tetrahydro level during pupal development (Perry and Miller, 1965). It was concluded that aminopterin affects DHF reductase in the house fly because the amount of N^5-formyl THF was appreciably lower in larvae treated with a growth-inhibiting dose of aminopterin.

Since the original sterilization of house flies by aminop-

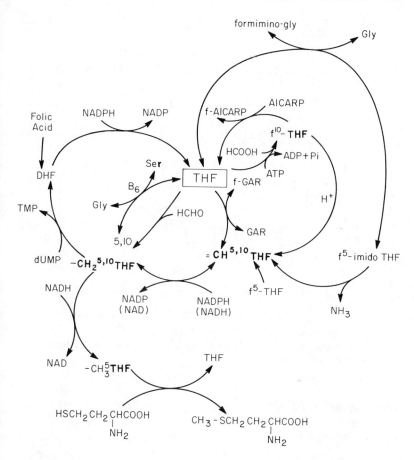

FIG. 7. Interconversions of folic acid coenzyme forms.

terin (Mitlin et al., 1954), progress in folate chemistry has seen the development of smaller molecular weight inhibitors of DHF reductase. The structure and function of these compounds have been reviewed by Hitchings and Burchall, (1965). The general formula of such inhibitors is given in Table 10 along with some examples of substituents and their effects. Thus it appears some new, potentially active compounds are available and should be tested for chemosterilant effects.

TABLE 10

EFFECTS OF 5- AND 6- SUBSTITUENTS ON THE IN-
HIBITORY ACTIONS OF 2,4-DIAMINOPYRIMIDINES IN
THE GROWTH OF *L. CASEI*[a]

No.	Pyrimidine substituent 5	6	50% I.C. μg/ml
1	CH_3	H	20
2	CH_3	CH_3	5
3	C_6H_5O	H	0.15
4	$C_6H_5CH_2-$	H	0.2
5	$C_6H_5CH_2-$	CH_3	0.8
6	C_6H_5	H	0.6
7	$-CH_2CH_2CH_2CH_2$		1.0
8	$-CH=C(CH_3)-CH=CH-$		0.02
9	$-CH=C(CH_3)-CH=N-$		0.08
10	H	C_6H_5	100
11	CH_3	C_6H_5	40
12	C_6H_5	C_6H_5	100
13	C_6H_4Cl	$C_6H_5CH_2$	100

(From Hitchings and Burchall, 1965.)

[a]A–B can be C=C, N=C, or C=N. The bonds extended join
through additional atoms.

URACIL, 5-FLUORO-

Synonyms

5-FU
FU
NSC 19893
ENT 25297

Structure

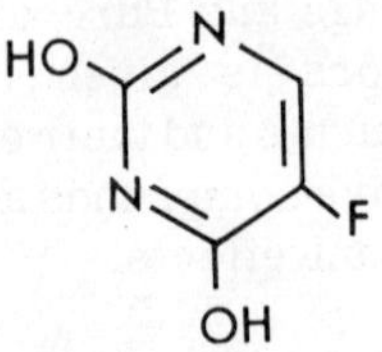

$C_4H_3FN_2O_2$ Mol. wt. 130.0

Physical Properties

Physical form   Crystalline powder
Color   White
Odor   Odorless
Melting point   281 to 283°C

Solubility. Practically insoluble in chloroform, benzene, and diethyl ether. Soluble in water (1.25 percent), in ethanol (0.59 percent), and in methanol (1.82 percent). The solubility in aqueous solutions increases with increasing pH.

Stability. Very stable; solutions of 1 mg/ml or higher concentration can be stored at freezer temperatures for several months without decomposition.

Methods of Determination

The principal methods for determination of fluorouracil are microbiological assays and chromatography followed by spectrophotometric measurements.

Biochemistry

Fluorouracil is an analog of uracil and acts as a classical antimetabolite of that nucleotide. It blocks the methylation of deoxyuridylic acid to form thymidylic acid and thus inhibits synthesis of DNA (Heidelberger et al., 1958). In the form of fluorouridine diphosphate it is incorporated into RNA. This antimetabolite does possess a degree of selectivity for neoplastic tissue since uracil is preferentially utilized by neoplasms. In Ehrlich ascites cells, fluorouracil was anabolized to the ribose nucleoside, to its mono-, di-, and triphosphates, and to fluorodeoxyuridine monophosphate.

The incorporation of fluorouracil into sRNA also alters the characteristic elution profile of the acceptor RNA from a methylated albumin column (Sueoka and Yamane, 1963). This may be the result of alteration of the specificity of sRNA for activating enzyme or a change in some physicochemical property.

Two main effects of FU are recognized. First, on RNA synthesis. FU can be incorporated into RNA as an abnormal nucleotide and it can also inhibit incorporation of orotic acid and uracil into RNA (Bosch et al., 1958, and Harbers et al., 1959). In *E. coli* it appears fluorouracil may block the induced synthesis of certain enzymes and cause other alterations in RNA and protein synthesis (Horowitz et al., 1960).

The second main mechanism of action is blockage of DNA synthesis by virtue of the inhibition of TMP synthetase caused by fluorodeoxyuridine monophosphate (Heidelberger, 1963). Resistance to the chemical developed through elimination of the metabolic pathways by which fluorouridylic acid and deoxyribofluorouridylic acid are synthesized.

In the Walker tumor, FU depressed incorporation of uniformly labeled C^{14}-arginine into histones, and into acid-insoluble nuclear proteins (Busch et al., 1961). Specific activity of microsomal and cytoplasmic proteins was also suppressed.

In the house fly, fluorouracil is effective as a sterilant only in females, whereas fluoroorotic acid, a precursor to pyrimidines, is active in both sexes. The reason for this difference in effect is not known, but one explanation could be that in the male fly fluorouracil is not converted to fluorouridylic acid or to fluorodeoxyuridine, whereas such conversions do occur in the female. On the other hand, both sexes are able to convert fluoroorotic acid to fluorooritidine-5-phosphate and by this alternate pathway the fluorinated pyrimidine is formed in vivo. Another explanation is based upon the faster sexual development of the male fly where motile sperm are present in new adults but ovarian development is incomplete in the newly emerged female. On this basis it must be assumed that fluorouracil and fluoroorotic acid exert their effects by different mechanisms or at a different stage of development in the reproductive cells of the house fly. The latter has been proposed by Painter and Kilgore (1965).

The difference in effect may be related to the observation that multiple injections of fluoroorotic acid caused a decrease in the ψ-uridylic acid content of sRNA in rat liver, whereas similar injections of fluorouracil had no apparent effect (Wagner and Heidelberger, 1962). It was also noted that radiolabeled fluoroorotic acid was incorporated into several RNA fractions to a greater extent than fluorouracil. This indicates that in the rat, fluoroorotic acid is converted to the uridine nucleotides but fluorouracil apparently was not.

OROTIC ACID, 5-FLUORO

Synonyms

5-Fluoroorotic acid
5-FO
NSC 31712
ENT 26398

Structure

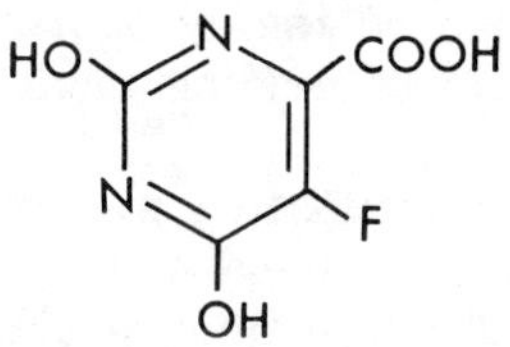

$C_5H_3FN_2O_4$ Mol. wt. 174.0

Physical Properties

Physical form	Crystalline solid
Color	White
Odor	Odorless
Melting point	(.H_2O) 255°C (decarboxylation) (sublimes at 260 to 270°C in vacuo to give anhydrous fluorootic acid)

Solubility. Approximately 0.2 g per 100 ml water.

Stability. Very stable, solutions can be stored at refrigerator temperatures for extended lengths of time without decomposition.

Methods of Determination and Purification

Two dimensional thin-layer chromatography has been used to separate a mixture containing 5-FO, FU, and other nucleotides (Hawrylyshyn et al., 1964). The solvents employed were ethyl acetate: acetone: water (70:40:10) and ethyl acetate: methanol: ammonium hydroxide (75:25:1); and fluoroorotic acid was detected by examination of the chromatograph under short-wave ultraviolet light.

Microbiological assays and ultraviolet spectrophotometry are the principal methods used for quantitative determinations.

Biochemistry

The most effective of the halogenated orotic acids as an inhibitor of the enzymatic conversion of orotic acid to uridine nucleotides is 5-fluoroorotic acid (Stone and Potter, 1957). The inhibition of dihydroorotase and of orotidine-5-phosphatase leading to the synthesis of uridine nucleotides has long been recognized.

A technique for evaluating pyrimidine nucleotide synthesis in the intact organism based upon the release of $C^{14}O_2$ from carboxyl-labeled pyrimidine precursors has been developed (Rabkin et al., 1962). The evidence presented for the specificity of the assay is convincing and the method can be used to determine the degree of inhibition, the time of onset, and duration of the biochemical effectiveness.

Multiple injections of 5-FO caused a decrease in the ψ-uridylic acid content of sRNA of rat liver (Wagner and Heidelberger, 1962). It was also noted that radiolabeled 5-FO was incorporated into several RNA fractions to a greater extent than 5-FU (cf. FU section).

It has been suggested that the carcinostatic effects of FO (and of FU) may be explained on the basis of a transfer of electrons between nucleic acids (Goudot, 1963). This assumes that such transfer would be necessary for the initiation of all cellular multiplications. The loss of a pair of electrons from DNA, thereby initiating molecular splitting, would not occur in the presence of RNA containing 5-FO because of the energy levels. Such transfers would occur only if the nucleic acids were free of their protective protein coat.

ANTIBIOTICS

These compounds are another biological class of chemicals which have been studied extensively in microbial systems and many of the preceding remarks concerning the mode of action of antimetabolites applies to antibiotics as well.

CARBAMIC ACID, AZIRINO[2′,3′: 3,4]PYRROLO-[1-2a]-IN-
DOLE-4,7-DIONE, 6-AMINO-1, 1a, 2,8,8a, 8b-HEXAHY-
DRO-8-(HYDROXYMETHYL)-8a-METHOXY-1,5-DI-
METHYL ESTER

Synonyms

Porfiromycin
Methyl mitomycin
Antibiotic pigment D
NSC 56410
ENT 50825

Structure

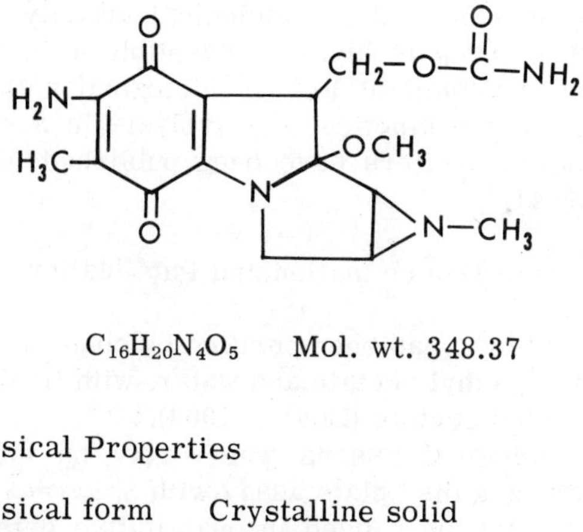

$C_{16}H_{20}N_4O_5$ Mol. wt. 348.37

Physical Properties

Physical form   Crystalline solid
Color   Dark purple
Odor   Odorless
Melting point   199 to 202° C

The ultraviolet spectrum is identical with that of mitomycin C, and in methanol or water exhibits λ max. around
217 and 360 mμ (Herr et al., 1960, and Webb et al., 1962). The
infrared spectrum of porfiromycin in a mineral oil suspension
was reported by Herr et al. (1960), who also presented optical
rotation characteristics of a 0.1 percent solution of porfiromycin in methanol.

Solubility. Moderately soluble in polar organic solvents; soluble in dimethyl formamide; slightly soluble in water; insoluble in hydrocarbon solvents.

Stability. Samples which had been stored in dry crystalline form showed no detectable degradation after six months at 70°C, but acidic or alkaline solutions deteriorate rapidly (Herr et al., 1960). Solutions containing 1 mg/ml in methanol and 0.1 M phosphate buffer pH 7 (approximately 1:25) showed no loss of activity after storage in the refrigerator for 2 months (Hanka, 1960). Solutions of porfiromycin have maximum stability between pH 4 and 9.

Twelve different products of acidic and alkaline degradation have been identified, the kinetics of their transformations quantified, and many of the dissociation constants and apparent equivalent weights established (Garrett, 1963). The biological activities of the degradation products were different and it was concluded that the fused ring aziridine portion of the molecule is essential for biological activity. Like most aziridines, this group is highly susceptible to acid-catalyzed solvolysis and concomitant loss of biological activity. Additional details of the kinetics of solvolysis in acetate, phosphate, and borate buffers have been published (Garrett and Schroeder, 1964).

Methods of Determination and Purification

The antibiotic has been purified by countercurrent distribution between ethyl acetate and water, with final recrystallization from ethyl acetate (Duvall, 1963).

Microbiological assays which rely on the inhibition zone diameter of a disc plate assay with *S. aureus* UC-607 on nutrient agar have been used in quantitative determinations of porfiromycin (Hanka, 1960). A turbidimetric assay capable of detecting as low as 0.001 μg/ml is especially useful in determining porfiromycin in tissues.

Porfiromycin may be chromatographed on paper using the solvent systems shown in Table 11. Paper chromatographic assays which rely on ultraviolet scanning, and biological activity against *S. lutea* have been developed (De Boer et al., 1961).

A spectrophotometric method based upon absorbancy at 363 mμ has shown good correlation with the plate disc assay against *S. aureus* (Garrett and Schroeder, 1964).

TABLE 11

SOLVENT SYSTEMS FOR PAPER CHROMATOGRAPHY

Solvent system	R_f
Butanol: H_2O (84:16)	0.71[a]
Methanol: benzene: H_2O (1:1:2)	0.13[a]
Ethylacetate: H_2O (saturated)	0.98[a]
Butanol: acetic acid: H_2O (4:1:5) (upper phase)	0.83 to .85[b]
Benzene: methanol: 0.01 M phosphate buffer pH 6.8 (20:1:1)	0.09[c]

[a]Wakaki et al. (1962).
[b]Wagner and Gitterman (1962).
[c]Lefemine et al. (1962).

Biochemistry

The biological effects of porfiromycin are virtually identical to those of mitomycin. In vitro studies have shown that porfiromycin (like mitomycin C) inhibits purine metabolism but also appears to have one or more additional sites of action (Pittillo and Quinnelly, 1962).

Porfiromycin, generally inactive in the natural oxidized state, has been activated metabolically by a lysate of *Sarcina lutea;* the activation requires NADPH (Iyer and Szybalski, 1964). Activated porfiromycin seems to act as a bifunctional alkylating agent, as evidenced by cross-linking of complementary strands of DNA. The activating component is sedimented from a cell-free lysate by centrifugation at 198,000 X *g* for 90 min. It has also been shown that a commercial preparation of diaphorase will activate mitomycin in the presence of NADPH. It appears that the NADPH-dependent enzymic reduction of porfiromycin is necessary for in vivo cross-linking of DNA, since chemically reduced porfiromycin is capable of cross-linking complementary strands of DNA in vitro (Iyer and Szybalski, 1964). The cross-linking reaction is estimated to involve one cross-link per 2,000 nucleotide residues and appears to be favored by a high content of guanine and cytosine in the DNA. The activation of porfiromycin is described below. The sites indicated by X and Y are believed to be the sites which react in the cross-linking of DNA. The site Z represents another point in the molecule which cannot be excluded as a reactive center.

C^{14}-labeled porfiromycin was shown to alkylate nucleic acids and become attached to the nucleic acid molecule (Weiss-

(From Iyer and Szybalski, 1964, Science, 145(3627): 55–8. Copyright 1964 by the American Association for the Advancement of Science.)

bach and Lisio, 1965). RNA and DNA were alkylated to the same
extent and contained about one cross-link per 500 nucleotide
residues. It was suggested that the principle attachment of
porfiromycin to DNA is not across the double helix to form
cross-links. This hypothesis is supported by the observation
that heat denatured DNA is alkylated as well as native DNA.
It was concluded that most of the porfiromycin molecules at-
tach to the nucleic acids through a monofunctional alkylation.
Fragmentation of the DNA may also occur after alkylation.

The influence of alkylation of DNA on the biological and
enzymatic activities has been investigated (Pricer and Weissbach, 1965). Alkylated DNA was utilized only 1/3 to 1/4 as well
as native DNA as a primer for DNA or RNA polymerase. The
alkylated DNA was degraded more slowly than native DNA by
certain exonucleases and phosphodiesterases.

Synthetic polyribonucleotides were alkylated by C^{14}-
porfiromycin (and H^3-mitomycin) at least four times as easily
on guanine as on the other bases (Lipsett and Weissbach, 1965).
Alkylation of sRNA produced both monoguanyl- and diguanyl-
porfiromycin, the latter probably a consequence of inter-
strand linkage. In agreement with the observations of Brookes
and Lawley, (1961) alkylation of guanine components labilizes
the guanine-ribose bond and thus creates "depurinated strands"
in sRNA on storage.

In normal *Staphylococci* and in some biochemical mutants, porfiromycin selectively inhibited synthesis of DNA
(Laiko, 1964).

The products of acidic and alkaline solution transformation of porfiromycin were identified spectrophotometrically
and assayed for biological activity (Garrett, 1963). The fused
ring aziridine appears to be mandatory for biological activity.
This structure is resistant to alkali and maintains its activity
through various alkali-induced structural alterations. The
aziridine group is highly susceptible to acid-catalyzed solvolysis and its degradation results in loss of biological activity.

Low concentrations of porfiromycin completely inhibited cell division and nearly abolished synthesis of DNA in
Hela cells (Magee and Miller, 1962). Selective inhibition of
DNA synthesis along with nearly normal production of RNA
and protein was observed.

It seems important to note that although porfiromycin
and mitomycin show similar biological activities, mitomycin
(at levels 10 to 50 times the effective dose of porfiromycin)

is not effective as a chemosterilant (LaBrecque, personal communication). An explanation of this difference in biological activity can probably be related to the presence of the methyl group at the 1a position resulting in alteration of permeability or transport properties. The effects of porfiromycin on insects have not been studied in sufficient detail to know if activation is necessary for antifertility activity.

GLUTARIMIDE, 3-[2-(3,5-DIMETHYL-2-OXOCYCLOHEXYL)-2-HYDROXYETHYL]-

Synonyms

Cycloheximide
Actidione
NSC 185
ENT 15541

Structure

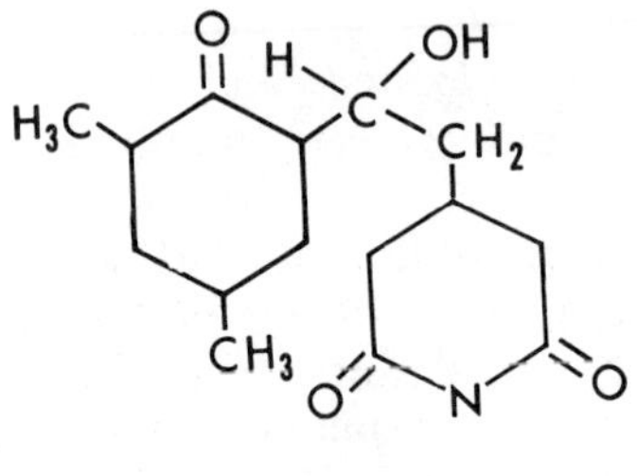

$C_{15}H_{23}NO_4$ Mol. wt. 281.11

Physical Properties

Physical form	Crystalline solid
Color	White
Odor	Odorless
Melting point	Racemic mixture 139 to 149° C
	1-form 114 to 115° C

Solubility. In water, 2 percent; in amyl acetate, 7 percent. Also soluble in chloroform, ether, acetone, methanol,

ethanol, and other common organic solvents except saturated hydrocarbons. Cycloheximide can be recrystallized from amyl acetate, water, or 30 percent methanol, giving a product which melts at 119.5 to 121°C.

Stability. Cycloheximide is very stable (at least 30 days in water and much longer in organic solvents) unless the pH is above 8.0 when degradation is quite rapid (Dr. Malcolm R. Siegel, personal communication). The degradation at room temperature by dilute alkali is accompanied by the formation of a volatile, fragrant ketone, 2,4-dimethylcyclohexanone. The compound is destroyed by boiling at pH 7 for 1 hr, but shows no loss of activity after 15 min boiling. It is not destroyed by boiling at pH 2 for 1 hr. Degradation of cycloheximide in 0.1 N hydrochloric acid was followed using thin-layer chromatography with ethyl acetate as the developing solvent (R_f 0.47) (Garrett and Notari, 1966). At 80°C degradation was approximately 50 percent complete after 3 to 6 hr. Additional detailed studies on the kinetics and mechanism of degradation in pharmaceutically useful pH ranges have been reported by Garrett and Notari (1965).

Methods of Determination

A bioautographic system based upon inhibition of cellular dehydrogenase activity has been developed (Schuurmans et al., 1964). Paper chromatograms were developed in the appropriate solvent by the descending method at 30°C (± 1) in the dark on Whatman #1 paper strips, and were then dried in a ventilated oven overnight at 27°C. The R_f values for the solvent systems employed are listed in Table 12.

A spectrophotometric analysis has been developed which is based upon the reaction of the imide with alkaline hydroxylamine producing a hydroxamic acid which is then converted to the brightly colored ferric hydroxamate (Forist and Theal, 1959). The method is rapid, precise, and accurate but other functional groups such as anhydrides, acid chlorides, lactones, and esters are capable of forming hydoxamic acids and will cause interference. In addition, high concentrations of transition elements, carbonyls, or ions capable of complexing with the ferric ion will affect the intensity of the color. The instability of the color is also inconvenient.

Another method is based upon the color reaction with resorcinol which will occur with compounds capable of form-

TABLE 12

SOLVENT SYSTEMS FOR PAPER CHROMATOGRAPHY

Solvent system (0.4 μg cycloheximide)	R_f
n-Butanol: acetic acid: H_2 (25:6:25) (butanol phase)	0.80
n-Butanol saturated with $2N$ NH$_4$OH	0.83
i-Amyl alcohol (layer 0.5 cm deep), 5% Na$_2$HPO$_4$ (1 cm)	0.72
Dry methanol buffered at pH 5.5 with 0.05 M acetate (1.64 g anhydrous sodium acetate and 0.14 ml glacial acetic acid per 400 ml of dry methanol)	0.74

(From Schuurmans et al., 1964.)

ing an α, β-unsaturated ketone upon being heated with hydrochloric acid (Takeshita et al., 1962). All of the resorcinols tested gave a yellow coloration when heated with cycloheximide in hydrochloric acid. Using resorcinol, the absorption of the colored product at 400 mμ is linear up to 10 μg/ml. Carbohydrates are sensitive to this reagent and their presence will interfere in the estimation of cycloheximide by this method.

Neither of the foregoing spectrophotometric methods is able to distinguish cycloheximide from its degradation product, anhydrocycloheximide. A method for determining cycloheximide and its degradation products has been devised based upon the relative examination reactivities of the carbonyl compounds, (Garrett and Notari, 1965). The method is useful in both aqueous and methanolic solutions and can be used in conjunction with spectrophotometry, or imide analytical methods, to study degradation rates of an unknown amount of cycloheximide.

Biochemistry

Cycloheximide has been shown to inhibit protein synthesis in both whole cells and in cell-free systems of Saccharomyces pastorianus (Siegel and Sisler, 1963, 1964a,b). The specific site of action was traced to the transfer of amino acids from sRNA to ribosomal protein. It was subsequently found that among resistant and susceptible yeast, the resistance or susceptibility is determined by the ribosomes and not by the supernatant enzymes (Siegel and Sisler, 1965). This provided further evidence that the site of action of cycloheximide is at the ribosomal site.

Cycloheximide has also been shown to inhibit protein synthesis in mammalian cells (Young et al., 1963, Gorski and Axman, 1964) and to inhibit the transfer of amino acids from sRNA to polypeptide chains in cell-free systems prepared from mammalian cells (Ennis and Lubin, 1964a,b). In addition to the inhibition of the transfer mechanism, Wettstein et al. (1964) found evidence indicating that the antibiotic prevented normal breakdown of GTP-dependent ribosomes which is coupled with protein synthesis. The breakdown of polyribosomes was inhibited to about the same extent as incorporation of amino acids into protein.

Bennett et al. (1964) found the antibiotic inhibited synthesis of DNA in vivo, but subsequently, in vitro studies indicated this action to be secondary to the inhibition of protein synthesis (Bennett et al., 1965). Young and Hodas (1965) reported inhibition of incorporation of radio-labeled leucine and thymidine in Hela cell monolayers.

It appears that the primary site of action of cycloheximide in microbial systems has been established. The inhibitory effect of cycloheximide on the transfer of amino acids from sRNA, and thus of protein synthesis, may explain the other effects of the drug on nucleic acid synthesis which have been reported.

ALKALOIDS

The effects of alkaloids on the mitotic process of the cell make these compounds particularly interesting chemosterilants. Extension of data obtained with microbial systems to that of insects seems justified and for this reason should provide a fruitful field for antifertility investigations.

MONOCROTALINE

Synonyms

NSC 28693
ENT 41120

Structure

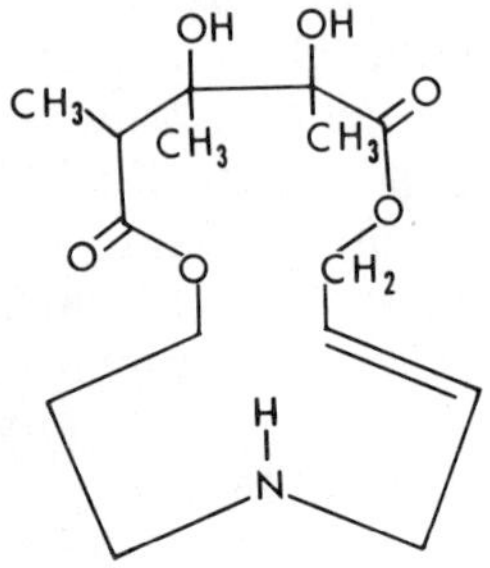

$C_{16}H_{23}NO_6$ Mol. wt. 325.10

Physical Properties

Physical form	Crystalline solid
Color	White
Odor	Odorless
Melting point	196 to 197° C

Solubility. Sparingly soluble in ethanol and chloroform; low solubility in most other solvents; readily soluble in water in the presence of acids (C. C. J. Culvenor, personal communication).

Stability. Stable over a period of months in neutral or slightly acid aqueous solutions (or in ethanol) if kept cold and out of light; readily hydrolyzed by dilute sodium hydroxide at room temperature (C. C. J. Culvenor, personal communication).

Methods of Determination and Purification

Monocrotaline can be purified by recrystallization from ethanol. The alkaloid has been determined by gas, thin-layer, and paper chromatography (Chalmers et al., 1965). Thin-layer chromatography appears to be more sensitive than the other methods. Silica gel plates were developed in methanol and monocrotaline was detected with iodine vapors. On ascending paper chromatography using n-butanol: 5 percent acetic acid (1:1) as the developing solvent system, the R_f value was 0.39. The retention time in gas chromatography was 19.5 min on an SE-30 column.

Biochemistry

Monocrotaline, when administered (25 $\mu g/ml$) to human embryo liver cells in tissue culture, caused increase in nuclear size, bizarre cells, abnormal mitoses, multinucleated cells, and amitotic divisions and features similar to those of neo-plastic cells (Hurchinson and Hill, 1960). In the same report it was noted that Hela cells were not affected by monocrotaline.

The addition of cysteine reduced by 80 to 90 percent the cytological damage caused by monocrotaline in allium root tips (Avanzi, 1961). The mechanism of protection is not known but is believed to be by reduction of the oxygen tension in a manner analogous to similar effects noted in radiobiological results. The implication of an oxygen dependence of the cyto-logical effect is substantiated by that of other chemical mutagens, i.e., 8-ethoxycaffeine and KCN (Kihlman, 1955, 1956, and Lilly and Thoday, 1956).

COLCHICINE

Synonyms

NSC 757
ENT 31149

Structure

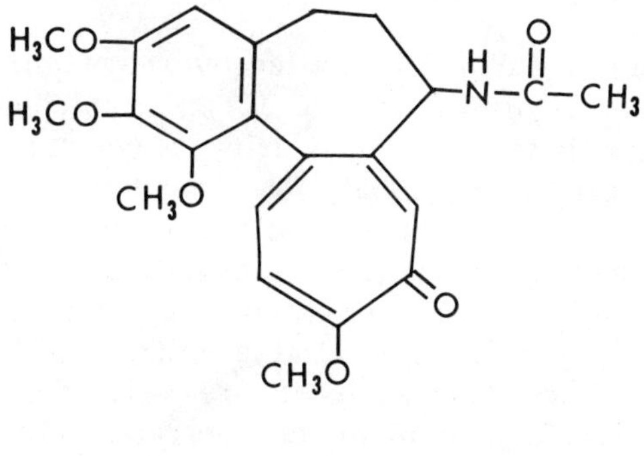

$C_{22}H_{25}NO_6$ Mol. wt. 399.43

Physical Properties

Physical form	Crystalline solid or amorphous powder
Color	Yellow
Odor	Odorless
Melting point	142 to 150° C
Optical rotation	Levorotatory in chloroform and aqueous solutions; in aqueous solutions $(\alpha)_D^{25} = -410$ to $435°$ C

Determinations of specific rotatory power of colchicine should preferably be made in ethanol solutions because the reading in ethanol is not affected by temperature or concentration (Bellet and Fabre, 1961).

Ultraviolet, N.M.R. and IR spectra have been reported for colchicine and some analogs (von Schreiber et al., 1961). In the ultraviolet, λ max. in 95 percent ethanol were noted at 350.5 mμ (log ϵ 4.22), and at 243 mμ (log ϵ 4.47).

Solubility. 4.5 percent in water, 0.45 percent in ether, 1 percent in benzene; freely soluble in alcohol or chloroform; insoluble in petroleum ether. Forms two crystalline compounds with chloroform, $B \cdot CHCl_3$ and $B \cdot 2CHCl_3$, which do not give up their chloroform unless heated between 60 to 70° C for a considerable time.

Stability. Undergoes auto-oxidation upon exposure to light.

Methods of Determination and Purification

Colchicine can be purified by recrystallization from ethyl acetate. Analyses of 1 to 10 μg of colchicine in tissue extracts have been performed using a gas chromatographic method (Parker et al., 1963). The retention times are given for several alkaloids chromatographed on 5 percent SE-30 at five different temperatures. Although response to a given weight of sample was not linear it is apparent that by proper conditioning of the column reliable values could be attained.

The color produced by the reaction of colchicine with concentrated sulfuric acid, or concentrated sulfuric acid plus ferric chloride, or ferric ammonium sulfate, serves as a rapid quantitative determination (Graham, 1964). The most successful paper chromatographic separation employs paper impregnated with 30 percent formamide in methanol or ethanol and development in benzene: chloroform (2:1). Colchicine is then located by its fluorescence in ultraviolet light or phosphotungstic acid spray.

Biochemistry

Many of the characteristic effects of colchicine parallel those produced by x-rays.

An effect of colchicine on sulfur metabolism is indicated by the report that intraperitoneal injection of colchicine increased urinary excretion of taurine in rats (Kostos and Kocsis, 1961). Apparently the extra urinary taurine did not arise from preformed tissue taurine.

Colchicine caused a definite inhibition of anaerobic glycolysis but very slight effect on the pentose cycle of erythrocytes (Sonka et al., 1961).

It was surprising to note that levels of colchicine which blocked dividing eggs in metaphase did not show any effect on the ATPase activity of the mitotic apparatus (Sauaia and Mazia, 1961).

Effects of this alkaloid have been observed on a variety of enzyme systems. Colchicine caused a slight, but passing, decrease in the DNase activity of blood plasma in mice while the transaminase activity underwent a prolonged increase (Truhaut and Bohoun, 1963). Administration of colchicine to guinea pigs, mice, and rats caused a decrease in alkaline and acid phosphatase activity of various internal organs (Kemeny et al., 1963a,b). Three activities of hypoxanthine oxidase, all of which were inhibited by colchicine, are (1) aerobic production of uric acid from hypoxanthine, (2) the increase in this activity upon addition of methylene blue, and (3) anaerobic reduction of methylene blue (Roussors, 1963).

Colchicine has been shown to inhibit liver xanthine oxidase and xanthine dehydrogenase activities in rats (Affonso et al., 1961). The enzyme activities in the blood serum, however, actually increased (Affonso et al., 1962). Colchicine inhibited DNase, and the dephosphorylation and deamination of deoxyribonucleotides (Ebner and Strecker, 1950). Another report of interference with nitrogen metabolism is indicated by

TABLE 13

EFFECTS OF COLCHICINE ON LABELING OF NUCLEAR
PROTEINS OF EHRLICH ASCITES CELLS

Fractions	Control average cpm I standard error		With colchicine (24 hr prior to arginine-C^{14})	
Whole homogenate	4160	+590	2630	+480
Acid insoluble	4260	+500	2895	+370
Histones	5700	+680	3850	+760
Microsomes	3090	+1000	1320	+320
Mitochondria	1860	+280	920	+140
Cytoplasmic sap	3230	+1340	1130	+310

(From Busch et al., 1961.)

the report that uric acid excretion was reduced without increasing the serum uric acid levels (Longo and Zinsser, 1960).
    Colchicine suppressed the uptake of uniformly labeled
C^{14}-arginine into protein of the Ehrlich ascites tumor cells
(Busch et al., 1961). The labeling of cytoplasmic proteins exceeded that of the nuclear proteins as shown in Table 13.

MISCELLANEOUS

PHOSPHORIC TRIAMIDE, HEXAMETHYL-

Synonyms

Hempa
HMPA
HMP
ENT 50882

Structure

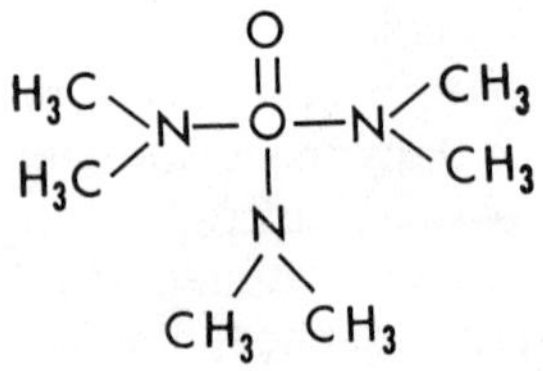

$C_6H_{18}N_3OP$ Mol. wt. 179.02

Physical Properties

(Generously supplied by T. B. Rice, Eastman Chemical Products, Inc.)

Physical form	Liquid
Color	Water-white
Odor	Mild amine
Melting point	6 to 8° C
Boiling point	(1 to 1.5mm Hg) 70.72° C
	(739.4mm Hg) 230 to 232° C

Refractive index $n_D^{25} = 1.4586 - 1.4590$

Solubility. Soluble in water and all common plasticizers, and in both polar and nonpolar solvents.

Stability. Storage tests in steel drums indicate that hempa is stable under normal storage conditions.

Methods of Determination

The best method available is the gas chromatographic method described in the section on alkylating agents (Bowman and Beroza, 1966). Colorimetric phosphate analyses may also be used.

Biochemistry

Metabolic effects of hempa have not been extensively investigated and very little is known about its biochemistry.

Hodgson and Casida (1961) found no indication of a microsomal enzyme in rat liver which would metabolize hempa and cause the release of formaldehyde although certain other N,N-dialkyl derivatives of a noncarbamate structure tested were metabolized in this manner.

Hempa has frequently been reported to be effective in the coordination of metals. Its action as a sterilant might be related to this property in that binding of essential metal cofactors might block any of several enzyme systems.

UREA, THIO-

Synonyms

Thiourea
ENT 3582

Structure

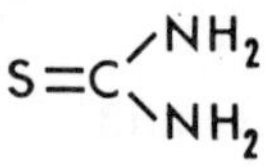

$$S=C\begin{smallmatrix}\nearrow NH_2 \\ \searrow NH_2\end{smallmatrix}$$

CH$_4$N$_2$S   Mol. wt. 76-07

Physical Properties

Physical form	Crystalline solid
Color	White
Odor	Odorless
Melting point	176 to 180° C

Solubility. Soluble in 11 parts water and in ethanol; sparingly soluble in ether.

Stability. Stable under normal storage conditions at room temperature.

Methods of Determination

It would be futile to try to list all of the accepted methods of determination but a few of the recently developed methods are worthy of note. A chromatographic method useful in determination of sulfates, and compounds which can be converted to them, has been devised (Brouwer, 1964). The compounds are detected on paper by a modification of the method of Feigl and Aufricht (1939). After the precipitation of BaCl$_2$,, in the presence of KMnO$_4$, the paper is decolorized by exposure to nitrous fumes. The sulfate-containing spots persist because MnO$_4$ has become incorporated in the crystal.

Microgram amounts of thiourea can be detected by a spectrophotometric method based on reaction with nitrous acid (Seiffarth and Ardelt, 1964). The HSCN thus formed reacts with bromine to give BrCN, which in turn reacts with pyridine and barbituric acid. The intensity of the developed color is measured at 589 mμ. There is no interference from biuret, cyanates, cyanuric acid, dicyanodiamide, melamine, thiocyanates, or urea.

Biochemistry

Thiourea is well recognized for its effectiveness as a protective agent against physiological damage caused by radiation or by "radiomimetic" alkylating agents. Since both radiation and "radiomimetic" chemicals are effective as chemosterilants it is difficult to imagine biochemical reactions of thiourea which might be related to its antifertility effects. In consideration of possible effects on enzyme systems, one is forced to consider the report of in vitro inhibition of oxidative phosphorylation of lettuce mitochondria (Ulitzur and Poljakoff-Mayber, 1963). The same workers, however, noted that thiourea sometimes actually stimulated the process in vivo.

It has been suggested that the protective effect of thriourea against radiation-induced hemolysis of erythrocytes is based upon its ability to form inclusion compounds with proteins in the protoplasm (Kriger and Parkhomenko, 1960). This binding to proteins may be related to the sterilizing effects of thiourea. A rather unexpected effect is the enhancement of thiamine biosynthesis reported to occur in rats which were fed thiourea (Meghal and Nath, 1963).

SUMMARY OF BIOCHEMICAL EFFECTS CITED

Apholate

Inhibited DNA and LDH synthesis in house fly eggs (p. 169); (Kilgore and Painter, 1964).

Reduced PAS-positive material in mosquito ovary (p. 170); (Hazard, personal communication).

Reduced alkaline phosphatase activity in gonads of southern corn rootworm (p. 171); (Mendoza, 1964).

Weakened and inactivated sperm (p. 171); (Mendoza, 1964).

Tepa

Clumped chromatin at anaphase stage in testes of boll weevil (p. 179); (Hedin et al., 1966b).

Increased depolymerase activity in tumor-bearing rats (p. 00); (Chernov and Presnova, 1963).

Inhibited nucleic acid biosynthesis (p. 182); (Chernov and Presnova, 1963).

Reduced concentration of RNA and DNA in malignant tissues (p.182); (Grushina, 1955, and Chernov and Zakharova, 1957).

Reduced body growth, tumor growth, and utilization of food in the rat (p.182); (Allison et al., 1954).

Increased glycolysis of Yoshida sarcoma cells (p.182); (Hori et al., 1963).

Inhibited glycolysis of Ehrlich ascites tumor cells and stimulated alkaline phosphatase activity (p.182); (Maruyama and Uchida, 1960).

Metepa

Rapidly degraded in mosquitoes (p.185); (Plapp et al., 1962).

Thiotepa

Rapidly converted to tepa in the rat, rabbit, dog, and several insect species (p.189); (Craig et al., 1959, Mellett and Woods, 1960, and Parish and Arthur, 1965).

Found to be associated with protein in blood serum of treated cancer patients (p.190); (Bateman et al., 1960).

Shown to be bound to the nuclear fraction in rats (p.190); (Ruddon and Mellett, 1964).

Altered SH metabolism (p.191); (Schuberth and Sorbo, 1963).

Decreased SH content in the blood serum and in tumor tissue of rats (p.191); (Kulik, 1963).

Inhibited dehydrogenase activity in Ehrlich ascites tumor cells (p.191); (DiPaola, 1963a,b).

Prolonged metaphase of dividing cells in tissue culture (p.191); (Oishi, 1961).

Caused sticky and condensed chromosomes (p.192); (Umemo, 1959).

Altered depolymerase activity of normal and tumor cells (p.192); (Chernov and Presnova, 1963).

Reduced incorporation of H^3-thymidine into DNA (p.192); (MacDonald et al., 1963).

Caused formation of large molecular aggregates of DNA in vitro (p.192); (Klemm and Obrecht, 1962).

Inhibited incorporation of C^{14}-formate into purines of

RNA and DNA in sensitive tumors but not in resistant tumors (p.192); (Wheeler and Alexander, 1964b).

Inhibited incorporation of adenine-8-C^{14} into DNA (p.192); (Wheeler and Alexander, 1964b).

Increased serum albumin in cancer patients (p.193); (Shimizu, 1961).

Altered incorporation of C^{14}-glycine into both histone and nonhistone fractions of nuclear protein (p.193); (Pradhan and West, 1964).

Inhibited incorporation of C^{14}-glycine into cytoplasmic proteins (p. 193); (Pradhan and West, 1964).

Reduced serum properdin level of rabbits (p.193); (Blumberg and Bass-Shadkin, 1964).

Reduced level of total and fraction III protein in rat liver (p.193); (Kaji, 1962).

Decreased incorporation of C^{14}-glycine into cellular protein of Ehrlich ascites cells (p.193); (Perevoshchikova, 1964).

Reduced glycogen content and simultaneously increased glucose content of ascitic cells (p.193); (Burdzhanadze et al., 1965).

Inhibited respiration of human cancer cells but stimulated aerobic metabolism in vitro (p.194); (Katchman et al., 1963).

Inhibited anaerobic glycolysis of liver carcinoma cells in vitro (p.194); (Tsukagoshi et al., 1959).

Depressed P:O ratio in normal cells (p.194); (Tsukagoshi et al., 1959).

Reduced oxygen consumption in normal cells (p.194); (Tsukagoshi et al., 1959).

Inhibited oxidation of α-ketoglutarate in mitochondria in vitro (p.194); (Maruyama, 1962).

Altered 5-aminolevulinic acid metabolism in mice with tumors (p.194); (Akashi, 1964).

Therapeutic effect against Ehrlich ascites cells was synergized by certain furocoumarins (p.194); (Vermel, 1964, and Vermel and Tsetlin, 1964).

Produced typical x-ray type dose-response curve against mammalian cells (p.194); (Berry, 1964).

OPSPA

Appeared to react with some precursor of nucleic acid biosynthesis in rats (p. 197); (Maller and Heidelberger, 1957a).

Reduced albumins and increased α-globulins in hepatectomized rats (p. 198); (Leonardi et al., 1959).

TEM

Was degraded in vivo to cyanuric acid (p. 201); (Nadkarni et al., 1954).

Activity in rats bearing Walker tumor was enhanced by pretreatment with glucose (p. 201); (Connors et al., 1964b).

Cytostatic effects in rats was reduced by treatment with cysteine just prior to TEM, but administration of cysteine 30 min. before enhanced the effects of TEM (p. 201); (Pliess, 1960).

Inhibited incorporation of C^{14}-formate into purines and of adenine-8-C^{14} into DNA (p. 202); (Wheeler and Alexander, 1964a).

Exerted a selective effect on male reproductive system (p. 202); (Jackson et al., 1955).

Principal effect was on spermatocytes and on spermatids (p.202); (Jackson et al., 1959).

Decreased extractibility of DNA in spermatozoa (p.202); (Berenbaum, 1962a).

Affected nondividing differentiating cells (p. 203); (Berenbaum and Calley, 1962, and Pliess, 1961).

Affected spermatid development and spermatogonia (p. 203); (Fox et al., 1963b).

Exerted specific effect on testicular germinal epithelium (p. 203); (Steinberger, 1962).

Suppressed antibody synthesis (p. 204); (Berenbaum, 1962b).

Delayed development of antibody titer (p. 205); (Cassi et al., 1962).

Reduced albumins and increased α-globulins in hepatectomized rats (p. 205); (Leonardi et al., 1959).

Altered purine metabolism in rats (p. 205); (Takemasa, 1958).

Caused formation of large molecular aggregates of DNA in vitro (p. 205); (Klemm and Obrecht, 1962).

Depressed uptake of P^{32} into Ehrlich ascites cells (p. 205); (Krepsz et al., 1964).

Was incorporated into DNA, one mole per mole of DNA (p. 205); (Trams et al., 1961).

Decreased glycogen and alkaline phosphatase in marrow and peripheral blood of rats and guinea pigs (p. 205); (Squadrito et al., 1961).

Alkylated nicotinamide, pyridoxine, adenine, thiamine, riboflavin, folic acid, methionine, and lysine in vitro (p. 205); (Duntze et al., 1962).

2-Chloroethylmethanesulfonate

Reacted in vivo with SH groups (p. 207); (Roberts and Warwick, 1958a, 1959b).

Showed striking activity against lymphoma 8 whether the tumor was well established or recently innoculated (p.207); (Schmidt, 1960).

Altered anaerobic glycolysis (p. 207); (Briggs, 1960).

Inhibited incorporation of C^{14}-glycine into ethanol-acetone insoluble fraction (p. 209); (Coles et al., 1960).

2-Fluoroethylmethanesulfonate

Altered nucleic acid synthesis (p. 211); (Ricciardi et al., 1959).

4-Fluorobutylmethanesulfonate

Caused accumulation of citrate in kidney and brain of mice (p. 213); (Parker and Walker, 1957).

Dimethylmyleran

Reduced acid-soluble SH compounds in the brain of rats (p. 214); (Calcutt, 1965).

Caused erratic fluctuation of acid-soluble and protein-bound SH values (p. 214); (Calcutt, 1965).

Decreased glutamate, aspartate, and taurine in the free amino acid pool of plasma (p. 214); (Rouser et al., 1962).

Toxicity to rats was not reduced by administration of cysteine (p. 214); (Roberts and Warwick, 1959a,b).

Reacted principally with SH groups (p. 215); (Roberts and Warwick, 1959a,b).

Appeared to be truly radiomimetic (p. 215); (Alexander, 1961).

Chlorambucil

Inhibited several general glycolytic enzymes (p. 218); (Brecher and Baker, 1965).

Alkylated hemoglobin in vitro (p. 219); (Linford, 1963b).

Was incorporated into DNA fraction in vivo (p. 219); (Trams et al., 1961).

Inhibited incorporation of arginine-C^{14} into acid-insoluble nuclear proteins (p. 220); (Busch et al., 1961).

Altered SH levels in rats (p. 220); (Calcutt, 1965).

Rapidly adsorbed by serum proteins (p. 220); (Linford, 1961).

Stimulated formate uptake by leukemic cells (p. 220); (Winzler et al., 1959).

Inhibited incorporation of lysine and glycine into protein (p. 220); (Pradhan and West, 1960).

Inhibited incorporation of glycine into acid-soluble nucleotides (p. 221); (Pradhan and West, 1960).

Inhibited incorporation of glycine, formate, adenine, and orotic acid (p. 221); (Pradhan and West, 1960).

Triphenyl Tin Chloride

Shown to be an uncompetitive inhibitor of ATPase (p. 223); (Pieper and Casida, 1965).

Triphenyl Tin Acetate

Inhibited oxidative phosphorylation (p.224); (Kaars-Sijesteijn et al., 1962).

Aminopterin

Inhibited dihydrofolic (DHF) reductase (p. 226); (Osborn et al., 1958).

Inhibited folate reduction through a noncompetitive mechanism (p. 226); (Peters and Greenberg, 1959).

Bound DHF reductase 10^4 to 10^5 times as tightly as did substrate and showed little discrimination among enzymes obtained from different sources (p. 226); (Bertino, 1963, and Werkheiser, 1963).

Lowered N^5-formyl tetrahydrofolate (THF) level in house fly larvae (p. 226); (Perry and Miller, 1965).

Fluorouracil

Blocked methylation of deoxyuridylic acid (dUMP) to thymidylic acid (TMP) (p. 229); (Heidelberger et al., 1958).

Was incorporated into RNA (p. 229); (Heidelberger et al., 1958).

Possessed a degree of selectivity for neoplasms (p. 229); (Heidelberger et al., 1958).

Altered the elution pattern of sRNA from a methylated albumin column (p. 229); (Sueoka and Yamane, 1963).

Inhibited incorporation of orotate and uracil into RNA (p. 229); (Bosch et al., 1958, and Harbers et al., 1959).

May block induce synthesis of certain enzymes (p. 230); (Horowitz et al., 1960).

Blocked DNA synthesis (p. 230); (Heidelberger, 1963).

Depressed incorporation of arginine-C^{14} into histones and into acid-insoluble nuclear proteins; and into microsomal and cytoplasmic proteins (p. 230); (Busch et al., 1961).

Fluoroorotic acid

Inhibited dihydroorotase and orotidine-5-phosphatase (p. 232); (Stone and Potter, 1957).

Reduced the ψ-uridylic acid content of sRNA (p. 232); (Wagner and Heidelberger, 1962).

Incorporated into several RNA fractions to a greater extent than fluorouracil (p. 232); (Wagner and Heidelberger, 1962).

Porfiromycin

Inhibited purine metabolism but appears to have additional sites of action (p. 235); (Pittillo and Quinnelly, 1962). Cross-linked DNA—one link per 2,000 nucleotide residues (p. 235); (Iyer and Szybalski, 1964).

Alkylated RNA and DNA to the same extent— one cross-link per 500 nucleotide residues (p. 236); (Weissbach and Lisio, 1965).

Alkylated sRNA producing mono- and diguanyl porfiromycin (p. 237); Lipsett and Weissbach, 1965).

Alkylated synthetic polyribonucleotides (p. 237); (Lipsett and Weissbach, 1965).

Labilized guanine-ribose bond (p. 237); (Lipsett and Weissbach, 1965, Brookes and Lawley, 1961).

Selectively inhibited DNA synthesis (p. 237); (Laiko, 1964).

Nearly abolished DNA synthesis (p. 237); (Magee and Miller, 1962).

Cycloheximide

Inhibited protein synthesis by *S. pastorianus* in vivo and in vitro by inhibition of transfer of amino acids from sRNA to ribosomal protein (p. 240); (Siegel and Sisler, 1963, 1964a,b).

Inhibited protein synthesis in mammalian cells (p. 241); (Young et al., 1963, Gorski and Axman, 1964).

Inhibited transfer of amino acids from sRNA to polypeptide chain in vitro with mammalian cells (p. 241); (Ennis and Lubin, 1964a,b).

Inhibited normal GTP-dependent breakdown of ribosomes which is coupled to protein synthesis (p. 241); (Wettstein et al., 1964).

Inhibited DNA synthesis secondarily to an inhibition of protein synthesis (p. 241); (Bennett et al., 1965).

Inhibited incorporation of leucine and thymidine into HeLa cells (p. 241); (Young and Hodas, 1965).

Monocrotaline

Caused liver cells to develop features of neoplastic cells (p. 243); (Hurchinson and Hill, 1960).

Cytological damage was reduced 80 to 90 percent by administration of cysteine (p. 243); (Avanzi, 1961).

Colchicine

Caused increased excretion of taurine in rats (p. 245); (Kostos and Kocsis, 1961).

Inhibited anaerobic glycolysis in erythrocytes (p. 245); (Sonka et al., 1961).

Blocked dividing eggs at metaphase but did not alter ATPase activity (p. 245); (Sauia and Mazia, 1961).

Inhibited DNase activity, increased transaminase activity in mice (p. 245); (Truhaut and Bohuon, 1963).

Decreased alkaline and acid phosphatase activity (p. 245); (Kemeney et al., 1963a,b).

Inhibited the following activities of xanthine oxidase: aerobic production of uric acid from hypoxanthine, the increase of this activity by methylene blue, anaerobis reduction of methylene blue (p. 245); (Roussors, 1963).

Inhibited liver xanthine oxidase and xanthine dehydrogenase activities (p. 245); (Affonso et al., 1961).

Increased blood xanthine oxidase and xanthine dehydrogenase activities (p. 245); (Affonso, 1961).

Reduced uric acid excretion without altering serum uric acid levels (p. 245); (Longo and Zinsser, 1960).

Suppressed uptake of arginine-C^{14} into protein of Ehrlich ascites cells (p. 246); (Busch et al., 1961).

Hempa

Not metabolized by microsomal enzyme (p. 247); (Hodgson and Casida, 1961).

Thiourea

Inhibited oxidative phosphorylation of mitochondria (p. 249); (Ulitzur and Poljakoff-Mayber, 1963).

Sometimes stimulated oxidative phosphorylation in vivo (p. 249); (Ulitzur and Poljakoff-Mayber, 1963).

Formed inclusion compounds with proteins in protoplasm (p. 249); (Kriger and Parkhomenko, 1960).

Enhanced thiamine biosynthesis (p. 249); (Meghal and Nath, 1963).

REFERENCES

Affonso, O. R., E. Mitidieri, and G. G. Villela. 1961. Effect of colchicine on rat liver xanthine oxidase. Nature (London), 192: 666–667.

_____, E. Mitidieri, and G. G. Villela. 1962. Effect of colchicine on rat blood serum xanthine oxidase. Nature (London), 193:64.

Alexander, M. L., and E. Glanges. 1965. Genetic damage induced by ethyleneimine. Proc. Nat. Acad. Sci. U.S.A., 53:282–288.

Alexander, P. 1961. Mechanisms of the cytotoxic action of the radiomimetic alkylating agents. Radiobiol., Proc. 3d Australasian Conf., Sydney, Australia, 1960, 287–297.

_____, and J. T. Lett. 1960. Biological significance of changes produced in deoxyribonucleic acid of cells treated with radiomimetic alkylating agents. Biochem. Pharmacol., 4:34–48.

_____, and Z. B. Mikulski. 1961. Differences in the response of leukemia cells in tissue culture to nitrogen mustard and to dimethyl myleran. Biochem. Pharmacol., 5:275–282.

Allen, E., and W. Seaman. 1955. Method of assay for ethyleneimine derivatives. Anal. Chem., 27:540–543.

Allison, J. B., R. W. Wannemacher, Jr., R. Hill, J. F. Migliarese, and M. L. Crossley. 1954. Dietary protein and tumor-host relationship in the rat. J. Nutr., 54:593–600.

_____, R. W. Wannemacher, Jr., L. Prosky, and M. L. Crossley. 1956. Nutritive value of protein and tumor-host relationship in the rat. J. Nutr., 60:297–307.

Ausman, R. K., E. E. Crevar, H. Hagedorn, T. J. Bardos, and J. L. Ambrus. 1961. Studies in the pharmacodynamics of mechlorethamine and AB 100. J. Amer. Med. Ass., 178:735–738.

Avanzi, S. 1961. Chromosome breakage by pyrrolizidine alkaloids and modification of the effect by cysteine. Caryologia, 14:251–261.

Bardos, T. J., N. Datta-Gupta, P. Hebborn, and D. J. Triggle. 1965. Comparative chemical and biological activities of alkylating agents. J. Med. Chem., 8:167–174.

Bateman, J. C., H. N. Carlton, R. C. Calvert, and G. E. Lindenbald. 1960. Investigation of distribution and excretion of C^{14}-tagged triethylenethiophosphoramide following injection by various routes. Int. J. Appl. Radiat., 7:287–298.

Bellet, P., and P. Fabre. 1961. Rotatory power of the medicinal colchicine. Ann. Pharm. Franc., 19:117–119.

Bender, D. F., E. Sawicki, and R. M. Wilson, Jr. 1965. Spectrophotometric determination of alkylating agents with 4-picoline and o-dinitrobenzene. Analyst, 90:630–635

Bennett, L. L., Jr., D. Smithers, and C. T. Ward. 1964. Inhibition of DNA synthesis in mammalian cells by actidione. Biochem. Biophys. Acta, 87:60–69.

_____, V. L. Ward, and R. W. Brockman. 1965. Inhibition of protein synthesis in vitro by chyloheximide and related glutarimide antibiotics. Biochem. Biophys. Acta, 103:478–485.

Berenbaum, M. C. 1961. The action of antimitotic substances on the immune response. Path. Biol. (Paris), 9:963–966.

_____. 1962a. Histochemical evidence for crosslinking of DNA (deoxyribonucleic acid) by alkylating agents in vivo. Biochem. Pharmacol., 11:1035–1042.

_____. 1962b. Effect of cytostatic agents on the production of antibody to T. A. B. vaccine in the mouse. Biochem. Pharmacol., 11: 29–44.

_____, and M. Calley. 1962. Effects of antitumor agents on nondividing cells. Nature (London), 196:656–658.

Beroza, M., and A. B. Borkovec. 1964. The stability of tepa and other aziridine chemosterilants. J. Med. Chem. 7:44–49.

Berry, R. J. 1964. A comparison of effects of some chemotherapeutic agents and those of x-rays on the reproductive capacity of mammalian cells. Nature (London), 203:1150–1153.

Bertino, J. R. 1963. The mechanism of action of the folate antagonists in man. Cancer Res., 23:1286–1306.

Beslekoev, T. I., and L. N. Surodeikina. 1964. Influence of thiotepa on the blood protein composition in sarcoma M-1. Vop. Onkol., 10:45–48.

Block, J., and H. Jackson. 1957. The action of triethylenemelamine on the fertility of male rats. Brit. J. Pharmacol., 12:1–7.

Blum, M. S., and J. J. Pratt, Jr. 1960. Relations between structure and insecticidal activity of some organotin compounds. J. Econ. Entom., 53:445–448.

Blumberg, M., and Kh. Bass-Shadkin. 1964. Properdin level in blood serum of the rabbit in certain pathological conditions. Latvijas PSR Zinantnu Akad. Vestis, 1964:46–50.

Bock, R., S. Gorbach, and H. Oeser. 1958. Analysis of triphenyltin compounds. Angew. Chem. (Eng.), 70:272.

Bolognari, A. 1952. Quantitative variation in the content of glutathione in the fertilized eggs of Paracentrotus lividus. Arch. Sci. Biol. (Bologna), 36:40–47.

Borkovec, A. B. 1962. Sexual sterilization of insects by chemicals. Science, 137:1037–1037.

_____, and C. W. Woods. 1963. Aziridine chemosterilants. Sulfur-containing aziridines. Advances Chem. Ser., 41:47–55.

_____, S. C. Chang, and A. M. Limburg. 1964. Effect of pH on sterilizing activity of tepa and metepa in male houseflies. J. Econ. Entom., 57:815–817.

Bosch, L., E. Harbers, and C. Heidelberger. 1958. Studies on fluorinated pyrimidines. V. Effects on nucleic acid metabolism in vitro. Cancer Res., 18:335–343.

Bowman, M. C., and M. Beroza. 1966. Gas chromatographic determination of trace amounts of the insect chemosterilants tepa, metepa, methiotepa, hempa, and apholate, and the analysis of tepa in insect tissue. J. Ass. Official Anal. Chem., 49: 1046-1052.

Brecher, A. S., and B. S. Baker. 1965. The inhibition of some gly-colytic enzymes by chlorambucil. Biochem. Pharmacol., 14: 638-640.

Briggs, D. E. 1960. Biochemical studies with methanesulfonyl esters, especially 2-chlorethyl methanesulfonate. Biochem. J., 77: 186-194.

Brookes, P., and P. E. Lawley. 1961. Reaction of mono- and difunc-tional alkylating agents with nucleic acids. Biochem. J., 80:496-503.

_____, and P. E. Lawley. 1964. Alkylating agents. Brit. Med. Bull., 20:91-95.

Brouwer, Th. 1964. New detection method for the chromatographic investigation of sulfur compounds. Chem. Weekblad, 60:208-210.

Buffa, P., and R. A. Peters. 1939. The in vivo formation of citrate induced by fluoroacetate and its significance. J. Physiol., 110:488-500.

Burdzhanadze, V. A., Sh. I. Mardakhiashvili, and A. S. Dzotsenidze. 1965. Hydrocarbon metabolism in an ascitic carcinoma dur-ing anticarcinoma chemotherapy. Soobshch. Akad. Nauk Gruz. SSR. 37:213-220.

Busch, H., D. C. Firszt, A. Lipsey, E. Kohen, and S. Amer. 1961. Inhibition by antitumor agents of labeling of nuclear proteins in vivo with L-arginine-U-C[14]. Biochem. Pharmacol., 7:123-134.

Calcutt, G. 1965. The effects of some cancer chemotherapy agents on the sulphydryl levels of normal rat tissues. Brit. J. Cancer, 19:883-893.

_____, and T. A. Connors. 1963. Tumor sulphydryl levels and sensi-tivity to the nitrogen mustard merophan. Biochem. Pharma-col., 12:839-845.

_____, T. A. Connors, L. A. Elson and W. C. J. Ross. 1963. Reduc-tion of the toxicity of "radiomimetic" alkylating agents in rats by thiol pretreatment. II. Mechanism of protection. Bio-chem. Pharmacol., 12:833-837.

Cassi, E., G. C. Scaltrini, R. Bombara, and S. Tognella. 1962. Anti-body formation and antineoplastic drugs. Modified hetero-agglutinin production in mice treated with prednisolone, alkylating agents and 6-mercaptopurine. Boll. Ist. Sieroter. Milan, 41:377-388.

Chalmers, A. H., C. C. J. Culvenor, and L. W. Smith. 1965. Charac-terization of pyrrolizidine alkaloids by gas, thin-layer, and paper chromotography. J. Chromatogr., 20:270-277.

Chang, S. C. 1965. Chemosterilization and mating behavior of male house flies. J. Econ. Entom., 58:669-672.

_____, and A. B. Borkovec. 1964. Quantitative effects of tepa, metepa, and apholate on sterilization of male houseflies. J. Econ. Entom., 57:488–490.

_____, and A. B. Borkovec. 1965. Structure-activity relationships in tepa and hempa. Analogs of J. Econ. Entom., 59:1359–1362.

_____, P. H. Terry, and A. B. Borkovec. 1964. Insect chemosterilants with low toxicity for mammals. Science, 144:57–58.

_____, A. B. Borkovec and C. W. Woods. 1966. Fate of tepa uniformly labeled with C^{14} in male house flies. J. Econ. Entom., 59: 937–944.

Chernov, V. A., and Zh. F. Zakharova. 1957. Effect of triethyleneimino phosphoramide (TEP) on the metabolism of nucleic acids in cancer and in animal organs with transplanted cancer (rat sarcoma "45"). Vop. Onkol., 3:289–295.

_____, and Zh. F. Presnova. 1963. The change in nucleic acid depolymerase activity in rats with transplanted tumors under the influence of ethyleneimine derivatives. Vop. Onkol., 9:70–78.

Coles, N. W., R. M. Johnstone, and J. H. Quastel. 1960. Effects of alkylating agents on the incorporation of glycine-1-C^{14} into tissue proteins in vitro. Cancer Res., 20:1523–1529.

Connors, T. A., and L. A. Elson. 1962. Reduction of the toxicity of radiomimetic alkylating agents in rats by thiol pretreatment. Biochem. Pharmacol., 11:1221–1232.

_____, A. Jeney, and M. Jones. 1964a. Reduction of the toxicity of "radiomimetic" alkylating agents in rats by thiol pretreatment. III. The mechanism of the protective effect of thiosulfate. Biochem. Pharmacol., 13:1545–1550.

_____, B. C. V. Mitchley, V. M. Rosenoer, and W. C. J. Ross. 1964b. Effect of glucose pretreatment on the carcinostatic and toxic activities of some alkylating agents. Biochem. Pharmacol., 13:395–400.

Craig, A. W., and H. Jackson. 1955. The metabolism of P^{32}-labeled triethylenephosphoramide in relation to its antitumor activity. Brit. J. Pharmacol., 10:321–325.

_____, B. W. Fox, H. Jackson. 1958. Sensitivity of the spermatogenic process in the rat to radiomimetic drugs and x-rays. Nature (London), 181:353–354.

_____, B. W. Fox, and H. Jackson. 1959. Metabolic studies of P^{32}-labeled triethylenethiophosphoramide. Biochem. Pharmacol., 3:42–50.

Crossley, M. L., J. B. Allison, R. P. Parker, E. Kuh, and D. R. Seegar. 1953. Chemotherapy of tumors in rats with certain ethylenephosphoramides. Proc. Soc. Exp. Biol. Med., 83:438–447.

Crystal, M. M. 1963. The induction of sexual sterility in the screwworm fly by antimetabolites and alkylating agents. J. Econ. Entom., 56:468–473.

Dame, D. A., and H. R. Ford. 1964. Chemosterilization and its permanency in mosquitoes. Nature (London), 201:733–734.

Davison, A. N. 1955. The conversion of Schradan and Parathion inhibitors of cholinesterase by mammalian liver. Biochem. J., 61:203–209.

Davison, C., R. S. Rozman, and P. K. Smith. 1961. Metabolism of bis-β-chloroethyl sulfide (sulfur mustard gas). Biochem. Pharmacol., 7:65–74.

DeBoer, C., A. Dietz, N. E. Lummis, and G. Savage. 1961. In Gray, P., B. Tabenkin, and S. G. Bradley, Antimicrobial Agents Annual, 1960, pp. 17–22, New York, Plenum Press.

Di Paola, J. A. 1963a. In vitro test systems for cancer chemotherapy. I. Inhibition of dehydrogenases and growth in the Ehrlich ascites tumor. Cancer Res., 23:184–190.

_____. 1963b. In vitro test systems for cancer therapy. II. Correlation of in vitro inhibition of dehydrogenase and growth with in vivo inhibition of Ehrlich ascites tumor. Proc. Soc. Exp. Biol. Med., 114:384–387.

Dixon, F. J., D. W. Talmage, and P. H. Maurer. 1952. Radiosensitive and radioresistant phases in the antibody response. J. Immun., 68:693–700.

Dixon, M. 1952. Manometric Methods, 3d ed., Cambridge, Cambridge University Press.

Duntze, W., H. W. Goedde, S. Frank, and H. Holzer. 1962. Alkylation of nicotinamide and nicotinic acid by tetramin-(1-aziridino-2-hydroxybut-3-ene) and other carcinostatic ethyleneimine derivatives. Z. Krebsforsch, 64:503–518.

Duvall, L. R. 1961. 2-Chloroethyl methanesulfonate. Cancer Chemother. Rep., 14:180–187.

_____. 1963. Porfiromycin. Cancer Chemother. Rep., 30:35–43.

Ebner, H., and H. Strecker. 1960. Über die wirkung des colchicins in vivo auf die alkalische phosphatase der rattenleber. Experentia, 6:388–389.

Elson, L. A., and L. F. Lamerton. 1949. The influence of the protein content of the diet on the response of Walker rat carcinoma 256 to x-radiation. Brit. J. Cancer, 3:414–426.

Ennis, H. L., and M. Lubin. 1964a. Dissociation of nucleic acid and protein synthesis in mammalian cells in culture. Bacteriol. Proc. Amer. Soc. Microbiol., 1964:103. (Abstr., p. 89.)

_____, and M. Lubin. 1964b. Cycloheximide and acetoxycycloheximide: inhibitors of transfer of amino acids from aminoacyl-s-RNA to polypeptide in mammalian cells. Fed. Proc., 23:269. (Abstr., p. 1009.)

Epstein, J., R. W. Rosenthal, and R. J. Ess. 1955. Use of γ-(4-nitrobenzyl) pyridine as analytical reagent for ethyleneimines and alkylating agents. Anal. Chem., 27:1435–1439.

Fahmy, O. G., and M. J. Fahmy. 1957. Mutagenic response to the alkylmethane-sulfonates during spermatogenesis in Drosophila melanogaster. Nature (London), 180:31–34.

Feigl, F., and W. Aufricht. 1939. Detection of barium and sulfate by spot tests. Rec. Trav. Chim., 58:1127–1132.

Forist, A. A., and S. Theal. 1959. Spectrophotometric determination of cycloheximide. Anal. Chem., 31:1042–1044.

Fox, B. W., H. Jackson, A. W. Craig, and T. D. Glover. 1963a. Effect of alkylating agents on spermatogenesis in the rabbit. J. Reprod. Fertil., 5:13–21.

————, M. Partington, and H. Jackson. 1963b. Action of alkylating agents on sea urchin gametes. Exp. Cell Res., 29:137–143.

Friedman, O. M., and E. Boger. 1961. Colorimetric estimation of nitrogen mustards in aqueous media-hydrolytic behavior of bis (beta-chloroethyl) amine. Anal. Chem., 33:906–910.

Garrett, E. R. 1963. The physical chemical characterization of the products, equilibrium, and kinetics of the complex transformations of the antibiotic porfiromycin. J. Med. Chem., 6:488–501.

————, and R. E. Notari. 1965. Cycloheximide transformations. II Kinetics and stability in a pharmaceutically useful pH range. J. Pharm. Sci., 54:209–215.

————, and R. E. Notari. 1966. Cycloheximide transformations. II Kinetics and mechanism in aqueous acid. J. Org. Chem., 31: 425–434.

————, and W. Schroeder. 1964. Prediction of stability of pharmaceutical preparations. XII. Stability, spectrophotometric, and biological assay of the antibiotic porfiromycin in pharmaceutically useful pH range. J. Pharm. Sci., 53:917–923.

Gasparic, J., and A. Cee. 1962. Identification of organic compounds. XLV Separation and identification of organotin compounds by paper chromatography. J. Chromatogr., 8:393–398.

Gavosto, F., G. Maraini, and A. Pileri. 1960. Proliferative capacity of acute leukemia cells. Nature (London), 187:611–612.

Glaser, R. W. 1925. Hydrogen ion concentrations in the blood of insects. J. Gen. Physiol., 7:599–602.

Goldenthal, E. I., M. V. Nadkarni, and P. K. Smith. 1958. The excretion of radioactivity following administration of tri-C^{14}-s-triazine in normal mice. J. Pharmacol. Exp. Ther., 122:431–441.

————, M. V. Nadkarni, and P. K. Smith. 1959. A study of comparative protection against lethality of triethylenemelamine, nitrogen mustard, and x-irradiation in mice. Radiat. Res., 5:571–583.

Gorski, J., and M. C. Axman. 1964. Cycloheximide (actidione) inhibition of protein synthesis and the uterine response to estrogen. Arch. Biochem., 105:517–520.

Goudot, A. 1963. Transfer of electrons between deoxyribonucleic acid (DNA) or ribonucleic acid (RNA) slightly altered in chemical structure. C. R. Soc. Biol. (Paris), 256:3528–3531.

Graham, H. D. 1964. Color reactions of veratrum alkaloids with sulfuric acid and sulfuric acid reagents. J. Pharm. Sci., 53:86–91.

Grushina, A. A. 1955. The effect of triethyleneiminophosphoramide (TEP) on the metabolism of nucleic acids (RNA and DNA) in the transplantable rat sarcoma "45". Vop. Onkol, 1:51–59.

Haddow, A., and W. C. J. Ross. 1956. Tumor growth-inhibitory alkyl sulfonates. Nature (London), 177:995–996.

Hancock, W., and E. Q. Laws. 1956. Simultaneous determination of traces of benzene and toluene. Analyst, 81:37–41.

Hanes, C. S., and F. A. Isherwood. 1949. Separation of the phosphoric esters on filter paper chromatograms. Nature (London), 164:1107–1112.

Hanka, L. J. 1960. Porfiromycin, a new antibiotic. IV. Microbiological assays. Antimicrob. Agents Ann., 1960:37–44.

Hano, K., and A. Akashi. 1964. Influence of anticancer agents on the metabolism of 5-amino-levulinic acid in normal and tumor-bearing mice. Gann, 55:25–40.

Hansch, C., R. M. Muir, T. Fujita, P. P. Maloney, F. Geiger, M. Streich. 1963. The correlation of biological activity of plant growth regulators and chloromycetin derivatives with Hammett constants and partition coefficients. J. Amer. Chem. Soc., 85:2817–2824.

Harbers, E., N. K. Chadhuri, and C. Heidelberger. 1959. Studies on fluorinated pyrimidines. VIII. Further biochemical and metabolic investigations. J. Biol. Chem., 234:1255–1262.

Hardon, H. J., H. Brunink, and E. W. van der Pol. 1960. Colorimetric determination of triphenyltin residues. Analyst, 85:847–849.

Hawrylyshyn, M., B. Z. Senkowski, and E. G. Wollish. 1964. Thin-layer chromatography of fluoropyrimidines. Microchem. J., 8:15–22.

Hazard, E. I., C. S. Lofgren, D. B. Woodward, H. R. Ford, B. M. Glancey. 1964. Resistance to the chemical sterilant, apholate, in Aedes aegypti. Science, 145:500–501.

Hedin, P. A., G. Wiygul, and N. Mitlin. 1966a. Absorption and metabolism of C^{14} tepa by the boll weevil. J. Econ. Entom. 60:215–218.

——, G. Wiygul, D. A. Vickers, A. C. Bartlett, and N. Mitlin. 1966b. Sterilizing effect of the chemosterilant tepa on the male boll weevil with respect to dosage, permanency of sterility, gonadal changes, and its biological turnover. J. Econ. Entom. 60:209–214.

Heidelberger, C. 1963. Biochemical mechanisms of action of fluorinated pyrimidines. Exp. Cell. Res. Suppl., 9:462–471.

——, and M. E. Baumann. 1957. Studies on OPSPA. I The effect of several phosphoramides on transplanted tumors. Cancer Res., 17:277–283.

——, L. Griesbach, O. Cruz, R. J. Schnitzer, and E. Grunberg. 1958. Fluorinated pyrimidines. VI Effects of 5-fluorouridine and 5-fluoro-2-deoxyuridine on transplanted tumors. Proc. Soc. Exp. Biol. Med., 97:470–475.

Herok, J., and H. Goette. 1963. Radiometrische untersuchungen über das verhalten von triphenylzinnacetat in pflanze und tier. Int. J. Appl. Radiat., 14:461–479.

Herr, R. R., M. E. Bergy, T. E. Eble, H. K. Jahnke. 1960. Porfiromycin, a new antibiotic. II. Isolation and characterization. Antimicrob. Agents Ann., 1960:23–26.

Hitchings, G. H., and J. J. Burchall. 1965. Inhibition of folate bio-synthesis and function as a basis for chemotherapy. Advances Enzym., 27:417–468.

Hodgson, E., and J. E. Casida. 1961. Metabolism of N:N-dialkyl carbamates and related compounds by rat liver. Biochem. Pharmacol., 8:179–191.

Hori, M., E. Ito, T. Takeuchi, and H. Umezawa. 1963. Inhibitory effects of antitumor substances on growth and glycolysis of Yoshida rat sarcoma cells. Penishiriv Sono Ta Koseibusshitsu Ser. A., 16:1–6.

Horowitz, J., J. J. Saukkonen, and E. Chargoff. 1960. Effects of fluoro-pyrimidines on the synthesis of bacterial proteins and nucleic acids. J. Biol. Chem., 235:3266–3272.

Huennekens, F. M. 1963. The role of dihydrofolic reductase in the metabolism of one-carbon units. Biochemistry, 2:151–159.

Hurchinson, V., and K. R. Hill. 1960. The effect of a Senecio alkaloid (monocrotaline) on human embryo liver in tissue culture. Brit. J. Cancer, 14:637–646.

Iyer, V. N., and W. Szybalski. 1964. Mitomycins and porfiromycin: chemical mechanism of activation and cross-linking of DNA. Science, 145:55–58.

Jackson, H. 1964. Effects of alkylating agents on fertility. Brit. Med. Bull., 20:107–114.

_____, and M. Bock. 1955. The effect of triethylenemelamine on the fertility of rats. Nature (London), 175:1037–1038.

_____, B. W. Fox, and A. W. Craig. 1959. The effect of alkylating agents on male rat fertility. Brit. J. Pharmacol., 14:149–157.

_____, B. W. Fox, and A. W. Craig. 1961. Antifertility substances and their assessment in the male rodent. J. Reprod. Fertil., 2: 447–465.

Jaenicke, L., and C. Kutzbach. 1963. Folsaüre and Folat-Enzyme. Fortschr. Chem. Org. Naturstoffe, 21:183–274.

Kaars-Sijesteijn, A., Rijkens, J. G. A. Luijten, and L. C. Willemsens. 1962. On the antifungal activity and antibacterial activity of some trisubstituted organogermanium, organotin, and organo-lead compounds. Antonie van Leeuwenhoek, 28:346–356.

Kaji, H. 1962. Electrophoretic studies on serum proteins and tissue proteins of liver and of tumor in malignant tumor-bearing bodies. II. Electrophoretic studies on tissue proteins of the liver and of the tumor in malignant tumor-bearing bodies and the influence of irradiation and some agents upon them. Sun-fujinka no Shimpo, 14:271–295.

Katchman, B. J., R. E. Zipf, and J. P. F. Murphy. 1963. The effect of chemotherapeutic agents upon the metabolism of infant human cancer cells. An in vitro technic for cell sensitivity. Clin. Chem., 9:511–529.

Kemeny, Gy., T. Feszt, M. Guendisch, and Cs. Hadnagy. 1963a. Action of urethan, trypaflavine, colchicine and quinonediethylamine on tissue phosphatase. Fiziol. Norm. Pat., 9:163–167.

_____, T. Feszt, M. Gundisch, and Cs. Hadnagy. 1963b. The action of antimitotic compounds (colchicine, urethan, and trypaflavine) on the alkaline and acid phosphatases of tissues. Arch. Int. Pharmacodyn., 141:176–180.

Kihlman, B. 1955. Studies on the effect of oxygen and chromosome breakage induced by 8-ethoxycaffeine. Exp. Cell. Res., 8:404–407.

_____. 1956. Factors affecting the production of chromosome aberrations by chemicals. J. Biophys. Biochem. Cytol., 2:543–555.

Kilgore, W. W., and R. R. Painter. 1964. Effect of the chemosterilant, apholate, on the synthesis of cellular components in developing house fly eggs. Biochem. J., 92:353–357.

Klassen, W., and F. Matsumura. 1966. Resistance to a chemosterilant, metepa, in Aedes aegypti mosquitoes. Nature (London), 209:1155–1156.

Klatt, O., A. C. Griffin, and J. S. Stehlin, Jr. 1960. Method for determination of phenylalanine mustard and related alkylating agents in blood. Proc. Soc. Exp. Biol. Med., 104:629–631.

Klemm, D., and P. Obrecht. 1962. Effect of various cytostatic drugs on the ultracentrifuge pattern of deoxyribonucleic acid. Arzneimittel forschung, 12:468–469.

Kostos, V. J., and J. J. Kocsis. 1961. Effect of colchicine on taurine excretion. Proc. Soc. Exp. Biol. Med., 106:659–660.

Kostova, A. G., and L. B. Leonteva. 1960. Alkanesulfonic acids. XXIII Synthesis and properties of some esters of methanesulfonic acid. Zh. Obshch. Khim., 30:3451–3452.

Krepsz, I., A. Pupp, and F. Gyergyay. 1964. Effect of cytostatic substances on the incorporation of radiophosphorous in Ehrlich ascites carcinoma. Rev. Med., 8:382–384.

Kriger, Yu. A., and I. M. Parkhomenko. 1960. Protective action of thiourea. Biofizika, 5:278–281.

Kroller, E. 1960. Triphenyl tin compounds as plant growth protecting agents and the determination of the residue. Deut. Lebesm. Rundschau, 56:190–193.

Kulik, G. I. 1963. Effect of thiophosphoramide (Thio-Tepa) on sulfhydryl groups of transplanted tumors and the blood serum of rats. Fiziol. Zh., Akad. Nauk. Ukr. RSR, 9:268–270.

Laiko, A. V. 1964. Selective action of some antitumor antibiotics on nucleic acids of Staphylococci and their mutants. Antibiotiki, 9:711–716.

Lefimine, D. V., M. Dann, F. Barbatschi, W. K. Hausmann, V. Zbinovsky, P. Monnikendam, J. Adam, and N. Bohonos. 1962. Isolation and characterization of mitomycin and other antibiotics produced by Streptomyces verticillatus. J. Amer. Chem. Soc., 84:3184–3185.

Leonardi, A., A. Ingrami, B. Murelli, and R. Re. 1959. Antitumor substances and protein metabolism. III. Activity of some alkylating substances. Atti Soc. Lombarda Sci. Med. e Biol., 14:276–280.

Lilly, L. J., and M. J. Thoday. 1956. Effects of cyanide on the roots of *Vicia fabia*. Nature (London), 177:338–339.

Linford, J. H. 1961. Some interactions of nitrogen mustards with constituents of human blood serum. Biochem. Pharmacol., 8:343–347.

——. 1962a. The recovery of free chlorambucil from solution in blood serum. Biochem. Pharmacol., 11:693–706.

——. 1962b. Modification of the structure of hemoglobin by chlorambucil. Nature (London), 195:1066–1067.

——. 1963a. The influence of pH on the reactivity of chlorambucil. Biochem. Pharmacol., 12:317–324.

——. 1963b. The role of absorption in controlling the rate of reaction of chlorambucil with protein. Canad. J. Biochem., 41: 931–939.

Lipsett, M. N., and A. Weissbach. 1965. The site of alkylation of nucleic acids by mitomycin. Biochemistry (Wash.), 4:206–211.

Longo, F. W., and H. H. Zinsser. 1960. Effectiveness of anabolic agents Nilevar and colchicine in the therapy of patients who form uric acid stones. J. Urol., 84:766–770.

Mac Donald, G. O., A. N. Stroud, A. M. Brues, and W. H. Cole. 1963. In vivo and in vitro assay for drug effect on cancer cells. Ann. Surg., 157:785–796 (discussion 796–797).

Maeda, H., T. Nishimura, and M. Koyama. 1964. Stabilizing triethylenemelamine. Japan. Pat. 7778 (to Dainippon Ink and Chemicals, Inc.).

Magee, W. E., and O. V. Miller. 1962. Dissociation of the synthesis of host and viral deoxyribonucleic acid (DNA). Biochim. Biophys. Acta, 55:818–826.

Maller, R. K., and C. Heidelberger. 1957a. Studies on OPSPA. II Distribution and excretion of radioactivity following administration of OPSPA-C^{14} and OPSPA-P^{32} to the rat. Cancer Res., 17:284–290.

——, and C. Heidelberger. 1957b. Studies on the tumor-inhibitory properties of OPSPA. IV Metabolism of OPSPA in the rat and human. Cancer Res., 17:296–301.

Maruyama, M., and M. Uchida. 1960. Mode of action of RC4, a new anticancer agent containing the ethyleneimino ring. I. Effects of RC 4 and allied agents of glycolysis, respiration, hexokinase, and phosphatase of Ehrlich ascites tumor cells and on cholinesterase of human blood. Gann, 51:189–199.

——. 1962. Mode of action of o,o'-p-phenylene N,N',N'',N'''-tetraethylenetetramide diphosphate (RC-4), a new anticancer agent containing ethyleneimino rings. V. Effect of various alkylating agents on oxidative phosphorylation. Nippon Nogei Kagaku Kaishi, 36:34–40.

Mazia, D. 1960. The analysis of cell reproduction. Ann. N. Y. Acad. Sci., 90:455–469.

Meghal, S. K., and M. C. Nath. 1963. Storage of tissue thiamine and its intestinal synthesis in hypo- and hyperthyroid rats. Ann. Biochem. Exp. Med., 23:169–172.

Mellett, L. B., and L. A. Woods. 1960. Comparative physiological disposition of thiotepa and tepa in the dog. Cancer Res., 20: 524–532.

Mendoza, C. E. 1964. Morphology of the southern corn rootworm (Diabrotica undecimpunctata howardi) reproductive systems and their histochemistry in relation to apholate. Phd. Dissertation, Iowa State University.

Miller, S., and A. S. Perry. 1965. Isolation, purification, and characterization of N^5-formyltetrahydrofolic acid (folinic acid) from the housefly. Life Sci., 4:1573–1580.

Millington, J. E., and F. L. M. Pattison. 1956. Toxic fluorine compounds. XII. Esters of ω-fluoroalcohols. Canad. J. Chem., 34:1532–1541.

Mitlin, N., M. S. Konecky, and P. G. Piquett. 1954. The effect of a folic acid antagonist on the house fly. J. Econ. Entom., 47: 932–933.

Murray, W. S., and W. E. Bickley. 1964. Effect of apholate on the southern house mosquito Culex pipiens quinquefasciatus. University of Maryland, Agr. Exp. Station Bull. A, 134, 37 pp.

Nadkarni, M. V., E. I. Goldenthal, and P. K. Smith. 1954. The distribution of radioactivity following administration of triethylenimino-s-triazine-C^{14} in tumor-bearing and control mice. Cancer Res., 14:559–562.

_____, E. I. Goldenthal, and P. K. Smith. 1957. The distribution of radioactivity following administration of triethylenephosphoramide-P^{32} in tumor-bearing and control mice. Cancer Res., 17:97–101.

_____, E. G. Trams, and P. K. Smith. 1959. Preliminary studies on the distribution and fate of TEM, Tepa, and myleran in the human. Cancer Res., 19:713–718.

_____, E. G. Trams, and P. K. Smith. 1961. Excretion and distribution studies with radio-isotope-labeled alkylating drugs in cancer patients. Cancer, 14:953–956.

Nakabayashi, K. 1958. Stabilization of ethyleneimine therapeutic preparations. U.S. Pat. 3,014,902.

Oishi, H. 1961. Cytological effects of chemicals on tumors. XIII. Phase optic observations on effects of carzinophilin and thiotepa upon dividing cells in tissue culture. J. Fac. Sci. Hukkaido Univ. Ser VI., 14:629–638.

Olin Mathiesen. 1962. Experimental Insect Sterilant No. 2174. Apholate. Olin Mathiesen Bull.

Osborn, M. J., M. Freeman, and F. M. Huennekens. 1958. Inhibition of dihydrofolic reductase by aminopterin and amethopterin. Proc. Soc. Exp. Biol. Med., 97:429–431.

Painter, R. R., and W. W. Kilgore. 1965. Chemosterilant effect of 5-fluoroorotic acid on house flies. J. Econ. Entom., 58:888–891.

Papac, R., D. A. G. Galtoh, M. Till, and E. Wiltshaw. 1958. Preliminary clinical trial of p, di-2-chloroethyl-amino-L-phenyl-alanine (CB 3025, melphalan) and of di-2-chloroethyl methane-sulfonate (CB 1506). Ann. N.Y. Acad. Sci., 68:1126–1127.

Parish, J. C., and B. W. Arthur. 1965. Mammalian and insect metabolism of the chemosterilant thiotepa. J. Econ. Entom., 58:976–979.

Parker, J. M., and I. G. Walker. 1957. A toxicological and biochemical study of ω-fluoro compounds. Canad. J. Biochem. Physiol., 35:407–417.

Parker, K. D., C. R. Fontan, and P. L. Kirk. 1963. Rapid gas chromatographic method for screening of toxicological extracts for alkaloids, barbiturates, sympathomimetic amines, and tranquilizers. Anal. Chem., 35:356–359.

Pattison, F. L. M., and J. E. Millington. 1956. The preparation and some cleavage reactions of alkyl and substituted alkyl methanesulfonates. The synthesis of fluorides, iodides, and thiocyanates. Canad. J. Chem., 34:757–768.

Perevoschikova, K. A. 1964. Action of some metabolic inhibitors upon the accumulation of amino acids and the incorporation of the latter into the proteins of tumor cells in vitro. Acta Un Int. Cancr., 20:941–944.

Perry, A. S., and S. Miller, 1965. The essential role of folic acid and the effect of antimetabolites on growth and metamorphosis of house fly larvae *Musca domestica* L. J. Insect Physiol., 11:1277–1287.

Petering, H. G., and G. J. Van Giessen. 1963. Colorimetric method for determination of uracil mustard and related alkylating agents. J. Pharm. Sci., 52:1159–1162.

Peters, J. M., and D. M. Greenberg. 1959. Studies on folic acid reduction. Biochim. Biophys. Acta, 32:273–274.

Peters, R. A. 1953. Significance of biochemical lesions in the pyruvate oxidase system. Brit. Med. Bull., 9:116–121.

Pieper, G. R., and J. E. Casida. 1965. House fly adenosinetriphosphatases and their inhibition by insecticidal organotin compounds. J. Econ. Entom., 58:392–400.

Pittillo, R. F., and B. G. Quinnelly. 1962. Studies on the antimicrobial action of porfiromycin. Antibiot. Chemother., 12:55–64.

Plapp, F. W., Jr., W. S. Brigley, G. A. Chapman, and G. W. Eddy. 1962. Metabolism of methaphoxide in mosquitoes, house flies and mice. J. Econ. Entom., 55:607–613.

Pliess, G. 1960. The chemical protection of tissues against irradiation. Deutsch. Ges. Path., 44:335–338.

_____. 1961. Bone marrow side-effects of tumor chemotherapy. Ver. Deutsch. Ges. Path., 45:203–207.

Pradhan, S. N., and W. L. West. 1960. Effect of chlorambucil on synthesis of proteins and nucleic acids in tumor-bearing mice. Cancer Res., 20:594–599.

_____, and W. L. West. 1964. Effect of thiotepa on the synthesis of protein and nucleic acids in tumor-bearing mice. Acta Un. Int. Cancr., 20:151–152.

Pricer, W. E., Jr., and A. Weissbach. 1965. Enzymatic utilization and degradation of DNA treated with mitomycin C or ultraviolet light. Biochemistry, 4:200–205.

Rabkin, M. T., E. W. Frederick, M. Lotz, and L. H. Smith, Jr. 1962. Pyrimidine metabolism in man. V. The measurement in vivo of the biochemical effect of antineoplastic agents in animal and human subjects. J. Clin. Invest., 41:871–883.

Ricciardi, S. L. Talarico, P. Altucci, C. Riccardi, and G. Consoli. 1959. Anticellular activity of some alkylsulfonates. VII. The probable mechanisms of the effect of 2-chloroethyl methanesulfonate (CB-1506) and 2-fluoroethyl methanesulfonate. Boll. Soc. Ital. Biol. Sper., 35:278–279.

Ristich, S. S., R. H. Ratcliffe, and D. Perlman. 1965. Chemosterilant properties, cytoxicity, and mammalian toxicity of apholate and other P-N ring chemicals. J. Econ. Entom., 58:929–932.

Roberts, J. J., and G. P. Warwick. 1957. Mode of action of alkylating agents: formation of S-ethylcysteine from ethyl methanesulphonate in vivo. Nature (London), 179:1181–1182.

_____, and G. P. Warwick. 1958a. Discussion: Part I. Comparative clinical and biological effects of alkylating agents. Ann. N.Y. Acad. Sci., 68:722–727.

_____, and G. P. Warwick. 1958b. Studies on the mode of action of tumor-growth-inhibiting alkylating agents. I. The fate of ethyl methane-sulfonate ("half myleran") in the rat. Biochem. Pharmacol., 1:60–75.

_____, and G. P. Warwick. 1959a. Metabolism of myleran (1:4-dimethanesulphonoxy-butane). Nature (London), 183:1509–1511.

_____, and G. P. Warwick. 1959b. Metabolic and chemical studies of myleran: formation of 3-hydroxytetrahydrothiophene-1, 1-dioxide in vivo, and reactions with thiols in vitro. Nature (London), 184:1288–1289.

_____, and G. P. Warwick. 1959c. Studies on the metabolism of myleran (1:4-dimethane-sulphonyloxybutane). Biochem. J., 72:3P.

_____, and G. P. Warwick. 1961a. Mode of action of alkylating agents. III. Formation of 3-hydroxytetrahydrothiophene-1:1-dioxide from myleran, S-(β-L-alanyl) tetrahydrothiophenium mesylate, tetrahydrophiophene, and tetrahydrothiophene-1:1-dioxide in the rat, rabbit, and mouse. Biochem. Pharmacol., 6:217–227.

_____, and G. P. Warwick. 1961b. II Studies on metabolism of myleran. Reaction of myleran with some naturally occurring thiols in vitro. Biochem. Pharmacol., 205–216.

Ross, W. C. J. 1958a. Aliphatic sulfonyloxy compound. Brit. Pat. No. 798,259 (to Nat. Res. Dev. Corp.).

_____, 1958b. In vitro reactions of biological alkylating agents. Ann. N.Y. Acad. Sci., 68:669–681.

_____, and W. Davis. 1957. Potentially cytotoxic alkyl sulfonates. J. Chem. Soc., 1957:2420–2422.

Rouser, G., K. Kelly, B. Jelinek, and D. Heller. 1962. Free amino acids in the blood of man and animals. V. Effects of myleran, dimethyl-myleran, and related compounds in chronic granulocytic leukemia. In Amino Acid Pools, 413–429, New York, Elsevier Publishing Company.

Roussors, G. G. 1963. Hypoxanthine oxidase from bovine small intestine. Biochim. Biophys. Acta, 73:338–340.

Ruddon, R. W. 1964. The interaction between biological alkylating agents and nucleic acids: relationship to the mechanism of drug action. Phd. Dissertation. University of Michigan.

_____, and L. B. Mellett. 1964. Distribution of C^{14}-labeled thiotepa (NSC 6396) and its metabolites in normal and tumor-bearing rats. Cancer Chemother. Rep. No. 39:7–13.

Sakai, H., and K. Dan. 1959. Studies on sulfhydryl groups during cell division of sea urchin egg. I. Glutathione. Exp. Cell. Res., 16:24–41.

Sauaia, H., and D. Mazia. 1961. Action of colchicine on the mitotic apparatus. Path. Biol. (Paris), 9:473–476.

Schmidt, L. H. 1960. Observations on the therapeutic activity and toxicity of 2-chlorethyl methanesulfonate (CB-1506) (NSC-18016). Cancer Chemother. Rep., 9:56–68.

Schmidt, M., and H. Ruf. 1963. The reaction of sodium selenide with triphenylchlorostannane and dimethyldichlorostannane. Ber., 96:784–785.

Schuberth, J., and B. Sörbo. 1963. The effect of alkylating agents on the excretion of taurine in the urine of rats. Experientia, 19:105.

Schuurmans, D. M., D. T. Duncan, and B. H. Olson. 1964. A bioautographic system employing mammalian cell strains, and its tives. III. Spectrophotometric determination of thiourea at the microgram level. Z. Anal. Chem., 204:184–189.

Sherman, J. K., and E. Steinberger. 1960. Effect of triethylenemelamine on reproductive capacity of mouse spermatozoa. Proc. Soc. Exp. Biol. Med., 103:348–350.

Shimizu, Y. 1961. Influence of some anticancer agents on serum protein in patients with malignant tumors. Gifu Ika Daigaku Kiyo, 8:2545–2557.

Siegel, M. R., and H. D. Sisler. 1963. Inhibition of protein synthesis in vitro by cycloheximide. Nature (London), 200:675–676.

_____, and H. D. Sisler. 1964a. Site of action of cycloheximide in cells

of *Saccharomyces pastorianus*. I. Effect of the antibiotic on cellular metabolism. Biochim. Biophys. Acta, 87:70–82.
_____, and H. D. Sisler, 1964b. Site of action of cycloheximide in cells of *Saccharomyces pastorianus*. II. The nature of inhibition of protein synthesis in a cell-free system. Biochim. Biophys. Acta, 87:83–89.
_____, and H. D. Sisler. 1965. Site of action of cycloheximide in cells of *Saccharomyces pastorianus*. III. Further studies on the mechanism of action and the mechanism of resistance in *Saccharomyces* species. Biochim. Biophys. Acta, 103:558–567.

Slater, E. C. 1949. A respiratory catalyst required for the reduction of cytochrome c by cytochrome b. Biochem. J., 45:14–30.

Smith, P. K., M. V. Nadkarni, E. G. Trams, and C. Davidson. 1958. Distribution and fate of alkylating agents. Ann. N.Y. Acad. Sci., 68:834–850.

Smith, W. W., and I. M. Alderman. 1962. Colchicine, colchicine derivatives, and endotoxin in irradiated animals. Radiation Res., 17:594–607.

Sŏnka, J., L. Kašpárek, and V. Kohoutek. 1961. The influence of several cytostatic agents on the sugar metabolism of erythrocytes. Folia Haematol., 78:75–88.

Squadrito, G., D. Ceruso, M. Emanuele, and G. Franco. 1961. Behavior of alkaline phosphatase and of glycogen in the bone marrow and peripheral blood after antimitotic agents. Arch. Atti Soc. Med.-Chiv. Messina, 5:322–331.

Steinberger, E. 1962. A quantitative study of the effect of an alkylating agent (triethylenemelamine) on the seminiferous epithelium of rats. J. Reprod. Fertil., 3:250–259.

Stone, J. E., and V. R. Potter. 1957. Biochemical screening of pyrimidine antimetabolites. III. The testing of drugs against a system with a monoxidative energy source. Cancer Res., 17:800–803.

Sueoka, N., and T. Yamane. 1963. Fractionation of aminoacylacceptor RNA and the coding problem. *In* Vogel, H. J., Bryson, V. and J. O. Lampen, eds., Informational Macromolecules, 205–227. New York, Academic Press.

Sumitomo Chemical Co., Ltd. Stabilized compositions of therapeutic imine derivatives. British patent 845,823.

Sykes, M. P., D. A. Karnofsky, F. S. Phillips, and J. H. Burchenal. 1953. Clinical studies on triethylene phosphoramide and diethyene phosphoramide, compounds with nitrogen mustard-like activity. Cancer, 6:142–148.

Takemasa, Y. 1958. Evaluation of the effect of chemotherapy on malignant neoplasms. I. Experimental studies. Igaku Kenkyu, 28:4691–4706.

Takeshita, M., H. Takahashi, and T. Okuda. 1962. Studies on streptomyces antibiotic cycloheximide. XIII. New spectrophotometric determination of cycloheximide. Chem. Pharm. Bull. (Tokyo), 10:304–308.

Tan, Y. L., and D. R. Cole. 1965. New method for determination of alkylating agents in biologic fluids. Clin. Chem., 11:58–62.

Timmis, G. M. 1960. The action of antimetabolites and biological alkylating agents on the synthesis of deoxyribonucleic acids and a possible relation between the mechanisms of action. Biochem. Pharmacol., 4:49–56.

_____, R. F. Hudson, R. D. Marshall, and H. R. Bierman. 1962. Temporarily alleviating the symptoms of chronic and acute myelocytic leukemias with 2,5-bis(methanesulfonyloxy)-hexane. U.S. patent 3,041,241.

Trams, E. G. 1958. Determination of bis(2-chloroethyl)amines and related compounds with 8-quinolinol. Anal. Chem., 80:256–259.

_____, M. V. Nardkarni, and P. K. Smith. 1961. Mechanism of action of the alkylating agents. I. Interaction of alkylating agents with nucleic acids. Cancer Res., 21:560–566.

Truhaut, R., and C. Bohuon. 1963. Influence of colchicine and N-deacetylthiocolchicine on the activity of deoxyribonuclease in blood plasma in mice. C.R. Soc. Biol. (Paris), 256:1631–1633.

_____, E. Delacoux, G. Brule, and C. Bohuon. 1963. Estimation of alkylating agents in biological fluids; method involving the color reaction with γ-(4-nitrobenzyl)pyridine. Clin. Chim. Acta, 8: 235–245.

Tsukagoshi, S., K. Maetani, N. Okamoto, and Y. Miura. 1959. Mechanism of the effect of carcinostats. I. Influence of carcinostats in the energy-enzyme production system. J. Jap. Biochem. Soc. (Seikagaku), 31:323–327.

Uecker, W. 1962. Inactivation of microorganisms by alkylating agents III. Reactivation of bacteriophages after their inactivation by 2,4,6-triethyleneimino-s-triazine (TEM). Zbl. Bakt. [Orig.], 187:218–232.

Ulitzur, S., and A. Poljakoff-Mayber. 1963. Oxidative phosphorylation in germinating lettuce seeds. J. Exp. Botany, 14:95–100.

Umemo, T. 1959. The combined effects of radiation and various chemicals on mitotic cells. XVI. Effect of combined use of x-rays and thiotepa on Yoshida sarcoma. Nippon Acta Radiol. (Nippon Igaku Hoshasen Gakkai Zasshi), 19:1597–1608.

Vermel, E. M. 1964. Search for antitumor substances of plant origin. Acta Un. Int. Cancr., 20:211–213.

_____, and A. L. Tsetlin. 1964. The antitumor activity of some furocoumarins. Vop. Onkol., 10:85–90.

Vogel, J., and J. Deshusses. 1964. Polarographic determination of acetoxytriphenyltin (Brestan) residue on vegetables. Helv. Chim. Acta, 47:181–185.

von Schreiber, J., W. Leimgruber, M. Pesaro, P. Schubel, T. Threlfall, and A. Eschenumoser. 1961. Syntheses des Colchicins. Helv. Chim. Acta, 44:540–597.

Wagner, A. F., and C. O. Gitterman. 1962. Methyl mitomycin. Antibiot. Chemother. N.Y., 12:464–468.

Wagner, N. J., and C. Heidelberger. 1962. Some effects of 5-fluoroorotic acid and 5-fluorouracil on the soluble ribonucleic acid of rat liver. Biochim. Biophys. Acta, 61:373–379.

Wakaki, S., Y. Harada, K. Uzu, G. B. Whitfield, A. N. Wilson, A. Kalowsky, E. O. Stapley, F. J. Wolf, and D. E. Williams. 1962. The identity of porfiromycin and methyl mitomycin. Antibiot. Chemother. N.Y., 12:469–471.

Waller, C. W., B. L. Hutchings, J. H. Mowat, E. L. R. Stokstad, J. H. Boothe, R. B. Angier, J. Semb, Y. SubbaRow, D. B. Cosulich, M. J. Fahrenbach, M. E. Hultquist, E. Kuh, E. H. Northey, D. R. Seeger, J. P. Sickels, and J. N. Smith, Jr. 1948. Synthesis of pteroylglutamic acid (liver L. casei factor) and pteroic acid. J. Amer. Chem. Soc., 70:19–22.

Webb, J. S., D. B. Cosulich, J. H. Mowat, J. B. Patrick, R. W. Broschard, W. E. Meyer, R. P. Williams, C. F. Wolf, W. Fulmor, C. Pidacks, and J. E. Lancaster. 1962. The structure of mitomycin A, B, and C Part I. J. Amer. Chem. Soc., 84:3185–3187.

Weissbach, A., and A. Lisio. 1965. Alkylation of nucleic acids by mitomycin C and porfiromycin. Biochemistry, 4:196–199.

Werkheiser, W. C. 1963. The biochemical, cellular, and pharmacological action and effects of the folic acid antagonists. Cancer Res., 23:1277–1285.

Wettstein, F. O., H. Noll, and S. Penman. 1964. Effect of cycloheximide on ribosomal aggregates engaged in protein synthesis in vitro. Biochim. Biophys. Acta, 87:525–528.

Wheeler, G. P., and J. A. Alexander. 1964a. Studies with mustards. V. In vivo fixation of C^{14} of labeled alkylating agents by bilaterally grown sensitive and resistant tumors. Cancer Res., 24:1331–1337.

————, and J. A. Alexander. 1964b. Studies with mustards. VI. Effects of alkylating agents upon nucleic acid synthesis in bilaterally grown sensitive and resistant tumors. Cancer Res., 24:1338–1346.

Wigglesworth, V. B. 1933. Effects of salts on the anal gills of mosquito larvae. J. Exp. Biol., 10:1626.

Williams, D. J., and J. W. Price. 1960. Paper chromatography of some organotin compounds. Analyst, 85:579–582.

Winzler, R. J., W. Wells, J. Shapira, A. D. Williams, I. Bornstein, M. J. Burr, and W. R. Best. 1959. Metabolism of human leukocytes in vitro. II. The effect of several agents on the incorporation of radioactive formate and glycine. Cancer Res., 19:377–387.

Young, C. W., and S. Hodas. 1965. Acute effects of cytotoxic compounds on incorporation of precursors into DNA, RNA, and protein of HeLa monolayers. Biochem. Pharmacol., 14:205–214.

————, P. F. Robinson, and B. Sacktor. 1963. Inhibition of the synthesis of protein in intact animals by acetoxycycloheximide and a metabolic derangement concomitant with this blockade. Biochem. Pharmacol., 12:855–865.

6

Field Development and Evaluation of Chemosterilants

D. E. WEIDHAAS

ENTOMOLOGY RESEARCH DIVISION
AGRICULTURAL RESEARCH SERVICE
U.S. DEPARTMENT OF AGRICULTURE
GAINESVILLE, FLORIDA

INTRODUCTION

A new approach to insect suppression or eradication, called the sterility principle or more simply insect steriliza- tion, has become an important field of research to entomol- ogists and others interested in insect biology and control. This approach offers new and unique methods of dealing with the problem of the control of insect pests as well as the prob- lem of elucidating insect biology. Several methods are cur- rently available for causing sterility in insect populations, including chemosterilization, radiation sterilization, cytoplas- mic incompatibility, and hybrid sterility. Chemosterilants have been shown to be highly effective in sterilizing both sexes of many species of insects and, are potentially the most versatile type of sterilizing agent for use in the sterility approach to control or eradication. Research may show that chemosteri- lants can be used effectively and safely in a variety of ways to treat natural populations, whereas inducing sterility into natural populations through the use of radiation, cytoplasmic incompatibility, or hybrid sterility will require mass production and release of millions of insects (the sterile-male technique). The ingenuity of researchers will be challenged and taxed to develop safe and effective ways of using chemosterilants to control various populations.

An important phase of research in the development and evaluation of chemosterilants is field testing of possible methods of utilizing chemosterilants against natural populations to determine their feasibility for control or eradication. One of the purposes of this chapter is to present and critically review research on such field evaluations. In some cases this research involves studies in large outdoor cages. In most cases it involves research with field populations as they exist in nature. This discussion of research on methods of utilizing chemosterilants under field conditions requires some consideration of the development of the sterile-male release technique where radiation was used to sterilize the insects. Chemosterilants may be used in place of radiation to sterilize insects for release. In some cases chemical sterilants may be more effective or economical or easier to use than radiation. In some species of insects they may cause complete sterility with less deleterious effects on vigor, longevity, mating competitiveness, or behavior than radiation. It is not the purpose of this chapter to review the research on sterility induced by radiation and the development and successful demonstration of the effectiveness of the release of radiation-sterilized insects for total population suppression. However, references to release of radiation-sterilized insects will be included where they are pertinent.

Another purpose of this chapter is to emphasize that the capability of causing sterility in insects offers entomologists an extremely versatile tool for use in basic biological studies, particularly on ecology, population levels, population dynamics, and behavior. Discussions on the development of chemosterilants or the sterility principle have concentrated on their value for providing new methods of control. It has generally been conceded that we will need much more basic biological information on economically important insect pests to fully evaluate the feasibility and practicability of the sterility principle. There has been relatively little emphasis given to the fact that sterility itself is a highly useful and versatile tool, either in laboratory or field studies, in developing this needed biological data. The release of radiation-sterilized

Anopheles quadrimaculatus Say males reported by Weidhaas et al. (1962) which failed to induce significant levels of sterility in natural populations led these researchers and coworkers to basic research of this type. They (Dame et al., 1964) used sterility as a biological tool or tag under field conditions to show that the most important factor responsible for their unsuccessful releases was behavioral differences between the colonized and wild strains of this species of mosquito. Following this research Fye and LaBrecque (1966) used sterility as a tag in laboratory studies to show that males or females of different strains of house flies mated more readily with individuals of the opposite sex of their own strain than with those of different strains. Their comparisons were made between a colony strain of house flies and house flies collected on Grand Turk Island in the Bahamas where they were conducting a sterile-male release experiment. In both of these instances sterility was used to show differences in behavior between strains of insects. Following the general theoretical considerations developed by Dr. E. F. Knipling (see Chapter 1) we can develop means of assaying population levels, dynamics, and behavior using sterility as the tool or tag. Because this author feels that sterility will be extremely useful as a biological tool, a special section on this type of research has been added. As we conceive new methods of control or eradication, consider their theoretical potentialities and practical feasibility, and attempt to develop and design the practical means of using them, we will need basic biological data on total populations of insects. Sterility as a biological tool should prove very useful in this type of research.

The general approach to the development of insect chemosterilants involves both laboratory and field studies. The search for effective chemosterilants, their minimum effective concentrations, their effects on individual sexes, vigor, longevity, mating competitiveness, and other factors are most easily accomplished in laboratory studies. However, when these studies have shown that a chemosterilant(s) holds promise for further development as a means of control, field studies are needed. Current methods of using chemosterilants are generally considered to be:

1. The release of sterile insects into natural populations.
2. The combination of chemosterilants with attractants,

baits, or lures for the treatment of natural populations.

3. Direct treatment of natural populations.
4. Integration of the use of chemosterilants with other conventional or new approaches to control.
5. Use of sterility as a biological tool.

The specific type of field tests to be conducted will be determined by the researcher's approach to the problem and may involve either an empirical approach to test the effectiveness of a particular method of utilizing chemosterilants or basic research on population biology, ecology, and dynamics to determine the feasibility of the method. In many instances both types of experimentation can be conducted simultaneously.

For example, let us consider a field test involving the release of chemosterilized insects. In many cases with many species of insects, sufficient data may not be available on total population numbers, population levels at different times, the population's capability of increasing its numbers from generation to generation or over certain periods of time, or behavioral characteristics such as mating and migration. Some researchers may argue that more basic biological information must be available before field experiments are undertaken. One approach to this problem would be the release and recapture of marked insects to determine population levels and dynamics. In this way information would be available to design a better release experiment. The researcher may also decide to proceed with the release of sterile insects and also mark them. He can then evaluate the release of sterile insects and determine basic biology through the recapture of marked and sterile insects. In any case, any field experiments should be well conceived and thoroughly planned to provide the maximum amount of data on the biology of the species as well as the feasibility of the particular method of using chemosterilants under investigation. Poorly designed experiments may not allow the researcher to decide whether a failure in a field experiment, such as the release of sterile insects, occurred because the method has no applicability to the insect he is studying or because he did not have sufficient insight into the biology of the species to use the method properly. Care should be taken that researchers do not rush into poorly designed experiments, for this approach may lead to unfounded discouragement with the method, particularly where insufficient basic biological data are available.

Initial tests under field conditions may involve studies with populations in large outdoor cages or small-scale field tests with natural populations. It is extremely important that field tests be conducted on isolated populations since migration from surrounding areas can cause complete confusion of data or lead to discouragement and failure, particularly where little is known about ecology, behavior, and population dynamics. Small islands have received considerable attention as sites for field tests.

Most chemosterilants are, potentially at least, extremely toxic and hazardous materials. Field experiments with these materials should not be conducted until the method in which they are to be be used is shown to present no hazard to any form of life.

FIELD STUDIES WITH CHEMOSTERILANTS

An extensive effort on the laboratory development and evaluation of chemosterilants has led to preliminary field testing of chemosterilants with a variety of insect species and different methods of utilizing these materials. This research is most easily and readily summarized by insect species which have been studied.

HOUSE FLIES

The first insect chemosterilants effective in sterilizing males as well as females were discovered in laboratory studies with house flies (LaBrecque et al., 1960, and LaBrecque, 1961). Considerable laboratory research indicating the potential of these materials led to field tests for the control of house flies. Chemosterilants might be used to sterilize these flies for release or for the treatment of natural populations. Experience with insecticidal methods of control has shown that a high proportion of house flies can be reached and killed through the use of poisoned baits. Consequently the first field experiments with chemosterilants involved the use of chemosterilant baits.

The first field experiment was conducted on a semi-isolated refuse dump on Bahia Honda Key in the Florida Keys (LaBrecque et al., 1962). This dump covered about 1 1/2 acres, but only half of it had any fly-breeding potential. Another dump 30 miles east on Long Key was left untreated and used as a check. The dump on Bahia Honda Key was treated each week with the exception of the second week, for nine consecutive weeks with 30 pounds of granular bait containing 67 percent cornmeal, 15 percent sugar, 15 percent powdered milk, 2.5 percent powdered egg, and 0.5 percent tepa. This dry granular bait was scattered over the fly-breeding areas in the dump. Prior to, during, and after the treatment, observations were made on house fly abundance and fertility. Abundance of house flies was determined by making counts of the number of house flies landing in 1 min on an 18 by 18 in. grid placed in 10 locations of heaviest breeding and activity of house flies. Sterility in the population was determined by collecting females and determining the viability of eggs of these females held individually in the laboratory.

In four weeks house fly abundance decreased from 47 to 0 per grid in the treated dump. A few flies were still present but the authors reported difficulty in finding a sufficient number for sterility determinations. The proportion of egg masses from females collected at the dump in which one or more eggs were viable decreased from 100 to 10 percent within four weeks. The percent hatch of all eggs laid by females collected at the dump was reduced to 1 percent within 5 weeks. Abundance and fertility remained at extremely low levels during the remainder of the treatments. Less than 20 flies were observed in the dump during the last 3 weeks of treatment. Within 1 week after treatment was stopped, egg viability increased to 50 percent and abundance increased to 3 per grid after 4 weeks. Abundance and fertility of flies at the check dump remained within pretreatment levels. A high degree of control was obtained but the population was not eradicated presumably because of incomplete isolation.

A second experiment on chemosterilant baits for house fly control was reported by Gouck et al., (1963). This experiment was carried out at a dump about 2 acres in size on Pine Island in Florida. A bait consisting of two parts of cornmeal, one part of adult fly food (six parts of dry milk, six parts of granulated sugar, and one part of dry egg yoke) and 0.75 percent apholate was applied to the dump. For the first 7 weeks the dump was treated with 40 pounds of bait once a week. Frequent rains occurred and it was decided to apply the bait more often. During the next 5 weeks, 15 pounds of

bait were applied each day for 5 days each week. Abundance
and fertility of flies at the dump were measured before, during, and after treatment and compared with similar data for
flies in an untreated dump located 11 miles away. During the
first 7 weeks grid counts of house flies decreased from 68
per grid to 5 to 20 and hatchability of eggs from 81 to 12 to
49 percent. After the bait was applied five times each week,
adult fly counts decreased to 3 to 0 per grid and egg hatchability to 2 to 12 percent. Male fertility decreased very little
until the bait was distributed five times each week and then
ranged from 0 to 46 percent. Complete eradication was not
achieved because the dump was not isolated from reinfestation. After the test was terminated, abundance and fertility
of flies returned to normal.

Following these two field experiments, researchers at
Gainesville, Florida, treated several poultry houses to study
the effects of chemosterilants on house flies (LaBrecque et
al., 1963, and LaBrecque and Meifert, 1966). Baits containing 0.5 percent metepa, 1 percent metepa, 2.5 percent hempa,
or 1 percent apholate were applied to poultry droppings under
caged hens. Again abundance and fertility of the house flies
was followed. When bait applications were made only once a
week, apparently sufficient bait was not available to the flies
to cause high reductions in abundance or fertility. However,
when semiweekly applications of bait were made, a high degree
of sterility and control was obtained. In one case where the
treated area was isolated, complete elimination of the population was assumed since only 3 flies were found during the 2 1/2
months after the treatment was discontinued.

The most comprehensive experiment conducted by researchers at Gainesville (Meifert et al., 1967) involved the
application of two chemosterilants—metepa and apholate—in
sweetened baits in pits of privies on two islands—Grand Turk
and Mayaguana—in the West Indies. Semiweekly treatments
were made on each island, first with granular baits, then with
sugar syrup. A 1 percent metepa liquid bait used on Grand
Turk caused a high degree of sterility in the house fly population and reduced fly abundance by more than 90 percent over
an 18-month period. A 1 percent liquid apholate bait produced
moderately high sterility over a 3-month period and approximately 50 to 80 percent reduction in fly abundance. The lower
effectiveness of apholate on Mayaguana was attributed to less
favorable areas for bait application rather than a reduced ef-

ficacy of the chemosterilant apholate. Complete eradication
was not achieved and failure to eradicate was attributed to
limitation of the bait application to privies. Flies fed in other
areas such as kitchens where the bait was not applied.

Other researchers have studied the effects of chemosterilants on house flies. Mathis and Schoof (1965) used
chicken-watering units containing 0.5 percent apholate and 12
percent sugar in water (pH 8.0) to treat house flies at a chicken
ranch. One bait dispenser was used for each 2,000 sq ft of
floor space. Bait stations were refilled five times over an
11-week period. These bait applications did not bring the house
fly population under control although the number of ovipositing
females as well as the viability of eggs was reduced. Apparently a sufficiently high degree of sterility was not induced
into the population.

Hansens and Granett (1965) and Hansens (1965) reported
studies on the chemosterilant apholate applied as bait applications to caged populations of susceptible and insecticide-
resistant house flies. Caged populations were maintained in
screened cages 6 by 6 by 7 ft located inside a beef barn. Populations were treated with a sugar bait of 2 percent apholate or
1/8-inch cords treated with about 100 mg of apholate per
lineal foot of cord. Cords were prepared by dipping in water
containing 30 percent apholate, 10 percent Karo syrup, 0.2
percent erythrosin, 1 percent Tween 20, and 0.2 percent methyl-
p-hydroxybenzoate. Sugar baits were supplied to caged populations by placing two dishes in each cage. Four parallel cords
were strung across other cages. Baits were replaced once a
week, cords, every 4 weeks. Untreated water and skim milk
were available constantly. Tests were continued for 2 to 3
months during the summer. The 2 percent apholate sugar baits
caused reductions of 90 percent or greater in the continuously
breeding house fly populations (both susceptible and insecticide
resistant). Apholate-treated cords caused reductions of only 64
percent.

In large outdoor cage tests Ratcliffe and Ristich (1965)
treated house flies with baits of apholate, metepa, and four bifunctional aziridine chemicals. Applications were made as
granular and liquid sugar baits, ribbon treatments, and residual treatments. The baits caused the highest degree of sterility
in the house flies and were more effective in causing sterility
than the ribbon and residual treatments.

Sacca and Stella (1964) applied liquid baits of tepa (15 percent sugar solution in water containing 0.0625 to 0.2 percent tepa with 1 percent malt extract as an attractant) to garbage dumps of small towns in Italy. They reported: (1) a high degree of sterility in treated populations, (2) a higher degree of sterility in females than males presumably resulting from treated males mating with females which escaped the treatment, (3) reductions in house fly population levels or prevention of build-up of large populations, and (4) increase of abundance and fertility following termination of the treatment.

SCREWWORM, *COCHLIOMYIA HOMINIVORAX* COQUEREL

The classic demonstration of the potential and efficacy of the sterility principle was the development and successful execution of the sterile-male release program with the screwworm. In this program radiation was used to sterilize released insects. This comprehensive program of development and successful eradication will not be discussed here since chemosterilants were not used. It should be pointed out that laboratory research has developed effective chemosterilants that are now being considered for limited field studies. However, no field research has yet been conducted. Hopefully, current research will develop attractants or baits that may be used with chemosterilants. Those interested in the release of chemosterilized insects should be thoroughly familiar with the development and application of the screwworm eradication program. References to literature concerning this program are many and are given in other chapters of this book. One of the most recent and comprehensive summaries of the development and execution of the entire program was recently published by Baumhover (1966).

MEXICAN FRUIT FLY, *ANASTREPHA LUDENS* (LOEW)

Two species of fruit flies have been eradicated from islands in the Pacific by the sterile male release technique. The melon fly, *Dacus cucurbitae* Coquillet, was eradicated from the 33-square mile island of Rota, Mariana Islands, by the release of flies sterilized in the pupal stage by exposure to 9,500 r of gamma radiation (Steiner et al., 1965). The oriental fruit fly, *Dacus dorsalis* Hendel, was eradicated from the island of Guam by the release of radiation-sterilized males when the population was at a very low level following a tropical storm (Steiner, unpublished data). Considerable research both in the laboratory and field on sterilization, mass-rearing, release techniques, and biology were conducted and will be of interest to those concerned with the development of the sterile male release technique.

Following successful laboratory research on chemo-sterilization of the Mexican fruit fly by Shaw and Sanchez Riviello (1962), these authors (1965) reported the effectiveness of tepa-sterilized Mexican fruit flies for control in a mango grove. The flies used for release were sterilized by immersing the puparia in a 5 percent aqueous solution of tepa (85 percent in ethanol) for 1 min and allowing them to dry for 24 hr. The flies actually picked up their sterilizing dose of tepa when they emerged and walked on the treated puparia. Sterile insects were released into the 10-acre mango grove known as El Bebedero in northeastern Morelas, Mexico. For release, puparia were placed in special release stations which were hung low in trees in the grove. The release stations were pans 8 1/2 in. square and 3 in. deep, which were rodent-proofed with hardware cloth and protected from the rain with a cone-shaped roof. Releases were made in 1962 and 1963 during the time the mangoes were developing and maturing. From April through June the largest number of sterile flies were released, about 1.5 million in 1962 and 8 million in 1963. The releases protected the mango crop during its development, maturation, and harvest, and the crop sold at a premium price. About 90 percent of the crop was harvested. The authors concluded: "The results of this two-year test at El Bebedero demonstrated that the release of chemosterilized flies will control the native fly population. In an isolated area this technique might effect eradication of the Mexican fruit fly." (Shaw and Sanchez Riviello, 1965).

An interesting application of the release of chemosterilized Mexican fruit flies was demonstrated along the international border of the United States and Mexico at Tijuana, Baja California (Shaw et al., 1966). Here the Mexican fruit fly is a serious threat to the fruit industry of California and Arizona because of the shipment of infested fruit from the interior of Mexico. From 1954 to 1963 the California Department of Agriculture applied an insecticidal spray at three-week intervals to all host trees in a 2 by 5 mile strip in California opposite Tijuana; the U.S. Department of Agriculture sprayed trees in

Tijuana, Tecate, and in Ensenada, some 65 miles away. A cooperative program between agencies of the United States, Mexico, and California was undertaken to release tepa-sterilized Mexican fruit flies in Tijuana, Tecate, and Ensenada. The release replaced the insecticide spray program carried on previously. Flies were sterilized as reported above for the release in the mango grove and released over 45 sq miles in Tijuana, 2 sq miles in Tecate and 4 sq miles in Ensenada. Flies were reared and sterilized in Mexico City and shipped once each week to San Diego. Only sterilized males were released in Tijuana and Tecate. Later both sterile males and females were released at Ensenada. Between April 23 and November 18, 1964, more than 4 million sterile fruit flies were released in the three areas. Ratios of sterile males to native females recaptured were always greater than 1,000:1. These releases apparently completely controlled the Mexican fruit fly in the areas since no host fruit grown in northern Baja California or in southwestern California was found infested with this fly. A similar program was carried out during 1965 with the same successful results.

MOSQUITOES

Research in the laboratory has shown that a number of species of mosquitoes are susceptible to chemosterilization. Furthermore, it has been shown that chemicals can cause sterility by a variety of methods of application including contact of adult tarsae with residual deposits, incorporation of the chemical into the adult food, spraying or dusting adults, and treating larval breeding water. Research in field studies has not yet successfully demonstrated how chemosterilants can be used to treat and sterilize natural infestations of mosquitoes without undue hazards to man or other forms of life. Although sterilants are highly effective when given in the adult food, we do not, at present, have attractants, baits, or lures or the methods of using them that are sufficiently effective to sterilize a large proportion of natural populations. Hopefully, research will develop more effective attractive agents and devices. Because of the potential hazards involved in the use of present chemosterilants, treatments as residual deposits on resting surfaces or as larval treatments cannot presently be considered feasible. Even if chemosterilants are shown to be safe for these types of treatment, it is still to be proven that residual treatments will sterilize a sufficiently large proportion of the males in a population to result in effective treatment. Research with known chemosterilants shows that high concentrations of these materials [10 parts per million (ppm) or higher] are needed to sterilize larvae in their breeding water. The ingenuity of researchers will be taxed to find safe and effective ways of utilizing chemosterilants in the treatment of natural populations of mosquitoes. The sterilization approach, however, offers a potential advantage for reaching a portion of the population that would not be reached with an insecticidal treatment since any males sterilized will be free to search out females of the natural population.

Chemosterilants may be used in place of radiation in the sterile male release technique. Research with some species of mosquitoes indicated that chemosterilants may cause less reduction of vigor and mating competitiveness than gamma radiation at dosages required for complete sterilization; however, further study is needed on this point. The feasibility of the sterile male release technique has not yet been demonstrated in the field. This technique may be particularly difficult to develop with species in which males do not disperse widely within or between breeding sites and with flood-water species where eggs remain dormant for long periods of time. The sterile-male technique appears to be more readily adapted to use with species of the genera *Culex* and *Anopheles*, since eggs are laid directly on the water surface and hatch within a few days. In places where a population breeds continually at low levels throughout a dry or unfavorable season or where populations could be reduced to extremely low levels through the use of insecticides, the release of sterile insects may be a means of controlling or eliminating a population. We might visualize that in some situations where a population was reduced to extremely low numbers but some reinfestation occurs, it might be more economical to release sterile males than to depend on repeated insecticidal applications.

Considerable research, however, is needed on population dynamics, dispersion, flight range, ecology, behavior, mass-rearing, and distribution techniques for the development of effective means of utilizing chemosterilants for the treatment of natural populations or for the release of sterile insects. If only a fraction of the total research on mosquito biology and control is directed toward this end we can expect some method of utilizing the sterility approach, alone or in conjunction with other methods, to be developed.

Very little research has been conducted on the treatment of natural populations of mosquitoes. This is a result of the possible hazards of such treatments, particularly where extensive areas would have to be treated and, of course, the fact that research on chemosterilization of mosquitoes is a relatively new field of study. Dame et al. (1964) conducted limited field studies to determine concentrations of the chemosterilant, tepa, which might be effective under field conditions when larval breeding water was treated. They dug small potholes at the edge of an existing mosquito breeding area. After the potholes had filled, they treated the water with a methanol solution of tepa to give a calculated concentration of 10 ppm. Third-instar larvae of *Aedes aegypti* (L.) were introduced into the treated potholes. One group was removed after 3 days and another group exposed similarly during a second 3-day period. Treated individuals were returned to the laboratory for determination of fertility. Only 20 percent of the eggs obtained from crosses of males and females exposed for the first 3 days hatched, but eggs from males and females of the second 3-day period hatched normally. Concurrent laboratory treatments in clean enamel pans produced 7 and 0 percent hatch for the first and second 3-day periods. These authors concluded that the sterilant broke down or became unavailable rapidly under field conditions. Furthermore, they pointed out the impracticability of using such high concentrations (equivalent to 10 to 30 pounds per acre depending on water depth) and the need for materials effective and safe at lower concentrations.

This author and co-workers (unpublished data) undertook some preliminary studies to determine the duration of residual deposits of tepa under field conditions. The studies were conducted near Lake Panasoffkee, Florida, within an extensive population of *Anopheles quadrimaculatus*. Twenty privy-type resting stations and smaller boxes constructed with walls and ceilings of tempered masonite were placed in active breeding areas of this mosquito. Inside resting surfaces were treated at a dosage of 500 mg/sq ft by painting on ethanol solutions of tepa. These deposits completely sterilized adults resting in these boxes for only 3 to 4 days. Attempts to find sterile females in the natural population in locations other than the treated boxes were not successful, indicating the small proportion of the population which was treated in this manner and the dispersion of treated adults within the area. One treated and one untreated privy-type station were placed side by side to see if adults might be repelled by the treatment. Both stations contained comparable numbers of males and females.

Lewallen et al. (1965) reported on preliminary studies in which they treated small, isolated seep holes in a desert region in San Diego County, California, containing natural populations of the mosquito *Culex tarsalis* Coquillet with the chemosterilant apholate. The amount of water in each pothole was calculated and then each pothole was treated at a dosage of 75 ppm of apholate. Treatments were applied by weighing the appropriate amount of technical apholate powder into plastic bottles, adding water, shaking, and pipetting the mixture evenly over the water surfaces. Three treatments were applied; the second 9 days after the first, and the third 13 days after the second. Eight-mesh hardware cloth was placed over the treated water for the protection of wildlife. At the time of the second treatment no reduction in egg rafts or larvae were noted. However, at the time of the third treatment no eggs were found although larvae were present in reduced numbers. One week after the third treatment no young larvae or egg rafts were found. Subsequently larval counts returned to normal. These authors point out that this study was preliminary and not of a magnitude for conclusive results.

To date there has been no field research reported on the release of mosquitoes sterilized by chemicals as a method of control or eradication. Considerable research in the laboratory has shown that mosquitoes can be sterilized effectively by chemicals and that chemosterilants can be used in place of radiation to sterilize insects for release. Dame et al. (1964) released chemosterilized *Anopheles quadrimaculatus* mosquitoes to study biology and behavior under field conditions. This work is covered in the section on sterility as a biological tool. Details are not given here except to note that the researchers were able to demonstrate behavioral differences in dispersing and mating ability between a colony and a wild strain of this mosquito.

Experiments with field releases of males of several species of mosquitoes sterilized by radiation have been conducted. It is not this author's intention to review the research on radiation-induced sterility. However, a brief resume of the results of field release of sterile mosquitoes will be of value to researchers interested in similar release experiments with chemosterilized mosquitoes.

Weidhaas et al. (1962) reported on their studies of the release of *Anopheles quadrimaculatus* males sterilized by gamma radiation into natural populations. Their research followed the laboratory research of Davis et al. (1959) who showed that dosages of 8,865 to 12,900 r of gamma radiation applied in the pupal or adult stage sterilized both sexes of this mosquito. However, sterile males appeared to be less than half as competitive as normal males in mating normal females under laboratory conditions.

Release of sterile males of *quadrimaculatus* into natural populations was of two types in two different areas. In the first release on a semi-isolated island off the southeast shore of Lake Ocheechobee, Florida, a total of 328,900 males (average of 3,700 per sq mile per week) were sterilized by exposure to 12,000 r and released. In this experiment males were released at 10 release stations so that no spot on the island was more than one fourth of a mile from a release point. Males were released three times a week over an 11-month period. In the second experiment, sterile males (exposed to 12,000 r in the pupal stage) were released at only two stations one eighth of a mile apart in the midst of an extensive *quadrimaculatus* breeding area along Lake Panasoffkee, Florida. A total of 104,700 (average of 9,500 per week) sterile males were released over and 11-week period when the natural population was relatively large. In both experiments, relative adult counts in resting stations in or near the release area as well as in the control areas, and the degree of sterility in females of the natural population were followed as criteria of the effect of the releases. Sterility or fertility of females of the wild population was determined by collecting females of the wild population, returning them to the laboratory, placing them individually in small glass vials containing water for egg deposition, and observing the hatchability of eggs. If females were not engorged it was necessary to give them a blood meal.

In the first experiment on Kreamer Island in Lake Okeechobee the release of sterile males may have influenced the abundance of the species during the first half of the experiment, when the natural population was in a seasonal decline, but had no effect when the population was increasing during the latter part of the experiment. The degree of sterility which was demonstrated in the wild females was never very great and of questionable significance. Release of sterile males in the second experiment failed to demonstrate con-

clusively any induced sterility in females of the wild population. The lack of success of these releases led these researchers to a series of experiments to uncover the reasons for
their failures. The reader is directed to a summary of these
studies by Dame et al. (1964) and the discussion of this point
later in this chapter. The researchers' conclusion was that the
laboratory colony of quadrimaculatus used in these releases
was behaviorally different from the wild strain of this species
and that the males of the colony strain were not able to seek
out females of the wild strain under natural conditions of the
field environment. Presumably the difference resulted through
selection of individuals from the wild population during colonization. This should be an important consideration in any
development of the sterile-male release technique.

Field tests with the release of sexually sterile *Aedes
aegypti* were undertaken and reported by Morlan et al. (1962).
Males were mass-reared (Fay et al., 1963) and sterilized by
exposure of pupae to a dosage of 11,000 to 18,000 r of gamma
radiation in Savannah, Georgia, and shipped for release to a
test area in and near Pensacola, Florida. Releases were made
in two years (1960 and 1961). In 1960 the release of sterile
males failed to demonstrate any conclusive differences in population trends or levels between the release and a check area.
In 1961 releases were made in two areas. In one of these
there was no reduction of the natural population. In the other
there was a reduction in the release area but there was also
a reduction in the check area. Morlan and his co-workers concluded that "Adaptation of the sterile male method for mosquito control requires additional investigation of the biology,
especially the dispersion of males under field conditions."
(Morlan et al., 1962).

In India, Krishnamurthy et al. (1963) reported that the
release of males of *Culex fatigans* (Wiedemann) sterilized by
gamma radiation caused some inviability of eggs in females
of the natural population. There was no reduction in mosquito
abundance, possibly because the numbers released were in-
adequate, but the results were sufficiently promising to justify
further studies.

CABBAGE LOOPER, *TRICHOPLUSIA NI* (HUBNER)

Laboratory studies by Howland et al. (1965) showed that
the cabbage looper could be readily sterilized with chemosterilants by contact with residual deposits or through adult feeding.

These same authors (Howland et al., 1966) conducted studies in 1962 and 1963 in large field cages (10 by 24 by 6 ft high) set over cabbage plants to evaluate the release of sterile males and a self-sterilizing chemosterilant technique on the reproductive potential of a single generation of cabbage loopers. In the sterile-male releases, newly emerged moths reared in the laboratory were sterilized by allowing them to feed on 1 percent tepa in 10 percent sugar solutions containing 1 percent of colloidal X-77® (alkyloxylpolyoxyethylene glycols, free fatty acids, isopropanol) and 1 percent of green food coloring. Excess solution was poured off and the deposit allowed to dry. Sterilized males were released along with untreated males and females into field cages at ratios of 20:1:1, 15:1:1, 10:1:1, 5:1:1, and 0:1:1. Effect on reproduction was determined by comparing representative number of larvae on cabbage plants to a control. Reductions in numbers of larvae ranged from 0 to 21 percent at the 5:1:1 ratio to 97 percent at the 20:1:1.

For the self-sterilizing technique, fluorescent black-lights (15 W) were enclosed in cellulose nitrate cylinders whose outer surfaces were coated with 8 percent tepa solutions as described above. Thirty or sixty pairs of virgin, untreated moths were placed in a cage which contained one of the treated lamps. The lamps were operated from 7 P.M. to 7 A.M. for 14 consecutive nights. In three experiments of this type larval populations were reduced 99, 65, and 82 percent compared to populations in a check cage. With the cabbage looper, cage tests indicate two possible methods of utilizing chemosterilants to be developed through further research.

BOLL WEEVIL, *ANTHONOMUS GRANDIS* BOHEMAN

During 1962 experiments were conducted by Davich et al. (1965) to study whether releases of apholate-sterilized male boll weevils could be used to eradicate artificially induced infestations of boll weevils in isolated plots of cotton. They discussed several factors of bionomics and research which make the application of the sterile-male technique to the boll weevil appear feasible. Gast and Vardell (1963) reported progress in rearing procedures that could be adapted to mass production of the boll weevil. This insect is a single-host species which can be reduced to very low levels through insecticidal applications. The researchers used small (1-acre plots for releases

and 1 to 6 acres for checks), isolated plots in Virginia, Tennessee, and Louisiana for their experiments. Small numbers
of virgin females and fertile males or gravid females alone
were introduced into the plots to establish a population. Subsequently sterile males were released into the plots to reduce
the reproductive potential of the parent and/or F_1 females.
The released males were sterilized by dipping them twice (24
hr apart) for 15 sec into a 2 percent solution of apholate in
water containing a small amount of Triton X-100 (1 drop per
10 ml). This treatment killed 50 to 60 percent of the males
within 1 hr after the second dipping. Living males were then
transported to the release plots and released in proximity to
the points where virgin females were released to establish the
populations. The releases made in the Virginia and Tennessee
plots did not eradicate the artificially introduced infestation,
and check infestations continued to thrive. The releases in the
Louisiana plot eradicated the boll weevil infestation there. In
this experiment a high ratio of sterile to fertile males was required to eradicate the infestation. The authors offered several
possible reasons for their success in Louisiana and failure in
the other two areas. They thought the important reason was
that in the Louisiana test they located the home range of all of
the females released to start the infestation and released the
males in these areas. The experiment established the possibility
of using the sterile-male technique for boll weevil eradication
even though the males used were low in mating competitiveness.
Further research is planned both to develop more effective
means of sterilizing the males and to further evaluate the
technique.

PINK BOLLWORM, *PECTINOPHORA GOSSYPIELLA* (SAUNDERS)

Some interesting studies in large field cages have been
conducted with the pink bollworm by Ouye and co-workers
(Ouye et al., 1965). Following successful laboratory studies
demonstrating effective sterilization of male pink bollworms by
topical applications of metepa, they studied the competitiveness of sterile males in large outdoor cages (6 by 6 by 36 ft).
Test insects were reared on an artificial diet. All males were
treated when less than 24 hr old by topical application on the
mesosternum of 30 or 15 μg of metepa dissolved in acetone.

Sterile males were released in cages with pairs of normal insects at a ratio of 9:1:1. The difference in the total number of F_1 larvae between cages containing the sterile males and normal pairs and control cages was used to determine competitiveness. Males sterilized with 30 μg of metepa were not competitive with normal males and no reduction in number of larvae was noted. Males sterilized with 15 μg of metepa, however, competed almost equally with normal males, causing an 81 percent reduction in the number of F_1 larvae.

Following these studies Ouye and Graham (1937) studied the effect of releasing sterile pink bollworm males, and the effect of winter cultural practices on a population in a large field cage over two cotton-growing seasons. The cage had two sections (each 0.2 acre in size, containing 10 rows of cotton 130 ft long); one to serve as a control, the other for the release of sterile males. Males were sterilized as in their previous cage tests. In 1964 males were released daily into the cage from April 28 to August 20 at an average ratio of seven sterile males to one normal fertile male. In 1964, sterile males were introduced on five consecutive days a week from May 28 until August 9. The ratio of sterile to fertile males varied from a high of 310:1 to 1:1 (when the greatest number of moths was emerging). A rotating stalk shredder was used following the 1964 season to reduce the number of overwintering larvae. During the 1964 season, population reduction resulting from the release of sterile males was calculated to be 80 to 90 percent of that of the untreated check. In spite of this reduction the population into which sterile males were released increased somewhat. In 1965, the release of sterile males controlled 98 percent of the population despite the escape of some moths from the control section to the treated section of the cage. During one consecutive 4-week period in 1965 no larvae were found in the section receiving sterile-male releases. This period was before the entry of moths from the control section was observed. The authors believe that they eradicated the caged population by the sterile-male releases. The infiltration of moths was an unfortunate occurrence which prevented them from concluding that eradication was in fact proved.

CODLING MOTH, *CARPOCAPSA POMONELLA* (LINNAEUS)

Research on the codling moth originally showed that topical applications of 40 μg of tepa would produce sterile competitive males. Further research, however, showed that at doses of 30 and 40 μg males were not competitive with untreated males. Reducing the dose applied topically to 15 μg of tepa resulted in sterile males which were competitive. Preliminary experiments have been conducted on the release of tepa sterilized males into an apple orchard at White Swan, Washington (Butt et al., 1965). In 1964, 97,797 sterile males were released, but the release was discontinued because the native population increased at a normal rate. Releases were made again in 1965; however, the ratio of sterile to native males was estimated and apparently did not exceed 3:1 during most of the season. Less females in the release area laid viable eggs than would have been anticipated. Fruit infestation was lower than expected. Control of the codling was not achieved, however, and the researchers attributed this lack of control to insufficient numbers of released sterile males. Earlier, Proverbs and Newton (1962) reported on experiments in which they released radiation-sterilized males of the codling moth in caged orchard trees.

Although the research under field conditions on the use of chemosterilants for control or eradication is still rather limited, excellent progress has been made with several species. In other cases with other species, laboratory research has approached the point where field studies can be planned. For example, Young and Cox (1965) have shown that the fall armyworm (*Spodoptera frugiperda* J. E. Smith) can be sterilized chemically by feeding tepa to the adults in sugar water. Harrell and his co-workers (1966) have described a suction-type light trap and collecting chamber designed in part for studies on treating moths of natural populations with chemosterilants. We can anticipate many developments in methods of releasing sterile insects or treating natural populations with chemosterilants through the use of traps and mechanical and chemical attractants. Much detailed research will be required. At the same time we will need basic studies on insect populations, their biology, dynamics, ecology, and behavior.

INSECT CHEMOSTERILANTS AS BIOLOGICAL TOOLS

Interest in the development and use of insect chemosterilants has centered, for the most part, on their usefulness in a new and unique approach to insect population control, suppression, or eradication, i.e., the sterility approach. We have tended to emphasize the theories behind the advantages of the use of chemosterilants, the possible ways that these sterilants could be used alone or in combination with other methods of control, and their chemistry, effectiveness, potentialities, and safety. As entomologists have proceeded with the development and evaluation of the sterility and other new approaches to control, they have agreed and attested to the fact that we lack needed basic biological data on economically important populations. To fully evaluate and determine the feasibility of new approaches to control we need much more data on ecology, behavior, mating, dispersion, flight range, and other biological factors. This need is particularly acute and apparent when we try to deal with total insect populations.

In our research and discussions of chemosterilants there has been little emphasis given to the fact that sterility itself can be a highly useful and versatile tool in basic biological studies. Our ability to sterilize males and/or females of many species of insects either chemically or by other means provides us with yet another means of tagging insects for later identification. Furthermore we can identify females that have mated with the sterile males. The tag is, of course, sterility itself. We have used this tag in our studies of permanence of sterility, mating competitiveness of sterile insects and other studies related to the evaluation of the potentialities of chemosterilants. A quick review of the theoretical concepts behind the sterility principle as developed and outlined by Dr. E. F. Knipling will show the reader that these theories provide not only the basic concepts underlying sterilization as an approach to control, but also the means of developing data on total populations for such factors as population levels and rate of increase or decrease.

The purpose of this section is to highlight the use of insect chemosterilants as biological tools or tags and provide examples of the data which can be obtained in this manner. The use of sterility as a tag to evaluate permanence of sterility, mating competitiveness, and other factors related to the effectiveness of chemosterilants may seem quite obvious. Less obvious, but of much interest, was the use of sterility to demonstrate behavioral differences between strains of the same species of insect. Before developing specific examples of the use of sterility as a biological tool, it might be well to briefly review the use of sterility in showing different behavioral traits of strains of the same species.

Weidhaas et al. (1962) reported results of their research in which they released radiation-sterilized males of *Anopheles quadrimaculatus*. They released 328,900 sterile males over an 11-month period into a natural population of *quadrimaculatus* on a semi-isolated island (Kreamer) in Lake Okeechobee, Florida, and another 104,700 sterile males over an 11-week period into a natural population of *quadrimaculatus* in an extensive breeding area near Lake Panasoffkee, Florida. They were unable to demonstrate that these sterile males could effectively seek out females of the natural populations and inseminate them. This failure to induce significant levels of sterility into natural populations by the release of sterile males led these researchers and co-workers into studies designed to explain their failure. The ways in which they used sterility as a biological tool are not mentioned here because this information is given in the specific examples which follow. However, using sterility as one means of tagging *quadrimaculatus* mosquitoes from a colony strain and the wild population they (Dame et al., 1964) were able to show that the most important factors responsible for their unsuccessful release experiment were differences in behavior between colonized and wild strains of this mosquito. Males from the colony were apparently incapable of seeking out and inseminating females of the natural populations when they had to compete with males of the natural populations under conditions existing in the natural habitat.

Following the lead developed in this research on *quadrimaculatus*, Fye and LaBrecque (1966) in laboratory experiments studied mating behavior of two strains of house flies—one a colony strain and the other a strain from a natural population of house flies. They sterilized the males of one strain and allowed these sterile males to compete with fertile males of the other strain in mating females of both strains. By determining the sterility and fertility of eggs of females from these crosses they showed a tendency of males and females from the colony strain and the wild strain to mate more readily with individuals of their own strain.

Sterility in insects, however achieved, will be useful in many ways as a biological tool in field studies. In considering the developmental research on chemosterilants, we find a rather generalized approach to the problem. Laboratory studies are conducted to find chemicals capable of causing sterility in insects and to evaluate their potential effectiveness. Successful laboratory research leads to field studies on the feasibility of various chemosterilant techniques. In the laboratory, major emphasis is given to evaluating the effects of the chemosterilant on the insect itself, i.e., (1) minimum effective concentration, (2) the stage most easily sterilized, (3) effect on individual sexes, vigor, longevity, and mating competitiveness, and (4) permanence of sterility. In these studies sterility is the tag which is used to determine the effects of chemosterilants on insects. In field studies some of these same factors may be evaluated. In field studies, however, the emphasis is generally changed from the study of the efficacy of the chemosterilant per se to the feasibility of using a particular chemosterilant technique for control or eradication. Now the important considerations are developing the technique, and understanding the biology of the insect involved. Sterility is an excellent means of tagging insects for field studies. There will be many advantages to using sterility alone or in combination with another marker such as dyes, paints, fluorescent materials, or radioactivity. For example one current method of estimating the number of insects in a given population is to release insects tagged with a visible marker so that the ratio of marked to wild insects recaptured can be used to estimate total numbers in the populations. If the marked insects that are released are also sterilized and released over sufficient time to thoroughly mix with the populations under study, then two indices for estimating total populations would be available: (1) the ratio of marked to wild insects recaptured and (2) the sterility found in females of the wild population. A double tag of this type would increase confidence in the results obtained and could confirm the fact that released insects had adequately mixed with the natural population.

To use sterility as a tag is more time-consuming and difficult than the use of visible markers. At present the only means of identifying sterility is to determine the hatchability of eggs. To identify sterile males requires determining the hatchability of eggs from fertile, virgin females mated to the sterile males. Unmated females (sterile) would have to be mated to normal, fertile males. Eggs produced by mated females can be examined for viability. This type of evaluation is relatively simple if the insect species behaves normally under caged conditions in the laboratory. It requires time, space, and effort, however, to capture, cage, and mate insects and provide suitable care, nutrition, and time for development, oviposition, and hatch of eggs.

Let us outline some specific types of field tests in which sterility can be used as a tag, and then give some examples of the types of studies which might be conducted. These studies could be grouped as follows:

1. Competitiveness of sterilized insects in mating fertile insects of natural populations.
2. Single or multiple matings by females.
3. The number of females that the average male can successfully fertilize.
4. Total numbers of insects in a population.
5. The rate of increase of an insect population from generation to generation or from the time required from one life cycle to the next.
6. Behavioral characteristics and differences in behavioral traits between strains.

COMPETITIVENESS OF STERILIZED INSECTS

One of the most important considerations in developing and evaluating the sterility approach of control or eradication is the ability of sterile insects to seek our their mates and compete successfully with normal, untreated insects in the population. The most obvious factor which may reduce the sterilized insects' ability to mate competitively with normal, fertile insects is some type of somatic damage caused by the sterilizing agent itself. It is quite possible that the expected amount of mating competitiveness will not be obtained in the field when sterilized insects are released or when natural populations are treated with chemosterilants, even though laboratory studies show that the sterilizing agents do not reduce the insects' ability to mate competitively with normal insects. Here competitiveness can be studied in the field through the use of sterility as a tag along with another marker which allows subsequent identification and capture of sterilized insects. Let us examine two theoretical examples of this type of study—one for the sterile-male release technique; the other for the use of chemosterilants in treating natural populations.

Let us assume that we are concerned about the competitiveness of males to be released in a sterile-male release experiment and that we have the capability of (1) releasing a known number of sterile males, (2) marking the released males for later identification, (3) determining the ratio of released sterile males to wild males in the natural population, and (4) assaying the degree of sterility produced in females of the natural population by the released sterile males. Since we are using a double tag we have a means of comparing the ratio of released to wild insects with the sterility obtained in wild females. If our released males are capable of dispersing in the natural population and competing fully and effectively with males of the natural population, then we can expect the degree of sterility found in females of the wild population to compare favorably with the expected degree of sterility calculated from the ratio of released to wild males. For example, if 10,000 males were released into a population of unknown size we might expect the following:

Ratio of released to wild males	Number of individuals in the wild population	Expected percent sterility in females of the wild population
1:9	90,000	10
1:4	40,000	20
1:3	30,000	25
1:1	10,000	50
3:1	3,333	75
4:1	2,500	80
9:1	1,111	90

When the calculated or expected degree of sterility agrees closely with that obtained in the wild population we are assured of competitive, naturally behaving males and can then calculate the number of males which would have to be released to attain a desired degree of sterility in the wild population. Where large differences occur between the expected degree of sterility and that obtained in the wild population we will know that either our males are not competitive in seeking out and fertilizing females or we know too little of the biology and ecology of the wild population to design a successful release experiment.

A similar hypothetical example can be given for the use of chemosterilants to treat natural populations. Let us assume that (1) some means, such as an attractive bait or lure, is available for treating the natural population, (2) a second type of marker such as a dye or radioactivity can be incorporated in the chemosterilant bait or treatment so that individuals sterilized by the treatment can be later identified, and (3) a means is available to survey the population at some location other than the bait or treatment area. If the bait or treatment completely sterilizes the males and females exposed to it we could expect the percentage of sterility found in females of the population which were not exposed to the bait or treatment to be equal to the percentage of the population which was exposed to and sterilized by the treatment. In cases where all individual males and females were not completely sterilized by the treatment or some were completely sterilized and some were partially sterilized, we would need to compare the degree of sterility found in females of the total population (both treated and untreated) to the degree of sterility expected on the basis of the percentage of the population affected. For example, if an average of 50 percent of the population was sterilized by the treatment, then 75 percent sterility should be found in the total population. Again correlation of expected and experimental results would prove the technique and the competitiveness of males, whereas lack of correlation would suggest further studies to improve the technique and elucidate biology.

A special example can be cited for using sterility as a means of studying competitive behavior of males. In the release of sterile males it is possible to have males from a colony strain that are no longer able to compete in the mating process under field conditions. This lack of competitiveness could be due to selection during colonization for adaption to laboratory or caged environments. The reader is referred to Dame et al. (1964) for a specific example of this type of problem with mosquitoes. Here we will simply outline a hypothetical model.

One means of studying and comparing the mating behavior of colony strains under field conditions would be to design an experiment in which sterile males from a colony were allowed to compete with fertile males of a wild population in mating virgin females of both strains under field conditions. In most cases the population of wild insects may be too large and dispersed to allow a simple experiment involving reasonable numbers of insects, time, and effort as described above. Furthermore, a large proportion of females of the natural population may be mated before any group of released colony males have a chance to mate with them. If a natural population can be located which contains active males, the following type of scheme could be developed. This scheme is patterned after the studies reported by Woodard et al. (1962) and Dame et al. (1964) with *Anopheles quadrimaculatus*.

Preliminary studies would have to be conducted to determine the location of a natural population with males that are actively mating. To accomplish this, virgin females from a laboratory colony could be marked with a visible marker, released into the natural population, and recaptured at given time intervals after release. Whether or not these females were mated by males of the wild population could be determined by dissection and examination for the presence of sperm or by allowing these females to oviposit in the laboratory and determining the viability of their eggs.

Once a natural population with active males is located, a rather simple experiment can be run as a preliminary evaluation. Sterile males of the colony strain can be released along with virgin, marked females of the colony strain into the natural population, allowing competition between laboratory and wild males in mating the virgin colony females. Subsequent recapture of the released females and the determination of the fertility and sterility of their eggs will permit a measure of the degree of mating by males of each strain. This type of test does not permit a quantitative determination of degree of mating by males of the two strains. However, it will demonstrate that males of the colony strain are capable of mating and competing to some degree under field conditions.

One method of comparing mating behavior and competitiveness of both strains would be to release marked, virgin females of the wild strain along with sterile colony males and marked, virgin colony females. In this case we would have a source of virgin females from each strain (each marked differently so they could be identified in subsequent recapture) available for mating by either sterile, colony males or fertile males of the wild population. Recapture of the released females and determination of the viability of their eggs would show whether a female had been mated by a colony or wild male (all matings by colony males would produce sterile eggs; all matings by wild males would produce normal fertility in eggs). In an experiment of this type it would not be necessary to know the total number of males in the wild population. If behavior and mating competitiveness were similar for each strain, we could expect that the same ratio of sterility to fertility would be found in eggs of females of both strains. For example, let us assume that the number of sterile colony males was one tenth or one fourth or equal to the number of actively mating males in the wild population capable of competing in the mating process with the colony males. Then we would expect 10, 25, or 50 percent of the females of each strain to develop sterile eggs. If the degree of sterility found in females of one strain differed from that found in other strains, good evidence would be found for some difference in behavior between the two strains under field conditions.

We have mentioned only a few hypothetical examples based on studies with mosquitoes of using sterility for studies on behavior particularly in relation to competitive mating. The ingenuity of researchers can adapt, develop, and devise the use of these markers in many other ways to fit the particular insect species or research problem they face. These examples are presented mainly to point to the usefulness of sterility.

So far we have considered the use of sterility as a tool mainly in evaluating the potentialities of chemosterilants in the sterility approach to control. In discussing mating competitiveness, however, we digressed somewhat to show that behavioral traits could also be studied. Sterility will also be useful as a tool in research on basic biology other than behavioral traits.

SINGLE OR MULTIPLE MATINGS BY FEMALES

Sterility has been used in laboratory studies and some field studies to determine whether females of a species mate only one time or more than once. There are, of course, other methods of determining whether the females are single or multiple maters. These include simple observation and the use of genetic markers. Although simple observation may show how many times a female(s) will copulate, it does not permit the researcher to know if sperm were transferred during copulation or if these sperm were utilized to fertilize eggs. Genetic markers such as visible mutations, insecticide-resistant strains, and sterility (dominant lethality) must be used to show successful fertilization. When males are sterilized by chemosterilants, through the induction of dominant lethal mutations in genetic material, the infertility of eggs of females can be followed to determine whether a female mates more than one time. The means of using sterility in this manner are applicable to either laboratory or field evaluations and studies, although field experiments will be much more difficult because they require more insects for release and the capture of females for evaluation.

When sterile males are released into a population and allowed to compete with wild males for mates with wild females, one can follow the fertility of individual females of the wild population. This requires the capture of wild females with procedures allowing the evaluation of hatchability of eggs from individual females. If these eggs from individual females are either "completely fertile" or "completely sterile," then an assumption of one successful fertilization can be made. Generally eggs from females are not 100 percent fertile. One may expect a small percentage of completely sterile egg batches or a small percentage of infertile eggs within an individual egg batch. Consequently, meaningful data can only be obtained by comparing the hatch of eggs from females collected during the release of sterile males with similar data for the natural population when no sterile males are released.

Dame and Schmidt (1964) reported an interesting method of tagging males of two species of mosquitoes, *Anopheles quadrimaculatus* and *Aedes aegypti*, with P^{32} which allowed them to identify females which mated to these males. Radioautographs of the spermathacae of females mated to these males showed radioactivity. Males were tagged by rearing the larvae in water treated with P^{32}. They further showed that males tagged with P^{32} and also sterilized with tepa were equally competitive with untreated males in mating females under laboratory test conditions. With this system one has available two effective methods of tagging males and following the mating process under field conditions. The release of fertile P^{32}-tagged males in addition to sterilized males would allow the evaluation of the presence of two tagging systems in females mated with these males. If the females mate successfully only once, one would expect to find radioactivity only in fertile females. If P^{32}-tagged sterile males were released in equal numbers with sterile males in a wild population, one could expect, if the female successfully mates only one time, that one half of the sterile females would also have radioactivity in their spermathacae and that all of the fertile wild females would have no radioactivity in the spermathacae. Deviations from these expectations would indicate females accepting more than one fertilization.

THE NUMBER OF FEMALES THAT THE AVERAGE MALE CAN SUCCESSFULLY FERTILIZE

In most cases the problem of determining how many females a male can successfully fertilize will be most simply and readily answered in the laboratory with caged insects. In laboratory tests of this type no special type of tag is necessary. One can place one or more males in cages with an appropriate excess of virgin females and follow the viability of eggs from individual females to determine the fertilizing capacity of an individual male or the average for a group of males. This same technique can be used in relatively large cages out of doors.

In field tests or in large cages where it is impossible to know or control the number of males or females present or the virginity of the females, some idea of the male's capacity to successfully inseminate more than one female could be determined by the release of fertile females alone. For example, let us assume that we have a field or caged population of insects for study in which the sex ratio is 1:1, into which we have the capability of releasing virgin females. If we simply release large numbers of virgin females into this population and find that a high percentage of them are mated, we can assume the males mate successfully more than once. However, we can not estimate how many females a male can successfully fertilize. To make such an estimate would require the release of known numbers of fertile, virgin females appropriately marked for later identification or the release of sterile, virgin females in combination with sterile males. For example, let us consider the release of 9,000 fertile females alone and the release of 9,000 sterile, virgin females in combination with 1,000 sterile males into natural or caged populations. We will assume that there are 1,000 males and 1,000 females in the population. When the fertile females are released alone, there will be only 1,000 males available to mate 10,000 females. Determination of the viability of eggs of a representative sample of individual females of the natural population, of the released females, or both, allows an estimate of inseminating capability of the males. If one found 10, 20, 50, or 100 percent of the females to be inseminated, then one could estimate that the average male could inseminate 1, 2, 5, or 10 or more females. The release of sterile females along with sterile males would permit a comparison of the percent insemination with the percent sterility and allow for more confidence in the data obtained. For example, if 9,000 sterile females plus 1,000 sterile males were released into 1,000 males and 1,000 females of a natural population, 2,000 males would be available for mating 10,000 females. If males can successfully inseminate 1, 2, or 5 or more females we could expect 20, 40, and 100 percent insemination of females. Fifty percent of the females of the natural population would be sterile.

Another advantage of the use of sterile females and males in field or cage studies of this type is that some information on the behavior of the released and wild insects can be obtained while the fertilizing potential of the males is being measured. In the case given above, the degree of sterility in females of the wild population would be expected to be 50 percent and the proportion of released to wild females would be expected to be 9:1. Any deviations from these expectations would indicate behavioral differences between released and wild insects or a poor experimental design. The same argument would apply to the expected degree of insemination of released and wild females.

We should perhaps point out that a definite answer under field conditions for the fertilizing capabilities of the average male is a valuable piece of data. It will immediately tell the researcher whether he can consider the release of sterile females only as a means of reducing insect populations. Furthermore, it will allow the researcher to know if the release of sterile females along with sterile males in a release experiment will have any effect in reducing the population. Ailam and Galun (1966) have published theoretical considerations covering this subject. Theoretically the release of sterile females can affect reproduction only by decreasing the number or percentage of females that can get mated. The release of sterile insects of both sexes will be more effective in reducing reproductive potential only when the males (both sterile and fertile) are incapable of fertilizing all of the females present. When both sexes of sterile insects are released, any advantage in reducing reproductive potential of the natural population would require the release of a greater number of sterile females than males and would depend upon the fertilizing capacity of the males.

An example of the theoretical reduction of a population that could be expected by the release of sterile females alone or by the release of sterile females and sterile males might be helpful. If we release 9,000 sterile females or 9,000 sterile females plus 1,000 sterile males for every 1,000 males and 1,000 females in the natural population, we could expect the following reduction in reproductive potential based on the number of times an average male mates.

Number of times the average male mates	Percent insemination; sterile females only released	Reduction in reproductive potential
1	10	90
2	20	80
5	50	50
10	100	0

Sterile females plus sterile males in ratio of 9:1

1	20	90
2	40	80
5	100	50
10	100	50

As long as the number of males present in the population is not sufficient to satisfy the mating requirements of the females, the reduction in reproductive potential (when both sterile females and males are released) is independent of the number of males released. The interested reader is referred to the article by Ailam and Galun (1966) for a mathematical treatment of this subject.

TOTAL NUMBER OF INSECTS IN A POPULATION

Of particular interest to entomologists concerned with field studies on the sterility approach is the total number of individuals in a population at a given time, for a given generation or under certain environmental conditions. This type of data is becoming more important as we develop and evaluate new approaches to control or to population regulation or suppression. Generally the release and recapture of insects marked with dyes, radioactivity, or other agents and the capture of insects from the natural population has been used to establish a ratio of released to wild insects. From this ratio an estimate of the size of the total population can be made. Estimates of this type are difficult to make and their reliability is often questioned, particularly with highly mobile insects. If insects released for estimating the number of individuals in natural populations were sterilized as well as marked with a visible tag, the researcher would have two methods of estimating the numbers in the total population. One of these would, of course, be the ratio of recaptured insects to captured wild insects. The other would be the degree of sterility in females of the wild population. For example, if one captured 1, 2, 4, or 9 times as many wild insects as were released, one could expect 50, 33, 20, or 10 percent sterility in females of the natural population. The numbers in the total population can be estimated from both of these data. Not only would there be a method of comparing the results of one system against the other to increase confidence in the data, but also the sterility data would indicate that the released insects had mixed with the natural population and behaved similarly. That in fact this mixture of released and wild insects did occur cannot be determined by the release of nonsterile tagged insects.

THE RATE OF INCREASE OF AN INSECT POPULATION

Perhaps the most difficult type of information to develop on population dynamics is the change in the total numbers of insects in a population from one generation to the next, or, for insects which breed continuously with all stages present at the same time, from the time required for the development of one life cycle to the time required for the next life cycle. The amount of change can differ under various situations, periods of time, or environmental conditions and may be an increase or decrease. In some cases there may be no change at all, with the total numbers of individuals remaining essentially constant.

When we consider insect populations that develop through discrete generations with little or no overlap between generations, we can study the increase or decrease in total numbers from generation to generation through the application of the principles developed by E. F. Knipling for the sterility approach to control or eradication. Here sterility becomes the tool or tag which allows the estimation of change in population numbers. Again we should emphasize that estimates of this type might be made more simply through the use of released marked insects. However, the use of sterile insects would allow the use of two means of estimating populations, would ensure that released insects mixed adequately with and behaved similarly to the wild population, and would confirm data obtained on the ratios of released to wild insects.

When studying populations that have discrete generations, one simply determines change from one generation to the next. It may be an increase, decrease, or no change at all. If the conditions which existed during the parent and F_1 generation permitted maximum possible increase in the numbers of the population, the estimate of the increase in population would represent its true biotic potential.

In working with insect populations which breed continuously with all stages of the insect present at the same time and without discrete generations, we might think that determining changes in the size of total populations over time would be much more difficult than with populations which develop through discrete generations. However, if we think in terms of the time required for the completion of one life cycle or generation, the problem of estimating changes in total populations, although more difficult, can still be accomplished. Estimates of the time required for each stage of the insect's development under different field conditions can be made and the time required for only one life cycle determined. The continual release of sterile, marked insects into this type of a population over the time required for two life cycles would permit researchers to compare averages for the ratios of released to wild insects and the sterility in the wild population in both a parent and an F_1 generation. With this type of data, estimates of changes in population levels can be made following the theories of the sterile-male technique developed by Dr. E. F. Knipling.

With populations that breed continuously throughout favorable seasons rather than develop through discrete generations, we may have an added advantage of being able to estimate their biotic potential under field conditions where both favorable and unfavorable factors influence the population level. Releases of sterile, marked insects over the time re-

quired for two or more generations should allow us to estimate a population's biotic potential. This can be understood if
we consider that the release of sterile insects gives us a
means of reducing the reproductive potential of a population
which, at the same time, has an inherent ability to replenish
its numbers. By measuring the amount of reduction in the
reproductive potential (percent sterility) in the parent to the
F_1 generation we can calculate the population's ability to increase its numbers. For example, if we release sterile insects into a natural population at a ratio of 19:1 we would
expect to reduce its reproductive potential by 95 percent. We
would expect that natural population to show some ability to
replenish its numbers. If the numbers of individuals in the
F_1 population is the same as in the parent generation, then we
can say the population has, at least, the ability to increase its
numbers twentyfold. If the ratio of released to wild insects is
sufficiently large to cause a reduction in reproductive potential greater than the insect's ability to increase its numbers,
then we can calculate its "biotic potential" under field conditions.

One problem which will make experiments of the type
described above particularly difficult is that the natural population may not remain at a constant level during the time of the
two life cycles required in the experimental procedure. If one
can find the ideal population which has attained a state of
balance with a constant population level, then evaluation of
potential increase will be relatively simple. One cannot determine, however, the population's maximum capability of increasing its numbers unless the sterility produced in the
natural population through release of sterile insects exceeds
its capability for increasing its numbers. With populations
which are continuous breeders but are either in the process of
increasing or decreasing in size during the parent and F_1 generation, studies of this type are more difficult. The researcher
will have to rely on some survey method for estimating population levels during the parent generation and the F_1 generation.
If he can determine the average increase or decrease and the
percent sterility for each generation, then he can calculate the
capability of the population to increase.

BEHAVIORAL CHARACTERISTICS AND DIFFERENCES IN BEHAVIOR BETWEEN STRAINS

One other interesting type of research relating to the development of the sterility method of control should be mentioned, for it may have an influence on the design of field experimentation. Here sterility is not needed as a tag, and experimentation falls within the realm of behavioral genetics. Recent work with mosquitoes (Weidhaas et al., 1962 and Dame et al., 1964) points the way to some interesting research with these insects and possibly others on behavioral traits and the genetic basis of these traits.

In studies on the release of sterile males of the common malaria mosquito *Anopheles quadrimaculatus*, the above authors showed that a colony of *quadrimaculatus* differs in behavioral traits from a wild strain of the same species. Fye and LaBrecque (1966) showed a difference in mating behavior between strains of the house fly. In both cases this difference in behavior somehow decreased the ability of males or females of one strain to seek out and copulate with males or females of a different strain as readily as they did with males or females of their own strain. The specific reason for this difference in behavior is unknown. It is quite possible, however, that a process of selection under different environmental conditions has led to these differences. It will be extremely interesting to attempt research directed toward establishing and evaluating the genetic basis of these differences in behavior.

The common malaria mosquito should be an excellent example of the possibilities of this type of research. The following line of research is included as a possible approach. Considerable background research with this mosquito has shown mating behavior of colony and wild insects under laboratory conditions to differ almost completely. Males and females of the laboratory colony mated readily under laboratory conditions. Seventy to ninety-five percent of the females of the laboratory were mated in 3 to 4 days when they were placed in cages (3 by 3 by 2 ft to 6 by 8 by 11 in.) with males of the same colony. Under the same cage conditions, males and females of a wild strain did not mate. Here was a definite difference in mating behavior of two strains. One hundred percent mating does not occur in the laboratory strain under these conditions. Presumably there exist in the wild strain individuals that will mate under laboratory conditions, since laboratory strains have been developed from wild stock. However, these colonies have been developed with difficulty. Techniques are now available to force-copulate mosquitoes. Consequently it should be possible to interbreed laboratory strains and wild strains through this technique. Assaying the mating ability of progeny from such crosses and selfing these progeny or backcrossing them to the original strains might uncover a genetic basis for such behavior. If simple mendelian inheritance were involved, with mating in cages a recessive trait, one could conclude that colonizing this particular strain involved selecting a homozygous recessive trait. Probably a behavioral difference related to a mating process is too complicated to be tied to a single gene phenomenon. However, research of this type should prove interesting and very important to an understand of field studies employing sterile insects.

REFERENCES

Ailam, G. and R. Galun. 1966. Optimal sex ratio for the control of insects by the sterility method. Ann. Entom. Soc. Amer. In press.

Baumhover, A. H. 1966. Eradication of the screw-worm fly, an agent of myiasis. J. Amer. Med. Assoc., 196(3):240–248.

Butt, B. A., D. O. Hathaway, and J. F. Howell. 1965. Codling moth sterile male release program at White Swan, Washington, Special Report AADF1-65-1, U.S. Dept. Agr., Entom. Res. Div., Yakima, Washington. 18 pp.

Dame, D. A., D. B. Woodard, and H. R. Ford. 1964. Chemosterilization of *Aedes aegypti* (L) by larval treatments. Mosq. News, 24(1):1–6.

_____, and C. H. Schmidt. 1964. P^{32}-labeled semen for mosquito mating studies. J. Econ. Entom., 57(5):699–672.

_____, D. B. Woodard, H. R. Ford, and D. E. Weidhaas. 1964. Field behavior of sexually sterile *Anopheles quadrimaculatus* males. Mosq. News, 24(1):6–14.

Davich, T. B., J. C. Keller, E. B. Mitchell, P. Heddleston, R. Hill, D. A. Lindquist, G. McKibben, and W. H. Cross. 1965. Preliminary field experiments with sterile males for eradication of the boll weevil. J. Econ. Entom., 58(1):127–131.

Davis, A. N., J. B. Gahan, D. E. Weidhaas, and C. N. Smith. 1959. Exploratory studies on gamma radiation for the sterilization and control of *Anopheles quadrimaculatus*. J. Econ. Entom., 52(5):868–870.

Fay, R. W., E. M. CcCray, Jr., and J. W. Kilpatrick. 1963. Mass production of sterilized male *Aedes aegypti*. Mosq. News, 23(3):210–214.

Fye, R. L., and G. C. LaBrecque. 1966. Sexual acceptability of laboratory strains of male house flies in competition with wild strains. J. Econ. Entom., 59(3):538–540.

Gast, R. T., and H. H. Vardell. 1963. Mechanical devices to expedite boll weevil rearing in the laboratory. U.S. Dept. Agr., ARS-33-89, 10 pp.

Gouck, H. K., D. W. Meifert, and J. B. Gahan. 1963. A field experiment with apholate as a chemosterilant for the control of house flies. J. Econ. Entom., 56(4):445–446.

Hansens, E. J. 1965. Effects of apholate on restricted populations of insecticide-resistant house flies, *Musca domestica*. J. Econ. Entom., 58(5):944–946.

———, and P. Granett. 1965. Effects of apholate on a restricted population of house flies. J. Econ. Entom., 58(1):157–158.

Harrell, E. A., W. W. Hare, and J. R. Young. 1966. A fan for handling live insects. J. Econ. Entom. In press.

Howland, A. F., P. Vail, and T. J. Henneberry. 1965. Effect of chemosterilants on fertility of cabbage loopers. J. Econ. Entom., 58(4):635–637.

———, P. Vail, and T. J. Henneberry. 1966. Results of cage experiments with sterile male releases and a chemosterilant technique for control of cabbage looper populations. J. Econ. Entom., 59(1):194–196.

Krishnamurthy, B. S., S. N. Ray, and G. C. Joshi. 1963. A note of preliminary field studies of the use of irradiated males for reduction of *Culex fatigans* Wied. populations. WHO/Vector Control 114.

LaBrecque, G. C., P. H. Adcock, and C. N. Smith. 1960. Tests with compounds affecting house fly metabolism. J. Econ. Entom., 53(5):802–805.

LaBrecque, G. C. 1961. Studies with three alkylating agents as house fly sterilants. J. Econ. Entom., 54(4):684–689.

———, and D. W. Meifert. 1966. Control of house flies *(Diptera: Muscidae)* in poultry houses with chemosterilants. J. Med. Entom. 3:(3-4):323–326.

———, C. N. Smith, and D. W. Meifert. 1962. A field experiment in the control of house flies with chemosterilant baits. J. Econ. Entom., 55(4):449–451.

———, D. W. Meifert, and R. L. Fye. 1963. A field study on the control of house flies with chemosterilant techniques. J. Econ. Entom., 56(2):150–152.

Lewallen, L. L., H. C. Chapman, and W. W. Wilder. 1965. Chemosterilant applications to an isolated population of *Culex tarsalis*. Mosq. News 25(1):16–18.

Mathis, W., and H. F. Schoof. 1965. Studies on house fly control. J. Econ. Entom., 58(2):291–293.

Meifert, D. W., G. C. LaBrecque, C. N. Smith, and P. B. Morgan. 1967. Control of house flies (*Musca domestica* L.) on some West Indies Islands with metepa, apholate, and trichlorfon baits. J. Econ. Entom. 60(2):480–485.

Morlan, H. B., E. M. McCray, Jr., and J. W. Kilpatrick. 1962. Field tests with sexually sterile males for control of *Aedes aegypti*. Mosq. News, 22(3):295–300.

Ouye, M. T. and H. H. Graham. 1967. Study on eradication of a confined population of pink bollworm by release of males sterilized with metepa. J. Econ. Entom. 60(1):244–247.

_____, H. M. Graham, R. S. Garcai, and D. F. Martin. 1965. Comparative mating competitiveness of metepa-sterilized and normal pink bollworms in laboratory and field cages. J. Econ. Entom., 58(5):927–929.

Proverbs, M. D., and J. R. Newton. 1962. Suppression of the reproductive potential of the codling moth by gamma irradiated males in caged orchard trees. J. Econ. Entom., 55(6):934–936.

Ratcliffe, R. H., and S. S. Ristich. 1965. Insect sterilant experiments in outdoor cages with apholate, metepa, and four bifunctional aziridine chemicals against the house fly. J. Econ. Entom., 58(6):1079–1082.

Sacca, G., and E. Stella. 1964. A field trial against *Musca domestica* L. by liquid baits of aphoxide. Riv. Parassit., 25(4):279–294.

Shaw, J. G., and M. Sanchez Riviello. 1962. Sterility in the Mexican fruit fly caused by chemicals. Science, 137:754–755.

_____, and M. Sanchez Riviello. 1965. Effectiveness of tepa-sterilized Mexican fruit flies released in a mango grove. J. Econ. Entom., 58(1):26–28.

_____, W. P. Patton, M. Sanchez Riviello, and L. M. Spishakoff. 1966. Mexican fruit fly control. Calif. Citrograph 51(5):209–214.

Steiner, L. F., E. J. Harris, W. C. Mitchell, M. S. Fujimoto, and L. D. Christenson. 1965. Melon fly eradication by overflooding with sterile flies. J. Econ. Entom., 58(3):519–522.

Weidhaas, D. E., C. H. Schmidt, and E. L. Seabrook. 1962. Field studies on the release of sterile males for the control of Anopheles quadrimaculatus. Mosq. News, 22(3):283–291.

Woodard, D. B., D. E. Weidhaas, and H. R. Ford. 1962. A method to study mating activity of *Anopheles quadrimaculatus* under field conditions. Proceedings of the Florida Anti-Mosquito Association, p. 24.

Young, J. R., and H. C. Cox. 1965. Evaluation of apholate and tepa as chemosterilants for the fall armyworm. J. Econ. Entom, 58(5):883–888.

7

Toxicological Aspects of Chemosterilants

WAYLAND J. HAYES, JR.

PESTICIDES PROGRAM
NATIONAL COMMUNICABLE DISEASE CENTER
PUBLIC HEALTH SERVICE
U.S. DEPARTMENT OF HEALTH,
    EDUCATION, AND WELFARE
ATLANTA, GEORGIA

Many of the compounds that show promise as chemosterilants are used in the palliative treatment of cancer or are analogs of carcinostatic compounds. This is true of alkylating agents, many antimetabolites, and some miscellaneous compounds such as colchicine and substituted ureas. Chemicals that offer some hope in treating cancer have been the subject of intensive study. It thus happens that much information is available on the biochemistry and the acute toxicity of some chemosterilants. There frequently is exact information on signs, symptoms, and pathological changes produced by the compounds in man. When known at all, information on the toxicity of these compounds to man includes knowledge of dosages that are generally tolerated and somewhat higher dosages that are frequently dangerous when given for a few days or a few weeks, as in the treatment of cancer. Unfortunately, information is often lacking on the effects of repeated dosages which are too small to produce a therapeutic or other effect that can be noticed in a week or two; in the few instances where such information is available, it is either because the compound is used in the treatment of a chronic disease (e.g., colchicine for gout), or because it has been studied in direct relation to its possible use as a chemosterilant for insects (e.g., metepa) or mammals (e.g., methyl methanesulfonate). Jackson (1966) has given an excellent discussion of the wide range of antifertility compounds considered for use in mammals.

In brief, the kinds of injury and the dosage necessary to produce them are known in connection with possible accidental exposure of workers to any of a large number of candidate chemosterilants, and the possible effects of repeated small exposures are usually unknown, as is the magnitude of repeated dosage that can be tolerated indefinitely. The few compounds that have been studied proved to be cumulative, and the effects of repeated dosage could not be predicted from the effects of one or a few doses. Thus, it is impossible to predict the effect that the long-repeated absorption of traces of most of the candidate chemosterilants would have on workers or others.

Some candidate chemosterilants, notably the alkylating agents, some antimetabolites, and some antibiotics, act as chromosomal poisons. Colchicine acts as a mitotic spindle poison. A number of candidate chemosterilants (e.g., the thioureas) apparently lack either of these effects, but do have reasonably well-recognized biochemical modes of action. Finally, it may be said that few if any candidate chemosterilants lack unexplained side effects.

ALKYLATING AGENTS

Because the alkylating agents produce a number of effects not frequently encountered with other classes of compounds, it seems desirable to outline their properties and later to explore to what extent other groups of candidate chemosterilants exhibit the same ones. Briefly, the effects of alkylating agents, which are discussed below in greater detail in connection with individual compounds, may be summarized in the following ways.

The compounds have little immediate pharmacological action, but are notable for their delayed effect, accompanied by a selective action against some proliferating tissues, namely: hematopoietic cells of the bone marrow and lymphoid tissues, the intestinal mucosa, germ cells, embryos, and tumors. Less frequently, nonproliferating cells are affected selectively. Metabolism of the compounds is rapid and frequently extensive.

Death following a single dose in the LD_{50} range is delayed. Although fluid loss and suppression of hematopoiesis occur, they fail to explain the mechanism of death. Sepsis is not prominent, and more severe loss of fluid from other causes is tolerated.

The manner of death following repeated doses of alkylating agents resembles the delayed lethal syndrome following a single dose except that gastrointestinal signs and pathology are less prominent.

The alkylating agents produce the following unusual effects: mutagenesis, teratogenesis, carcinogenesis, carcinostasis, and sexual sterilization, especially of males. Not all compounds have all of these properties for any one species. Mutagenesis has been demonstrated most often in insects, bacteria, fungi, and higher plants, although it has been produced in mammals also. Teratogenesis has been produced by alkylating agents in birds and mammals as well as in insects. A low grade of carcinogenic action has been observed in experimental animals dosed with certain chemosterilants, but some naturally occurring alkylating agents are strong carcinogens (Weisburger, 1966). A number of different kinds of tumors in various species including man are susceptible to palliative treatment with selected alkylating agents. Sterility has been produced by alkylating agents in the rat, mouse, rabbit, and dog as well as in insects, but not all alkylating agents produce sterility.

In mammals, sterility produced by these compounds is not necessarily accompanied by other toxic effects, and sterility does not involve any influence on the dynamics of spermatogenesis. This means that the order and duration of the different stages that lead to mature sperm are unchanged. The injury may involve destruction of one or more early cell types leading to aspermia as a result of at least partial atrophy of the seminal epithelium. A more subtle injury may affect the spermatids or spermatozoa with no histological evidence of action on earlier stages; sperm are produced that are normal in number, appearance, motility, and ability to penetrate ova, but the zygotes are incapable of sustained development. Jackson (1964) has emphasized the specificity of the effect of different alkylating agents on the different stages of spermatogenesis of mammals. Somewhat similar specificity is observed in insects (Fahmy and Fahmy, 1964).

A review of the alkylating agents has appeared recently (Hayes, 1964). Unlike this chapter, which is organized according to compound, the review was organized according to pharmacological effects, and it contained some information on compounds that have not been considered as chemosterilants.

Two new discoveries, however, are so basic they should be mentioned here. Both may help to explain why alkylating agents are only palliative in the treatment of leukemia and some other neoplasms against which they are initially effective. As reviewed by Moloney (1966), some compounds such as Cytoxan and tretamine that cause remission of malignant tumors have little or no effect on tumor viruses (Glynn et al., 1963). Secondly, Crathorn and Roberts (1966), in an effort to explain why two cell lines differed by a factor of about 2.5 in their sensitivity to mustard gas, proposed the hypothesis that the difference might depend on the existence of a mechanism for repairing the damage of DNA in cells less sensitive to action of the mustard. Using mustard gas tagged by radioactive sulfur, they were able to demonstrate not only alkylating of DNA, but also the subsequent, enzymatically mediated dealkylation of the DNA. Thus, the different ability of cells to repair their DNA must now be reckoned one of the variables that determine the observed specificity of alkylating agents in a wide variety of situations: for example, in relation to different tumors, different species of animals, or different stages in spermatogenesis.

TEPA

The oral LD_{50} of tepa for rats is 37 mg/kg, and its dermal LD_{50} for the same species is 87 mg/kg (Gaines and Kimbrough, 1964). The dosage used to treat cancer in man is only 1.2 to 2.0 mg/kg, given intramuscularly (Sykes et al., 1956). It was shown by Szybalski (1958) to be mutagenic in bacteria.

Apparently the effects of repeated doses have not been studied, but the metabolism has been investigated. Using isotopically marked tepa and paper chromatography, no unchanged tepa was detected in the urine of mice, and 80 percent was degraded to the inorganic phosphate. The animals excreted 60 to 80 percent of the radioactive phosphorus from tepa in 24 hr (Nadkarni et al., 1957). No unchanged tepa was excreted in human urine, but only about 30 percent of the dose was recovered (Nadkarni et al., 1959). Of the recovered material, 88 percent or more of the radioactivity was present as inorganic phosphate (Nadkarni et al., 1959). A high proportion of tepa can be recovered from the urine of rats (Crossley et al., 1953, Craig and Jackson, 1955); however, the majority is in the unchanged form (Craig and Jackson, 1955). Thus, tepa is not highly reactive in the rat, although a small fraction of the dose is probably metabolized extensively. In the dog, 13 to 15 percent of oral doses were recovered unchanged in the urine (Mellet and Woods, 1960).

THIOTEPA

Like tepa, thiotepa has been studied chiefly from the standpoint of metabolism. Using analytical methods specific for the two drugs, Mellett and Woods (1960) found that when thiotepa was given to dogs either intravenously or orally, it disappeared rapidly from the plasma, but the tepa metabolized from it reached a higher concentration and persisted longer. Thus, the concentration of tepa at four hr was as great as or greater than the concentration of thiotepa at two hr. At least 50 percent of the oral dose of thiotepa was absorbed intact. Rats excreted at least 95 percent of thiotepa and its metabolites within eight hr of intravenous or intra-arterial injection. The remainder was excreted about equally in the feces and expired air. Between 70 and 80 percent of the drug in the urine was unreacted, while 20 to 30 percent was in the form of tepa. There was evidence of traces of two or three other unidentified metabolites (Boone et al., 1962). In the rat, about two percent of injected thiotepa is expired as carbon dioxide (Boone et al., 1962), and this may come from the 20 to 30 percent metabolized to tepa. Dogs excrete 0.3 to 0.7 percent of thiotepa in the urine unchanged and 8 to 15 percent as tepa (Mellett and Woods, 1960). Craig et al. (1959)

studied the metabolism of thiotepa in the mouse, rat, rabbit, and dog in such a way that the results were strictly comparable. Each species converted the compound to tepa and each produced some inorganic phosphate and at least traces of other metabolites; however, the details of the biotransformation were not the same either quantitatively or qualitatively in any two of the species. Later studies (Parish and Arthur, 1965) were essentially confirmatory for the rat but permitted a comparison of the metabolism of thiotepa in that species and in insects.

A study done with thiotepa and chlorambucil may throw light on alkylating agents generally in regard to (1) the persistence of injury to bone marrow and (2) the development of tolerance in treated neoplasms. It was shown by Fisher and Roh (1964) that bilateral perfusion of the kidneys with either of these compounds inhibited the baseline of erythropoietin production and antagonized the response of the kidney to cobalt, which is a potent erythropoietic stimulus. These results were obtained even in situations in which no injury to the kidney was detected histologically. The results were not due to temporary anoxia, which may have accompanied the experimental procedure. Anoxia by itself actually increased the production of erythropoietin following cobalt. The authors considered that the slight fall in erythrocyte and hemoglobin values which occurs within a few days after systemic treatment with moderate dosages of alkylating agents was probably the result of direct effects on the bone marrow, but that persisting anemia might result from a reduced production of erythropoietin by the kidney.

Decreased production of erythropoietin may lead gradually to failure of treatment of neoplasms with alkylating agents because Stansly and Schiop (1966) found that induction of reticulum cell sarcoma and myeloerythroleukemia in mice by a virus could be inhibited by doses of erythropoietin obtained from rabbits. Delayed treatment with erythropoietin resulted in regression of tumors.

METEPA

Metepa caused no damage to the intestinal epithelium of rats, except following single doses in the fatal range. In the rat, the oral LD_{50} is 136 mg/kg, and the dermal LD_{50} is 183 mg/kg. The organ primarily affected by repeated small doses is the testis; the ovaries and bone marrow are damaged only at higher dosage levels. Metepa at an oral dosage of 5 mg/kg/day (about 4 percent of the acute oral LD_{50} level daily) produced severe reduction of fertility of male rats in 22 days, sterility within 70 days, and testicular atrophy within 77 days. Half that dosage produced a smaller reduction in fertility and only partial atrophy in some rats within 197 days. Dosages of 1.25 mg/kg/day or less produced no detectable effect on fertility and no histological change in the testis in 197 days. The survival of newborn rats was not affected by any dosage given to the sires (Gaines and Kimbrough, 1964).

In a separate study, it was found that a dosage of 2.5 mg/kg/day given by stomach tube to male rats for 422 days produced a slight reduction in the probability that a litter would be produced, a moderate reduction in the average number of young per litter, but no effect on the survival of the young after birth. This effect was evident at the first breeding begun after 56 doses. Three of the 20 treated males eventually developed lymphatic leukemia, and the other 17 showed after 303 days a slight but statistically insignificant reduction of circulating white blood cells. Under the same condition, a dosage of 0.625 mg/kg/day was not carcinogenic and did not impair fertility or alter the white blood cell count (Gaines and Kimbrough, 1966).

When male rats were observed after they had received 155 doses of metepa by stomach tube at the rate of 5.0 mg/kg/day, their fertility, which had reached almost zero, returned to normal within 150 days after the last dose; but within the total of 267 days they were observed after the last dose, two lymphatic leukemias, one chloroleukemia, and one astrocytoma, respectively, were found in 4 of the 20 animals. Such neoplasms did not occur in 35 control animals nor had they been detected in any untreated rats from the same colony during the 14 years since it was established (Gaines and Kimbrough, 1966).

Although, as already noted, mice excrete no unchanged tepa, they excreted a little over 16 percent of metepa unchanged in the urine in a study in which an additional 41 percent of the dose was found as metabolites and the remainder was not recovered (Plapp et al., 1962).

MORZID

The toxicity of this compound has been little studied. It has been shown to be a mutagen in bacteria (Szybalski, 1958). Radioactive morzid was metabolized in both rats and man to phosphate and morpholine, and the sulfur was oxidized to form N-(3-oxapentamethylene)-N', N'''-diethylenephosphoramide, a compound of equal potency against a test tumor. In addition, man excreted a considerable amount of uncharacterized metabolites (Heidelberger and Maller, 1958).

APHOLATE

The oral LD_{50} of apholate to rats is 98 mg/kg (Gaines and Kimbrough, 1964) or somewhat higher (Ristich et al., 1965). It requires about 15 percent of this dosage for 98 days to affect the blood, but 7.5 percent for the same period produces growth suppression, and 3.7 percent (3.7 mg/kg/day), also for 98 days, interferes with fertility of the male rat (Toxicology Section, Communicable Disease Center, unpublished results). It is not known whether apholate is carcinogenic.

Sheep are more sensitive than rats to apholate, for a daily dosage of 1.0 mg/kg/day led to the death of one out of two that received this doage, and higher dosages were uniformly fatal (Younger and Young, 1963). The surviving sheep tolerated 759 daily doses without clinical illness; the number of leukocytes and thrombocytes was decreased but gradually returned to normal during an additional period of 28 weeks after dosage was discontinued (Younger, 1965a). After approximately 195 doses of apholate at the rate of 1.0 mg/kg/day in another test, a ewe was bred by a ram treated in the same way. Dosage was continued. After a total of 345 doses the ewe delivered a grossly deformed lamb. The teratogenesis was attributed to apholate. Three other ewes treated in the same way delivered normal lambs (Younger, 1965b).

Three rams and three ewes tolerated apholate at a dosage of 0.5 mg/kg/day during a 494-day test. Microscopic examination of tissue taken by biopsy indicated no depression of oogenic or spermatogenic activity. The treated animals were bred; each ewe conceived and delivered two or more normal lambs during the test (Younger, 1965c). The author reported a slight leucopenia in the ewes, but it was of questionable statistical significance.

The acute toxicity of each of a number of analogs of apholate that are also alkylating agents is of the same order of magnitude and shows questionable correlation with the effectiveness of the same analog as a chemosterilant or with the concentration of it required to kill mouse fibroblast cells grown in tissue culture (Ristich et al., 1965).

TRETAMINE

The oral toxicity of tretamine is about 1 mg/kg or approximately the same as that of tetraethylpyrophosphate. Only 10 intraperitoneal doses at the rate of 0.37 mg/kg are carcinogenic for mice (Hendry et al., 1951b). Seven to eleven subcutaneous doses at the rate of 0.1 mg/kg are carcinogenic for rats (Walpole et al., 1954). Tretamine is mutagenic, at least in bacteria (Szybalski, 1958) and *Drosophila* (Auerbach and Robson, 1947, Fahmy and Fahmy, 1958). Cattanach (1957, 1959b) reported that some of the F_1 progeny of male mice treated with tretamine showed hereditary semisterility and that this trait was associated with cytologically demonstrable chromosomal translocations. The semisterility was associated with survival of the sperm but death of the zygote or embryo. He speculated that incomplete spermatogenesis and complete sterility in other F_1 offspring of treated male mice were caused by a dominant mutation. The injection of tretamine before mating also reduced the fertility of female mice, but a larger dose was necessary than in males. Cattanach (1959a) considered that the mechanism of action was the same in females as in males although direct evidence was not available. Only one F_1 progeny of treated mice was morphologically abnormal, and it did not breed (Cattanach, 1959b).

Tretamine is also teratogenic (Murphy et al., 1958). The required dosage in rats (0.2 mg/kg/day for 5 days beginning 4 days after mating) (Jackson and Bock, 1955) was larger than that needed to produce sterility in the male, and increasing doses were required as the fetus grew older.

In male rats, a single dose of tretamine at the rate of 0.2 mg/kg intraperitoneally produced subfertility promptly and sterility most marked 22 to 26 days after the dose and ending about 35 days after the dose (Bock and Jackson, 1957,

Craig et al., 1958, Jackson, 1958). The effect was thought to be on spermatocytes; mature sperm present at the time of treatment were not affected (Craig et al., 1958, Jackson, 1959). When the frequency of dosage with tretamine was increased to 0.2 mg/kg/day for 5 days intraperitoneally, recovery occurred 6 weeks after treatment (Bock and Jackson, 1957, Craig et al., 1958), but there was apparently a second brief period of sterility about 9 weeks after the last dose (Jackson, 1959). Thus, the effect resembled the combined action of single doses of tretamine and busulfan. The first period of sterility was thought to be caused by destruction of spermatocytes, the second by destruction of spermatogonia (Jackson, 1959). A quantitative, histological study (Steinberger, 1962) showed that the initial visible lesion caused by this dosage of tretamine (0.2 mg/kg/day intraperitoneally for 5 days) involved early generations of type A spermatogonia and began at least as early as the second day after initiation of treatment. A sharp decrease in the number of resting spermatocytes occurred on the tenth day after the start of treatment, and this decrease was soon reflected in the more mature spermatocytes. It appears that the effect of such doses on fertility involves a combination of this maturation depletion and the more subtle effect on the mature germinal cells which is also produced by low dosages (Steinberger et al., 1959).

When the same dosage of tretamine (0.2 mg/kg/day) was given to rats a total of 21 times in the course of 57 days, they remained sterile and aspermic for at least 8 weeks after dosage was stopped (Bock and Jackson, 1957).

Forty-one doses of tretamine at the lower rate of 0.05 mg/kg/day intraperitoneally during 57 days produced complete sterility in male rats beginning a few days after the first dose and lasting for 3 to 4 weeks after the last dose when full recovery took place (Jackson and Bock, 1955, Bock and Jackson, 1957). During the sterile period, the sperm were normal in number and motility and were able to penetrate ova, but the ova failed to develop to a significant degree. The sexual behaviour of the males remained normal (Jackson and Bock, 1955). No histological damage to the testis was observed following a dosage of 0.05 mg/kg five times each week (Jackson and Bock, 1955, Steinberger et al., 1959). The action of tretamine that permits fertilization but leads to early death of the resulting zygotes or embryos involves mature spermatozoa as well as other germinal cells.

When a similar experiment with tretamine (0.05 mg/kg/day intravenously for 29 days) was carried out in rabbits, the sperm were infertile but otherwise normal for about 50 days, after which matings became abruptly aspermic, although the volume of seminal fluid remained normal (Jackson, 1959).

Most of the effects of tretamine on fertility just mentioned were confirmed by Steinberger et al. (1959), who found, in addition, that the F_1 progeny of males that had regained fertility developed normally and were fully fertile, as was the F_2 generation.

Tretamine at a dosage of 0.2 mg/kg/day for 5 days before mating did not affect the fertility of female rats (Jackson and Bock, 1955). A single dose of 1.6 mg/kg, however, did reduce the fertility of female mice (Cattanach, 1959a).

The total intravenous therapeutic dosage of tretamine for man (0.12 mg/kg) (Sykes et al., 1956) is of the same order of magnitude as the smallest intravenous dosage (0.01 mg/kg/day) that produces temporary sterility in the rabbit (Jackson, 1959).

Following intravenous injection of radioactive tretamine in man and animals, the activity decreased rapidly in the blood and then maintained a low constant level for at least 48 hr. Mice excreted between 72 and 88 percent of radioactive tretamine in 24 hr, mostly in the urine, but 1 to 2 percent as exhaled carbon dioxide. Humans excreted about 30 percent in the urine after an oral dose but only about 20 percent after an intravenous dose. There was no unchanged compound in the urine. Chromatography revealed at least 16 metabolites in the urine, one of which is cyanuric acid. The metabolic pathway is unknown, but it has been postulated that the ethyleneimino group is excreted as the alkylated derivatives of normal metabolites (Smith et al., 1958, Nadkarni et al., 1959).

It is generally recognized that difunctional or polyfunctional alkylating agents are more effective than monofunctional agents in treating neoplasms (Ross, 1962). The difference may have the same basic cause as a difference observed in insects. Watson (1964) showed that the frequency of translocations in sperm from male *Drosophila* treated with tretamine increased substantially during storage of the sperm in the seminal receptacle of the female, although the frequency of sex-linked lethals increased only slightly during the same period. By contrast, the ratio of these effects of ethyleneimine remained constant during storage. The results were thought to indicate an essential difference in the way in which polyfunctional and monofunctional alkylating agents produce breaks in chromosomes.

METHYL METHANESULFONATE

This compound is apparently not outstanding as a chemosterilant for insects, but it is of interest because it has been shown to produce not only dominant lethal mutations in the sperm of mice, but also partial sterility in their offspring. A high proportion of dead implants occurred in female mice mated to males within the first two weeks after the males received a single intraperitoneal injection at the rate of 50 or 100 mg/kg. The result indicated the production of dominant lethals in sperm (Partington and Bateman, 1964). Histological examination (Partington and Bateman, 1964, Partington et al., 1964) showed that some earlier cell stages were injured by the higher dosage, but these effects, unlike those on the sperm (which were not accompanied by any visible alteration), did not lead to dominant lethals demonstrable by death of the early embryo (Partington and Bateman, 1964). Some progeny of male mice that had been mated in the second week after a single intraperitoneal dose of 50 mg/kg showed reduced reproductive capacity. Partial sterility was encountered in the F_2 generation also in both males and females, and complete sterility was found in one F_2 male (Jackson et al., 1964).

Jackson has pointed out that the possibility of transmissible injury raises the question of whether injuries that have not yet been detected are actually produced in stages of spermatogenesis that appear unaffected following treatment by an alkylating agent.

2-CHLOROETHYL METHANESULFONATE

This compound is of interest because, like its unchlorinated methyl and ethyl analogs, it exerts a sterilizing effect directly on spermatids and spermatozoa with no histological or functional evidence of injury to earlier stages (Jackson et al., 1961). Its mutagenicity in mammals apparently has not been tested, although it produces an unusually high proportion of visible mutations in *Drosophila* (Fahmy and Fahmy, 1956). Some of the surviving mutants were sterile, but others transmitted morphological abnormalities to the F_2 generation (Auerbach and Robson, 1947).

BUSULFAN

This compound, 1,4-dimethanesulfonoxybutane, has not been prominent as a chemosterilant, but an interesting phenomenon has been demonstrated with it that has not been looked for in connection with other alkylating agents. The phenomenon might be considered a special form of teratogenesis in which the "deformity" is complete loss of germ cells. Pregnant rats were injected on selected days from the fifth day after breeding until delivery, and young rats from other litters were injected on selected days from birth through the fifteenth day. The dosage of busulfan for mothers and for infant rats was the same, 10 mg/kg given intraperitoneally. Treatment between day 5 and 7 of fetal life (counting the day spermatozoa were found in the vaginal smear as day 0) apparently had no effect on the developing sex cells. Later treatments with busulfan led to increasing, permanent sterility of the young of either sex. Complete sterility was observed in male offspring of mothers injected from the thirteenth through the eighteenth day after breeding and in female offspring of mothers injected from the thirteenth through the sixteenth day. Treatment then became progressively less effective so that females treated with standard dosage of busulfan during their late fetal period were capable of normal reproduction, while males were normal if treated later than about 4 days post partum (Hemsworth and Jackson, 1962a,b).

OTHER DIESTERS OF SULFONIC ACID

A remarkable example of specificity is offered by busulfan and certain other members of a series of dimethanesulfonates of the form $CH_3-SO_2-O-(CH_2)n-O-SO_2-CH_3$. At a suitable dosage, the $n-1$ analog acts on very late cells in spermatogenesis so that sterility occurs during the first week after dosage (Fox and Jackson, 1965). The $n-2$ analog acts on cells of intermediate age producing sterility during the second to tenth weeks following dosage. The $n - 4$ analog (busulfan or Myleran) acts on early cells only, producing sterility during the seventh and subsequent weeks after dosage (Jackson, 1964).

CHLORAMBUCIL

Large doses of this nitrogen mustard derivative will produce in experimental animals the cytotoxic effects typical of alkylating agents in general and mustards in particular. Rather than discuss these effects again, let us see what selective action the drug possesses as described in *New Drugs* (American Medical Association, 1966).

Chlorambucil is used for the palliative treatment of chronic lymphatic leukemia, lymphosarcoma, and Hodgkin's disease. It apparently is of no value in any type of acute leukemia. Although chlorambucil may be effective in chronic granulocytic leukemia, busulfan is generally superior for this purpose. Chlorambucil depresses lymphocytic proliferation and maturation much more than it depresses granulocytes. When used therapeutically, lymphopenia, neutropenia, and thrombocytopenia tend to appear in that order. It is not always necessary to stop treatment when neutropenia first appears, but it must be remembered that the white blood cell count may remain depressed for 10 days after the last dose and that as the total dose approaches 6.5 mg/kg there is real danger of producing irreversible bone marrow damage. During treatment, complete blood studies must be made once a week and preferably more often.

Chlorambucil is usually given at the rate of 0.2 mg/kg/ day for 3 to 6 weeks in Hodgkin's disease and 0.1 mg/kg for a similar period in chronic lymphatic leukemia or lymphosarcoma. Although there is no evidence that chlorambucil is more effective than any other cytotoxic drug, the fact that it is absorbed well and more predictably from the gastrointestinal tract, produces fewer side effects, and may be less damaging to the bone marrow, makes it somewhat easier to handle than either nitrogen mustard or tretamine, which are used for the same kinds of cancer.

Chlorambucil was somewhat less effective than thiotepa (see above) in blocking the production of erythropoietin by the kidney (Fisher and Roh, 1964).

ANALOGS OF ALKYLATING AGENTS

HEMPA

Hempa has been studied more thoroughly than any other analog of the alkylating agents. In both male and female rats, the acute oral LD_{50} is greater than 2,500 mg/kg and the acute dermal LD_{50} is greater than 3,500 mg/kg (Kimbrough and Gaines, 1966). Jasper et al. (1965) found the acute oral LD_{50} for rats and guinea pigs to be 2,525 and 1,600 mg/kg, respectively. The acute dermal LD_{50} for guinea pigs and rabbits was 1,175 and 1,280 mg/kg, respectively.

Rats receiving a dosage in the LD_{50} range show involuntary urination, mild muscle fasciculations, bloody urine, and convulsions. Microscopic study shows that the hematuria may be based on necrotizing cystitis or on injury to the kidney tubules. Severe damage to the lungs and testes may be present also. Although hempa is an organic phosphorus compound and some of its effects suggest those of anticholinesterases, inhibition of cholinesterase cannot explain the symptomatology because poisoned rats show only a small reduction of plasma cholinesterase activity and no reduction of red cell enzyme activity.

Unlike the alkylating agents, hempa has little or no effect on blood formation; but, in spite of this, rats given 40 mg/kg/day for as much as 103 days were more susceptible than controls to pneumonia. The same dosage reduces male fertility and causes testicular atrophy in as little as 45 days, but longer dosage at 25 mg/kg/day had no observable effect on the testis or on fertility of the males. Females were distinctly more resistant; they reproduced normally while being dosed at the rate of 200 mg/kg/day, and the litters showed no teratogenesis (Kimbrough and Gaines, 1966).

Hempa has not been explored properly for possible carcinogenicity or mutagenicity. N,N-dimethylstearamide (Walpole et al., 1954) and trimethylolmelamine (Hendry et al., 1951a), however, are carcinogenic, and the latter caused mutation in *Drosophila* (Röhrborn, 1962). These compounds are analogs of alkylating agents but have not been proposed as chemosterilants.

The fact that so many of the actions of the analogs are the same as those of the alkylating agents suggests that alkylation may not be involved in the effects under discussion even in connection with the alkylating agents.

HEMEL

Jasper et al. (1965) reported that the oral LD_{50} values of hemel for rats and guinea pigs were 350 and 255 mg/kg, respectively. The acute dermal LD_{50} for rabbits was greater than 9,000 mg/kg.

ANTIMETABOLITES

Each antimetabolite owes its action to its imperfect chemical and metabolic resemblance to some compound normally present in the body. The kind of toxic effect depends on the vitamin or other properties of the corresponding normal metabolite, and the toxic effect may often be partially counteracted by large doses of the latter.

AMINOPTERIN

Aminopterin may be taken as an example of the antimetabolites proposed for use as chemosterilants. Its oral LD_{50} for rats is only 4.5 mg/kg, and only 2.8 percent of this dosage repeated eight times has a destructive action on the blood (Philips and Thiersch, 1949). Approximately the same dosage is known to produce abortion and teratogenesis in both man and rat (Thiersch and Philips, 1950). Dosages as low as 0.03 mg/kg/day lead to pallor, diarrhea, bleeding, and death when given to rats for as long as 28 days (Toxicology Section, Communicable Disease Center, unpublished results). The carcinostatic dosage for man is of the same magnitude: about 18 doses of 0.25 mg for infants or 0.5 mg for children (Sollmann, 1957).

Infant mice are distinctly less susceptible to aminopterin than their mothers perhaps because of a lack of development of and dependence on folic acid reductase. Sixteen-hour-old mice survived the subcutaneous injection of 10 μg of the compound (a dosage of about 12.5 mg/kg) but many of the mothers died in 3 to 4 days presumably as the result of ingesting urine from the seven or eight young in each litter (a maximal dosage of 3 to 4 mg/kg). The dead adults showed no gross injury but did exhibit profound bone marrow destruction (Toth and Shubik, 1964).

The principal action of aminopterin and other folic acid antagonists is to inhibit folic acid reductase, thereby preventing

conversion of desoxyuridylic to thymidylic acid. In one system, the affinity of the enzyme for the antagonist was almost
a thousand times that for folic acid (Karnofsky and Clarkson,
1963). Therefore, large doses of folic acid are usually ineffective in reversing toxic effects. However, folinic acid (10
mg) is helpful if given at the first sign of toxicity.

AMETHOPTERIN (METHOTREXATE)

The carcinostatic dose of amethopterin is 1.25 mg for
infants, 2.5 mg for children up to 3 or 4 years of age, and 5 to
10 mg for an older child or an adult repeated for 7 to 10 days
or more depending on clinical response. A daily dosage of 25
mg is given for 5 days and the course repeated at intervals in
treating metastatic uterine carcinoma. Although amethopterin
is tolerated in somewhat larger dosages than aminopterin, there
is no qualitative difference in effects at biologically equivalent
doses. Signs of toxicity are entirely similar. Usually the ear-
liest sign is the appearance of necrotic patches on the lips
or any mucosa of the oral cavity. Abdominal pain, vomiting,
and diarrhea may appear and, if dosage is not stopped, extensive ulceration develops in the esophagus, small intestine,
and colon. The gastrointestinal effects are accompanied by a
progressive reduction of leukocytes and platelets. The marrow is hypocellular but contains megaloblasts. Occasionally
alopecia or hyperpigmentation occur. Hepatic fibrosis has been
observed in some children who survived long enough to receive repeated treatment (Krakoff and Karnofsky, 1965).

S-TRIAZINE-2-4-DIAMINO-6-(2-FURYL)

This compound has apparently not been studied toxicologically. However, it is an analog of chloroguanide and pyrimethamine, which are antimalarial drugs. Although less similar
in structure to folic acid than is aminopterin, chloroguanide
and pyrimethamine nevertheless act as folic acid antagonists
by blocking the conversion of folic acid to folinic acid.
Chloroguanide (at a dosage of 87 mg of base per week
in adults) or pyrimethamine (at a dosage of 25 mg per week in
adults) may produce vomiting, abdominal pain, and diarrhea,

which are not sufficiently severe to stop therapy. Repeated dosage may lead to macrocytic normochromic anemia with a megaloblastic marrow, all of which responds to folinic acid (DiPalma, 1965).

5-FLUOROURACIL

5-Fluorouracil (5-FU or FU) is an analog of uracil and thymine (5-methyluracil). Its chief action is interference with the thymidylate synthetase system, thus causing marked inhibition of the synthesis of DNA. It was designed and synthesized for this purpose (Heidelberger et al., 1957). A less important mode of action involves incorporation of FU into RNA. A dosage of 15 mg/kg/day intravenously for five consecutive days and then 7.5 mg/kg/day on alternate days until the first sign of toxicity is necessary to produce regression of susceptible tumors. Unfortunately, the toxicity may be severe, and there is no proof that tumor regression is associated with increased survival time (Krakoff and Karnofsky, 1965). Early signs of toxicity include glossitis, diarrhea, reduction of white count and platelets. Toxicity may progress to severe ulceration of the gastrointestinal tract and aplasia of the bone marrow.

The fluorinated pyrimidines are teratogenic (Krakoff and Karnofsky, 1965).

5-FLUORO-OROTIC ACID

5-Fluoro-orotic acid (FO) is about 30 times as toxic by weight for man as FU (Krakoff and Karnofsky, 1965). Qualitatively it is similar to FU.

MISCELLANEOUS COMPOUNDS

Miscellaneous compounds suggested as chemosterilants include thiourea, ethylene urea, calcium arsenate, triphenyl tin hydroxide, and even tarter emetic and boric acid.

None of the wide range of materials have been studied toxicologically in this connection. Some information on them is available, but little or nothing is known of their effect on reproduction in mammals. Their acute oral toxicity is frequently not great.

ARSENIC

Calcium arsenate has been proposed for use against the apple maggot (Pickett and Patterson, 1963) at levels lower than those commonly used for insect control.

The "therapeutic dose" of arsenic trioxide (1 to 2 mg three times daily) that was used in the past as a tonic frequently led to mild poisoning. The threshold limit for arsenic in its uncombined form is 0.5 mg/m³. This would permit a maximal intake of 5 mg/man/day as arsenic or 6.6 mg/man/day as arsenic trioxide. Apparently, there is no evidence on whether the therapeutic dose influenced reproduction. Industrial records would have little bearing on the matter if the effects in mammals paralleled those in insects, for few women are exposed significantly to arsenic in industry.

Tolerance to arsenic can be produced in animals (Sollmann, 1957). The mountaineers of Styria and certain other regions consume arsenic once or twice weekly as a general stimulant and tonic. There is evidence that they gradually accustom themselves to doses of arsenic trioxide up to 400 mg/man/day that would ordinarily produce serious toxic effects (Sollmann, 1957). Survival of the population indicates that their intake of arsenic has no serious effect on reproduction.

Although it may have limited bearing on the interpretation of the toxicity of inorganic arsenic, it is interesting to note that certain organic arsenic compounds [e.g., arsanilic acid (4-aminophenyl arsonic acid) and 3-nitro-4-hydroxyphenyl arsonic acid] are effective as growth promoters in livestock, especially chickens, turkeys, and swine. The concentrations used in feed are 25 to 100 parts per million (ppm), and the dosage is approximately 0.043 to 0.52 mg/kg/day. Rats that were fed arsanilic acid for six generations at dietary concentrations of 100 and 200 ppm showed no decrease in reproduction in comparison to controls (Frost et al., 1955).

TRIPHENYL TIN

The two available studies of triphenyl tin apparently are not in good agreement. Klimmer (1964) reported an oral LD_{50} of 136 mg/kg and found that dosage at the rate of 1.25 mg/kg/day for 170 days failed to affect the blood. Van Esch and Arnoldussen (1962) found the material to be less toxic acutely but reported that a dosage of only 0.5 mg/kg/day for only 84 days led to injury to the blood. The same workers found that only twice this dosage for 28 days led to growth suppression and that the changes associated with poisoning by triphenyl tin—chronic brain edema and respiratory paralysis—are entirely similar to those caused by the highly dangerous triethyl tin. In connection with the latter, Magee et al. (1957) reported atrophy of the testes and accessory organs, but noted that the same thing occurred to a lesser degree in pair-fed controls, indicating that the atrophy may have resulted from starvation, which was present.

Unpublished studies of triphenyl tin hydroxide in the author's laboratory show that a dosage of 17.2 to 12.5 mg/kg/day, associated with a dietary level of 200 ppm, was tolerated by weanling rats during the 99 days of feeding without reduction of food intake, but it resulted in significant depression of the white blood cell count and less than normal weight gain. A dietary level of 400 ppm reduced food intake to about one-third of normal and led to death of rats in 34 days or less. Rats offered a dietary level of 100 ppm for 99 days received a dosage that decreased normally from 9.9 to 5.4 mg/kg/day as they grew older; this dosage range produced no detectable injury. In a separate study lasting 113 days it was found that dietary levels of 50, 100, and 200 ppm were also without effect on the reproduction of male rats.

THIOUREA

Thiourea is quickly absorbed from the gastrointestinal tract, widely distributed in the tissues and rapidly excreted. Up to 98 percent, mostly unmetabolized, was excreted by rats in 24 hr (Schulman and Keating, 1950). It is secreted in milk and crosses the placental barrier. The oral LD_{50} for rats is 125 to 640 mg/kg (Dieke et al., 1947) or even much higher (Dieke and Richter, 1945) depending on strain, species, and dietary factors. In rats the most striking effect of a large dose is pulmonary edema (MacKenzie and MacKenzie, 1943). Occurrence of edema can be influenced by prior administration of iodine or thyroxin. The underlying mechanism is not understood, but it is not directly related to the antithyroid effect described below.

The primary action of thiourea given in doses that can be tolerated for a time is inhibition of the formation of thyroid hormone chiefly by interference with the binding of iodine into an organic form. There is also some evidence that the drug inhibits the synthesis of thyroid hormone by blocking the coupling of iodotyrosines to form iodothyronines. Although the details of these mechanisms are not fully understood, it is clear that decreased formation of thyroid hormone leads to increased secretion of thyrotropic hormone by the anterior pituitary and, therefore, to hyperplasia of the thyroid gland. Thiourea does not cause hyperplasia of the thyroid if deficiency of thyroid hormone is compensated by injected hormone, or if the anterior pituitary is removed. Thiourea does not act synergistically with either thyroid hormone or thyrotropic hormone (Astwood, 1965).

Rats that received thiourea for over 3 years at a rate of 25 mg/kg/day showed no depression of growth and no increase of mortality or pathologic changes (Hartzell, 1945). Larger doses interfere reversibly with reproduction through action on the thyroid. The production of neutropenia in rats by thriourea may be prevented by simultaneous dosage with liver (Goldsmith et al., 1944). Rats that drank water containing 2,500 ppm (resulting in a dosage of about 120 mg/kg/day) developed hyperplasia of the thyroid progressing to adenomas, some of which eventually became malignant and metastisized to the lungs (Moore et al., 1953).

Thiourea was formerly used at a dosage of 1 to 2 gm by mouth (about 14 to 28 mg/kg/day) for treatment of hyperthyroidism. The higher dosage leads to a blood level of less than 50 ppm (Campbell et al., 1944). Thiourea has been replaced by propylthiouracil and methimazole because they produce less severe and less frequent side effects. The side effects of thiourea, however, were not serious. In fact, the drug is not necessarily more toxic than the newer ones; it was used at a dosage much greater than that now known to be effective for treatment of hyperthyroidism (Sollmann, 1957, Astwood, 1965). Thiourea has been used as a 1 percent solution to stimulate the healing of ulcers through stimulation of granulation tissue.

A number of analogs of thiourea have been used in medicine, and all of them have the same mode of action. Analogs that are proposed for use as chemosterilants but have not been used in medicine apparently have not been studied toxicologically, but their mode of action is almost certainly similar.

PORFIROMYCIN

This antibiotic isolated from *Streptomyces caespitosus* is an analog of mitomycin C, namely, *N*-methyl-mitomycin C. The toxicity of porfiromycin is similar to that of mitomycin C, which is better known because of its use against cancer.

Mitomycin C damages DNA (Shiba et al., 1959). In several species of experimental animals, it produces weight loss and delayed death associated with hypoplasia of the bone marrow and lymphoid tissues, and injury of the intestinal epithelium (Philips et al., 1960, Schwartz and Philips, 1961, Schwartz, 1962). The usual total dose by the intravenous route is about 1 mg/kg divided into four to ten daily injections. Even at this very low dosage, leucopenia and thrombocytopenia may occur (Karnofsky and Clarkson, 1963).

CYCLOHEXIMIDE (ACTI-DIONE®)

This antibiotic isolated from *Streptomyces griseus* is active against gram-positive bacteria and fungi, especially *Cryptococcus neoformans*. It has been used to treat systemic disease caused by *C. neoformans*, *Fusarium* (Carton, 1952), and *Candida albicans* (Schaberg et al., 1955). Rates of administration of cycloheximide have been as high as 180 mg/day intravenously, 720 mg/day intramuscularly, 20 mg/day intrathecally, and 30 mg/day intraventricularly. The highest total dosage for any one patient was 2,776 mg of which 2,681 mg were given by the intramuscular route. The only toxic effects observed were nausea and vomiting, and these could be controlled by Dramamine. Many of the patients showed temporary clinical improvement and a definite reduction of fever; a few apparently recovered although, in the absence of treatment, such disease is almost always fatal (Carton, 1952).

The highest daily dose given to an adult (735 mg) represents a rate about four or five times greater than the LD_{50} for the rat and twice that for the cat. It is clear that man is far less susceptible than these species to the toxic action of cycloheximide.

The LD_{50} values for the antibiotic quoted by Carton (1952) are: mouse, intravenously, 150 mg/kg; guinea pig, subcutaneously, 60 mg/kg; rabbit, intravenously, 17 mg/kg; cat, intraperitoneally, 4 mg/kg; and rat, subcutaneously, 2.7 mg/kg and intravenously, 2.5 mg/kg.

Rats that have received a fatal or near fatal dose show frothing and salivation, diarrhea, enlarged adrenals, hemorrhage of the stomach, liver congestion, and kidney damage (Greig and Gibbons, 1959). Hydrocortisone increased survival rate when given promptly and repeatedly; deoxycortosterone was ineffective (Greig and Gibbons, 1959).

COLCHICINE

The plant *Colchicum* was described in detail by Dioscorides, a Greek physician in the service of Nero (Holmstedt and Liljestrand, 1963). The physician warned of the danger of the plant, but there is some evidence this was necessary only because two or more related forms of greatly different potency were already recognized and used for the treatment of gout (Eigsti and Dustin, 1955). *Colchicum* apparently was first clearly recommended for the treatment of gout in the foot by Alexander of Tralles who died A.D. 605. Medical evaluation of the drug varied greatly chiefly because of its toxicity and lack of standardization of the herbal preparations (Eigsti and Dustin, 1955). Total synthesis was accomplished in 1959 (Schreiber et al., 1959, van Tamelen et al., 1959). According to Woodbury (1965) the drug now has no equal for the relief of acute attacks of gout. In such an attack, the drug is usually given orally at the rate of 0.5 mg/hr. The total dose usually required to relieve an attack is 4 to 8 mg, and it is recommended that patients continue to take from 0.25 to 2.0 mg/day prophylactically. Toxicity can occur, but it is usually the result of overdosage and is generally neither so serious nor so frequent as to require discontinuation of the drug at an appropriate dosage (Woodbury, 1965).

The therapeutic and toxic levels, however, are close. The highest recommended maintenance dose is about 0.028 mg/kg. This value may be compared with oral lethal doses of 0.125 mg/kg for both dogs and cats (Flury and Zernik, 1935). The lethal dose for the rat is between 1 mg/kg (Poe and Johnson, 1949) and 2 mg/kg (Orsini and Pansky, 1952). The lethal dose for the hamster is greater than 200 mg/kg (Orsini and Pansky, 1952). Man may be highly sensitive, for one death was reported following a dose of 7 mg (Woodbury, 1965).

Acute poisoning is the result of extensive vascular damage especially of the gastrointestinal tract and kidney leading to hemorrhagic gastroenteritis, hematuria, oliguria, and shock, a picture quite similar to that of acute arsenic poisoning. Large doses cause ascending paralysis that leads to death from respiratory failure. Eigsti and Dustin (1955) have emphasized the importance of central nervous system effects in the toxicity of colchicine. Chronic poisoning from colchicine may take the form of agranulocytosis, aplastic anemia, loss of hair, or myopathy.

Neither the therapeutic effect on gout nor the toxic effects, with the possible exception of the blood dyscrasias, are related to the antimitotic action of colchicine. However, toxic doses do, in addition to their other effects, stop mitosis at metaphase because these doses interfere with formation of the mitotic—or miotic—spindle. The first detailed autopsy in a fatal human case following discovery of the action of colchicine on cell division (Dustin, 1941) showed an abnormally high percentage of metaphase plates in the bone marrow, lymph glands, spleen, intestinal glands, liver, kidney, and both exocrine and endocrine tissues of the pancreas. The victim had survived 8 days following ingestion of 60 mg of colchicine with suicidal intent. Doses of the same order of magnitude (about 1 mg/kg) are used experimentally to disrupt spermatogenesis in mice. The drug is also known to be teratogenic (Eigsti and Dustin, 1955).

Concentrations as low as 0.001 ppm are capable of inactivating the spindle in tissue cultures (Bucher, 1945). However, some organisms such as *Chlamydomonas* are resistant requiring concentrations as high as 2,000 ppm (Cornman, 1942).

CONCLUSIONS

In conclusion, compounds that produce a relatively gradual onset of detectable injury that can be reversed by treatment or merely by removal from exposure tend to be safer in use than those that produce insidious effects whether acute or chronic. This means that compounds tend to be safer if there is a reliable test for their early effects. The test may be one that can be carried out in the laboratory or it may be a dependable clinical sign or symptom. Potentially the most rapid and frequently the most sensitive test involves symptomatology. This is especially true of compounds that are highly irritating or that produce early onset of nausea or other discomfort. Unfortunately the candidate chemosterilants often produce injury that is not easily detected but may be persistent.

The toxicology of some alkylating agents is unfavorable both qualitatively and quantitatively. For others, the toxicity is not greatly different quantitatively from that of pesticides now in safe use; but because of the *kind* of injury they produce, there is a real question whether any alkylating agent would be safe for use except under strict industrial controls.

So far as is now known, some of the analogs of alkylating agents are highly favorable from the standpoint of their level of toxicity. Some of these analogs produce one or more of the same undesirable kinds of injury as the alkylating agents, but whether this is true of all representatives of the group is not yet known. Even if undesirable kinds of injury are found experimentally, it may be that their production will require such high dosage levels that these potential injuries will constitute no practical problem.

The antimetabolites also show many of the same properties of the alkylating agents and their analogs. They tend to differ in that they affect females more than males both in insects and mammals. They also differ in that large doses of the normal metabolite may counteract the action of an antimetabolite, while no effective treatment against alkylating agents is known.

The toxicology of the miscellaneous compounds considered as chemosterilants has not been explored in relation to this proposed use, and if one or more of them really influence the reproduction of insects to a significant degree, we should learn at once whether they do the same thing to mammals.

Some of the chemosterilants show marked specificity for different species or even for different stages in spermatogenesis. The toxicity of each compound must be judged on the basis of its own dosage-response relationships. However, there is considerable reason to implicate changes in DNA or RNA in connection with the action of some of the compounds and to implicate disruption of the mitotic apparatus in connection with the action of others. Because these are undesirable changes, it would be important to learn whether it is possible to influence male fertility without changing nucleic acid or disrupting the mitotic spindle. It would be especially valuable to know whether there is anything peculiar about the reproduction of insects which would permit an entirely new approach to their sterilization. Although the physiology of insects seems to be similar to that of mammals in most respects (Winteringham and Barnes, 1955), notable differences are known, such as the presence of ecdysis and the importance of sex attractants in insects. If there is anything unique about male fertility in insects, it might be possible to influence the process by a chemical with insignificant toxic action in mammals.

REFERENCES

American Medical Association. 1966. New Drugs, Chicago.

Astwood, E. B. 1965. Thyroid and antithyroid drugs. *In* Goodman, L. S., and A. Gilman. The Pharmacological Basis of Therapeutics, 1466–1503, New York, Macmillan.

Auerbach, C., and J. M. Robson. 1947. The production of mutations by chemical substances. Proc. Roy. Soc. Edinburgh, B62: 271–283.

Bock, M., and H. Jackson. 1957. The action of triethylenemelamine on the fertility of male rats. Brit. J. Pharmacol., 12:1–7.

Boone, I. U., B. S. Rogers, and D. L. Williams. 1962. Toxicity, metabolism, and tissue distribution of carbon[14]-labeled $N,N'-N''$-triethylene thiophosphoramide (Thio-TEPA) in rats. Toxic. Appl. Pharmacol., 4:344–353.

Bucher, O. 1945. Uber die Wirkung sehr kleinen Colchicindosen nach Untersuchungen an in vitro gezuchteten Bindgewebszellen. Schwiez. Med. Wschr., 75:715–718.

Campbell, D., F. W. Landgrebe, and T. N. Morgan. 1944. Pharmacology of thiourea. Lancet, 1:630–632.

Carton, C. A. 1952. Treatment of central nervous system cryptococcosis: a review and report of four cases treated with actidione. Ann. Intern. Med., 37:123–154.

Cattanach, B. M. 1957. Induction of translocations in mice by triethylenemelamine. Nature (London), 180:1364–1365.

————. 1959a. The effect of triethylene-melamine on the fertility of female mice. Int. J. Radiat. Biol., 3:288–292.

————. 1959b. The sensitivity of the mouse testis to the mutagenic action of triethylenemelamine. Z. Verebungsl., 90:1–6.

Cornman, I. 1942. Susceptibility of *Colchicum* and *Chlamydomonas* to colchicine. Bot. Gaz., 104:50–61.

Craig, A. W., and H. Jackson. 1955. The metabolism of P^{32}-labelled triethylenephosphoramide in relation to its antitumor activity. Brit. J. Pharmacol., 10:321–325.

_____, B. W. Fox, and H. Jackson. 1958. Sensitivity of the spermatogenic process in the rat to radiomimetic drugs and X-rays. Nature (London), 181:353–354.

_____, B. W. Fox, and H. Jackson. 1959. Metabolic studies of P^{32}-labelled triethylene thiophosphoramide. Biochem. Pharmacol., 3:42–50.

Crathorn, A. R., and J. J. Roberts. 1966. Mechanism of the cytotoxic action of alkylating agents in mammalian cells and evidence for the removal of alkylated groups from deoxyribonucleic acid. Nature (London), 211:150–153.

Crossley, M. L., J. B. Allison, R. Wannemacher, J. Migliarese, R. P. Parker, E. Kuh, D. R. Seeger, and R. Partridge. 1953. Distribution of P^{32} following the injection of TEPA in rats. Proc. Soc. Exp. Biol. Med., 83:398–400.

Dieke, S. H., and C. P. Richter. 1945. Acute toxicity of thiourea to rats in relation to age, diet, strain and species variation. J. Pharmacol. Exp. Ther., 83:195–202.

_____, G. S. Allen, and C. P. Richter. 1947. The acute toxicity of thioureas and related compounds to wild and domestic Norway rats. J. Pharmacol. Exp. Ther., 90:260–270.

DiPalma, J. R. 1965. Chemotherapy of protozoan infections. I: Malaria. *In* DiPalma, J. R., Drill's Pharmacology in Medicine, 3d ed., 1376–1391, New York, McGraw-Hill.

Dustin, P., Jr. 1941. Intoxication mortelle par la colchicine. Étude histologique et hematologique. Bull. Acad. Roy. Med. Belg., 6:505–529.

Eigsti, O. J., and P. Dustin, Jr. 1955. Colchicine—In Agriculture, Medicine, Biology, and Chemistry, Ames, Iowa, Iowa State College Press.

Fahmy, O. G., and M. J. Fahmy. 1956. Mutagenecity of 2-chloroethyl methanesulfonate in *Drosophila melanogaster*. Nature (London), 177:996–997.

_____, and M. J. Fahmy. 1958. Discussion of mutagenic effects of alkylating agents. Ann. N.Y. Acad. Sci., 68:736–748.

_____, and M. J. Fahmy. 1964. Mutagenesis in relation to genetic hazard to man. Proc. Roy. Soc. Med., 57:646–650.

Fisher, J. W., and B. L. Roh. 1964. Influence of alkylating agents on kidney erythropoietin production. Cancer Res., 24:983–988.

Flurry, F., and F. Zernik. 1935. Zusammenstellung der toxischen und letalen Dosen für die gebraüchlichsten Gifte und Versuchstiere. *In* E. Abderhalden, Handbuch der Biologischen Arbeitmethoden, Abt. IV, T. 7B, Part II, 1289–1422, Berlin.

Fox, B. W., and H. Jackson. 1965. In vivo effects of methylene di-methanesulphonate on proliferating cell systems. Brit. J. Pharmacol., 24:24–28.

Frost, D. V., L. R. Overby, and H. C. Spruth. 1955. Arsenicals in feeds. J. Agr. Food Chem., 3:235–243.

Gaines, T. B., and R. D. Kimbrough. 1964. Toxicity of metepa to rats. With notes on two other chemosterilants. Bull. WHO, 31:737–745.

———, and R. D. Kimbrough. 1966. The sterilizing, carcinogenic and teratogenic effects of metepa in rats. Bull. WHO, 34:317–320.

Glynn, J. P., J. B. Moloney, M. A. Chirigos, S. R. Humphreys, and A. Goldin. 1963. Biological interrelationships in the chemo-therapy of Moloney virus leukemia. Cancer Res., 23:269–278.

Goldsmith, E. D., A. S. Gordon, G. Finkelstein, and H. A. Charipper. 1944. A suggested therapy for the prevention of granulo-cytopenia induced by thiourea. J. Amer. Med. Ass., 125:847.

Greig, M. E., and A. J. Gibbons. 1959. An antidote to cycloheximide (Acti-dione) poisoning. Toxic. Appl. Pharmacol., 1:598–601.

Hartzell, A. 1945. Thiourea (thiocarbamide): adult life span feeding experiments with rats. Contrib. Boyce Thompson Inst., 13:501–513.

Hayes, W. J., Jr. 1964. The toxicology of chemosterilants. Bull. WHO, 31:721–736.

Heidelberger, C., and R. K. Maller. 1958. Discussion on the distribu-tion and fate of alkylating agents. Ann. N.Y. Acad. Sci., 68:850–852.

———, N. K. Chaudhuri, P. Danneberg, D. Morren, L. Griesbach, R. Duschinsky, R. J. Schnitzer, E. Pleven, and J. Scheiner. 1957. Fluorinated pyrimidines, a new class of tumor-in-hibitory compounds. Nature (London), 179:663–666.

Hemsworth, B. N., and H. Jackson. 1962a. Effect of Busulphan on the developing gonad of the male rat. J. Reprod. Fertil. 5:187–194.

———, and H. Jackson. 1962b. Effect of Busulphan on the developing ovary in the rat. J. Reprod. Fertil., 6:229–233.

Hendry, J. A., F. L. Rose, and A. L. Walpole. 1951a. Cytotoxic agents: I. Methylolamides with tumor inhibitory activity, and related inactive compounds. Brit. J. Pharmacol., 6:201–234.

———, R. F. Homer, F. L. Rose, and A. L. Walpole. 1951b. Cytotoxic agents: III. Derivatives of ethyleneimine. Brit. J. Pharmacol., 6:257–410.

Holmstedt, B., and G. Liljestrand. 1963. Readings in Pharmacology, London, Pergamon Press.

Jackson, H. 1958. The effects of radiomimetic chemicals on the fertility of male rats. J. Fac. Radiol., 9:217–220.

———. 1959. Antifertility substances. Pharmacol. Rev., 11:135–172.

_____. 1964. The effects of alkylating agents on fertility. Brit. Med. Bull., 20:107–114.

_____. 1966. Antifertility Compounds in the Male and Female, Springfield, Charles C Thomas.

_____, and M. Bock. 1955. The effect of triethylenemelamine on the fertility of rats. Nature (London), 175:1037–1038.

_____, B. W. Fox, and A. W. Craig. 1961. Antifertility substances and their assessment in the male rodent. J. Reprod. Fertil., 2: 447–465.

_____, M. Partington, and A. L. Walpole. 1964. Production of heritable partial sterility in the mouse by methyl methanesulphonate, Brit. J. Pharmacol., 23:521–528.

Jasper, R. L., E. L. Silvers, and H. O. Williamson. 1965. Mammalian toxicity of two new insect chemosterilants. Fed. Proc., 24:641.

Karnofsky, D. A., and B. D. Clarkson. 1963. Cellular effects of anticancer drugs. In Cutting, W. C., R. H. Dreisbach, and H. W. Elliott, Annual Review of Pharmacology, 3:357–428, Palo Alto, California, Annual Reviews, Inc.

Kimbrough, R., and T. B. Gaines. 1966. The toxicity of hexamethylphosphoramide (HMPA) in rats. Nature (London), 211:146–147.

Klimmer, O. R. 1964. Part IV. Toxicological studies on triphenylacetate of tin (TPZA). Zbl. Veterinaermed. [A], 11:29–39.

Krakoff, I. H., and D. A. Karnofsky. 1965. Growth-inhibiting drugs: their anticancer, anti-immune, and teratogenic effects. In DiPalma, J. R., Drill's Pharmacology in Medicine, 1231–1262, New York, McGraw-Hill.

MacKenzie, C. G., and J. B. MacKenzie. 1943. Effect of sulfonamides and thioureas on thyroid gland and basal metabolism. Endocrinology, 32:185–209.

Magee, P. N., H. B. Stoner, and J. M. Barnes. 1957. The experimental production of edema in the central nervous system of the rat by triethyltin compound. J. Path. Bact., 73:107–124.

Mellett, L. B., and L. A. Woods. 1960. The comparative physiological disposition of ThioTEPA and TEPA in the dog. Cancer Res., 20:524–532.

Moloney, J. B. 1966. What is a virus? Hosp. Practice, 1:37–51.

Moore, G. E., E. L. Brackney, and F. G. Bock. 1953. Production of pituitary tumors in mice by chronic administration of a thiouracil derivative. Proc. Soc. Exp. Biol. Med., 82:643–645.

Murphy, M. L., A. D. Moro, and C. Lacon. 1958. The comparative effects of five polyfunctional alkylating agents on the rat fetus with additional notes on the chick embryo. Ann. N.Y. Acad. Sci., 68:762–781.

Nadkarni, M. V., E. G. Trams, and P. K. Smith. 1957. Studies with isotopically labeled triethylene melamine, triethylenephosphoramide and 1,4-dimethanesulfonoxybutane in cancer patients. Proc. Amer. Ass. Cancer Res., 2:235.

_____, E. G. Trams, and P. K. Smith. 1959. Preliminary studies on the distribution and fate of TEM, TEPA, and myleran in the human. Cancer Res., 19:713–718.

Orsini, M. W., and B. Pansky. 1952. The natural resistance of the golden hamster to colchicine. Science, 115:88–89.

Parish, J. C., and B. W. Arthur. 1965. Mammalian and insect metabolism of the chemosterilant thiotepa. J. Econ. Entom., 58: 976–979.

Partington, M., and A. J. Bateman. 1964. Dominant lethal mutations induced in male mice by methyl methanesulphonate. Heredity (London), 19:191–200.

_____, B. W. Fox, and H. Jackson. 1964. Comparative action of some methane sulphonic esters on the cell population of the rat testis. Exp. Cell. Res., 33:78–88.

Philips, F. S., and J. B. Thiersch. 1949. Studies of the actions of 4-amino-pteroylglutamic acid in rats and mice. J. Pharmacol. Exp. Ther., 95:303–311.

_____, H. S. Schwartz, and S. S. Sternberg. 1960. Pharmacology of mitomycin C. I. Toxicity and pathologic effects. Cancer Res., 20:1354–1361.

Pickett, A. D., and N. A. Patterson. 1963. Arsenates: effect on fecundity in some Diptera. Science, 140:493–494.

Plapp, F. W., Jr., W. S. Bigley, G. A. Chapman, and G. W. Eddy. 1962. Metabolism of methaphoxide in mosquitoes, house flies, and mice. J. Econ. Entom., 55:607–613.

Poe, C. F., and C. C. Johnson. 1949. Toxicity of colchicine, pilocarpine, and veratrine. Acta Pharmacol., 5:110–120.

Ristich, S. S., R. H. Ratcliffe, and D. Perlman. 1965. Chemosterilant properties, cytotoxicity, and mammalian toxicity of apholate and other P-N ring chemicals. J. Econ. Entom., 58:929–932.

Rohrborn, G. 1962. Chemische konstitution und mutagene wirkung. II. Triazinderivate. Z. Vererbungsl., 93:1–6.

Ross, W. C. J. 1962. Biological Alkylating Agents, London, Butterworths.

Schaberg, A., J. A. Hildes, and J. C. Wilt. 1955. Disseminated candidiasis. Arch. Intern. Med. (Chicago), 95:112–117.

Schreiber, J., W. Leimgruber, M. Pesaro, P. Schudel, and A. Eschenmoser. 1959. Synthese des colchicins. Angew. Chem. (Eng.), 71:637–640.

Schulman, J., and R. P. Keating. 1950. Studies on the metabolism of thiourea. I. Distribution and excretion in the rat of thiourea labeled with radioactive sulfur. J. Biol. Chem., 183:215–221.

Schwartz, H. S. 1962. Pharmacology of Mitomycin C. III. In vitro metabolism by rat liver. J. Pharmacol. Exp. Ther., 136:250–258.

_____, and F. S. Philips. 1961. Pharmacology of Mitomycin C. II. Renal excretion and metabolism by tissue hemogenates. J. Pharmacol. Exp. Ther., 133:335–342.

Shiba, S., A. Terawaki, T. Taguchi, and J. Kawamate. 1959. Selective inhibition of formation of deoxyribonucleic acid in Escherichia coli by Mitomycin C. Nature (London), 183:1056–1057.

Smith, P. K., M. V. Nadkarni, E. G. Trams, and C. Davison. 1958. Distribution and fate of alkylating agents. Ann. N.Y. Acad. Sci., 68:834–850.

Sollmann, T. 1957. A Manual of Pharmacology, 8th ed., Philadelphia, W. B. Saunders.

Stansly, P. G., and P. E. Schiop. 1966. Virus-induced murine leukemia: its inhibition and suppression by serum containing erythropoietin. Science, 152:1082–1083.

Steinberger, E. 1962. A quantitative study of the effect of an alkylating agent (triethylenemelamine) on the seminiferous epithelium of rats. J. Reprod. Fertil., 3:250–259.

_____, W. O. Nelson, A. Boccabella, and W. J. Dixon. 1959. A radiomimetic effect of triethylenemelamine on reproduction in the male rat. Endocrinology, 65:40–50.

Sykes, M. P., S. Philips, and D. A. Karnofsky. 1956. Comparative therapeutic activity of the nitrogen mustards and allied compounds. Med. Clin. N. Amer., 40:837–856.

Szybalski, W. 1958. Special microbiological system. II. Observations on chemical mutagenesis in microorganisms. Ann. N.Y. Acad. Sci., 76:475–489.

Thiersch, J. B., and F. S. Philips. 1950. Effect of 4-aminopteroylglutamic acid on early pregnancy. Proc. Soc. Exp. Biol. Med., 74:204–208.

Toth, B., and P. Shubik. 1964. Unexpected acute toxicity of aminopterin. Nature (London), 201:512.

van Esch, G. J., and A. M. Arnoldussen. 1962. Unpublished report of the National Institute of Public Health, Utrecht, Tox. 39/62. (Cited in Food and Agriculture Organization and World Health Organization. 1965. Evaluation of the Toxicity of Pesticide Residues in Food. WHO/Food Add./27.65).

van Tamelen, E. E., T. A. Spencer, Jr., D. S. Allen, Jr., and R. L. Orvis. 1959. The total synthesis of colchicine. J. Amer. Chem. Soc., 81:6341–6342.

Walpole, A. L., D. C. Roberts, F. L. Rose, J. A. Hendry, and R. F. Homer. 1954. Cytotoxic agents: IV. The carcinogenic actions of some monofunctional ethyleneimine derivatives. Brit. J. Pharmacol., 9:306–323.

Watson, W. A. F. 1964. Evidence of an essential difference between the genetical effects of mono- and bi-functional alkylating agents. Z. Vererbungsl., 95:374–378.

Weisburger, E. K. 1966. Carcinogenicity of alkylating agents. Public Health Rep., 81:772–776.

Winteringham, F. P. W., and J. M. Barnes. 1955. Comparative response of insects and mammals to certain halogenated hydrocarbons used as insecticides. Physiol. Rev., 35:701–739.

Woodbury, D. M. 1965. Analgesics and antipyretics. Salicylates and congeners; phenacetin and congeners; antipyrine and congeners; colchicine. *In* Goodman, L. S., and A. Gilman, The Pharmacological Basis of Therapeutics, 312–344, New York, Macmillan.

Younger, R. L. 1965a. Long-term toxicity studies in a sheep with apholate, an alkylating agent. Amer. J. Vet. Res., 26:1218–1220.

_____. 1965b. Probable induction of congenital anomalies in a lamb by apholate. Amer. J. Vet. Res., 26:991–995.

_____. 1965c. Low level feeding of a polyfunctional alkylating agent to sheep. Amer. J. Vet. Res., 26:1075–1078.

_____, and J. E. Young. 1963. Toxicologic studies and associated clinical and hematologic effects of apholate (an alkylating agent) in sheep—a preliminary report. Amer. J. Vet. Res., 24:659–669.

INDEX